Middle School 3-1

기말고사 완벽대비

영어 기출 문제집

중3

비상 | 김진완

구성과 특징

교과서의 주요 학습 내용을 중심으로 학습 영역별 특성에 맞춰 단계별로 다양한 학습 기회를 제공하여
단원별 학습능력 평가는 물론 중간 및 기말고사 시험 등에 완벽하게 대비할 수 있도록 내용을 구성

Words & Expressions

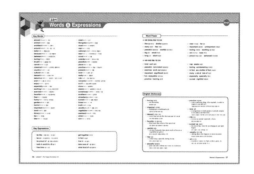

Step1
Key Words 단원별 핵심 단어 설명 및 풀이
Key Expression 단원별 핵심 숙어 및 관용어 설명
Word Power 반대 또는 비슷한 뜻 단어 배우기
English Dictionary 영어로 배우는 영어 단어

Step2 실력평가 단원별 수시평가 대비 주관식, 객관식 문제풀이

Step3 서술형 대비 학업성취도 및 수행능력평가 대비 서술형 문제풀이

Conversation

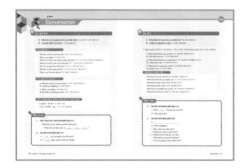

Step1 핵심 의사소통 소통에 필요한 주요 표현 방법 요약
핵심 Check 기본적인 표현 방법 및 활용능력 확인

Step2 대화문 익히기 교과서 대화문 심층 분석 및 확인

Step3 교과서 확인학습 빈칸 채우기를 통한 문장 완성 능력 확인

Step4 기본평가 시험대비 기초 학습 능력 평가

Step5 실력평가 단원별 수시평가 대비 주관식, 객관식 문제풀이

Step6 서술형 대비 학업성취도 및 수행능력평가 대비 서술형 문제풀이

Grammar

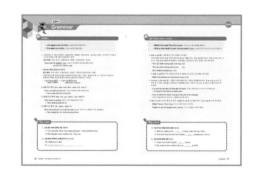

Step1 주요 문법 단원별 주요 문법 사항과 예문을 알기 쉽게 설명
핵심 Check 기본 문법사항에 대한 이해 여부 확인

Step2 기본평가 시험대비 기초 학습 능력 평가

Step3 실력평가 단원별 수시평가 대비 주관식, 객관식 문제풀이

Step4 서술형 대비 학업성취도 및 수행능력평가 대비 서술형 문제풀이

Reading

Step1 구문 분석 단원별로 제시된 문장에 대한 구문별 분석과 내용 설명
확인문제 문장에 대한 기본적인 이해와 인지능력 확인

Step2 확인학습A 빈칸 채우기를 통한 문장 완성 능력 확인

Step3 확인학습B 제시된 우리말을 영어로 완성하여 작문 능력 키우기

Step4 실력평가 단원별 수시평가 대비 주관식, 객관식 문제풀이

Step5 서술형 대비 학업성취도 및 수행능력평가 대비 서술형 문제풀이
교과서 구석구석 교과서에 나오는 기타 문장까지 완벽 학습

Composition

|영역별 핵심문제|

단어 및 어휘, 대화문, 문법, 독해 등 각 영역별 기출문제의 출제 유형을 분석하여 실전에 대비하고 연습할 수 있도록 문제를 배열

|단원별 예상문제|

기출문제를 분석한 후 새로운 시험 출제 경향을 더하여 새롭게 출제될 수 있는 문제를 포함하여 시험에 완벽하게 대비할 수 있도록 준비

|서술형 실전 및 창의사고력 문제|

학교 시험에서 점차 늘어나는 서술형 시험에 집중 대비하고 고득점을 취득하는데 만전을 기하기 위한 학습 코너

|단원별 모의고사|

영역별, 단계별 학습을 모두 마친 후 실전 연습을 위한 모의고사

교과서 파헤치기

- **단어Test1~3** 영어 단어 우리말 쓰기, 우리말을 영어 단어로 쓰기, 영영풀이에 해당하는 단어와 우리말 쓰기
- **대화문Test1~2** 대화문 빈칸 완성 및 전체 대화문 쓰기
- **본문Test1~5** 빈칸 완성, 우리말 쓰기, 문장 배열연습, 영어 작문하기 복습 등 단계별 반복 학습을 통해 교과서 지문에 대한 완벽한 습득
- **구석구석지문Test1~2** 지문 빈칸 완성 및 전문 영어로 쓰기

이책의 차례 # Contents

Lesson

3

For the Love of Our Country

 의사소통 기능

- 알고 있는 내용 진술하기

  A: Wasn't Jeong Yakyong a scholar in the Joseon Dynasty?

  B: Yeah, but it is said that he was also a detective.

- 허락 요청하기

  A: Is it okay if I take pictures in the museum?

  B: Sure. Go ahead.

 언어 형식

- 접속사 if

  I was not sure **if** he was telling the truth.

- 과거완료

  When I was sixteen years old, my family **had** already **made** an arrangement for me to marry him.

Words & Expressions

교과서

Key Words

- **afterwards**[ǽftərdz] 부 나중에, 그 뒤에
- **already**[ɔ:lrédi] 부 이미, 벌써
- **article**[á:rtikl] 명 기사
- **biography**[baiágəfi] 명 자서전, 전기
- **bring**[briŋ] 동 가져오다
- **chest**[ʧest] 명 서랍장, 큰 상자, 장롱
- **clinic**[klínik] 명 병원, 진료소
- **detective**[ditékiv] 명 형사, 탐정
- **disappointing**[dìsəpɔ́intiŋ] 형 실망시키는
- **Dynasty**[dáinəsti] 명 왕조
- **embarrassing**[imbǽrəsiŋ] 형 부끄러운, 당황스러운
- **female**[fí:meil] 명 여자 형 여자의, 여성의
- **fight**[fait] 동 싸우다
- **fortress**[fɔ́:rtris] 명 요새
- **fortune**[fɔ́:rʧən] 명 재산, 행운
- **gamble**[gǽmbl] 동 도박하다, ~을 도박으로 잃다
- **gambling house** 도박장
- **general**[dʒénərəl] 명 장군
- **horrible**[hɔ́:rəbl] 형 끔찍한
- **husband**[hʌ́zbənd] 명 남편
- **include**[inklú:d] 동 ~을 포함하다
- **independence**[ìndipéndəns] 명 독립, 광복
- **invention**[invénʃən] 명 발명품, 발명
- **Japanese**[dʒæpəní:z] 형 일본의 명 일본어
- **leave**[li:v] 동 맡기다, 남기다
- **locker**[lákər] 명 사물함
- **machine**[məʃí:n] 명 기계, 기구
- **Manchuria**[mænʧúərə] 명 만주 형 만주의

- **marriage**[mǽridʒ] 명 결혼, 혼인
- **marry**[mǽri] 동 결혼하다, 혼인하다
- **merchant**[mɔ́:rʧənt] 명 상인
- **move**[mu:v] 동 이동시키다, 이동하다
- **movement**[mú:vmənt] 명 (정치적·사회적) 운동
- **museum**[mju:zí:əm] 명 박물관, 기념관
- **musical instrument** 악기
- **object**[ábdʒikt] 명 물건
- **odd**[ɑd] 형 이상한
- **officer**[ɔ́:fisər] 명 경찰관, 장교
- **pilot**[páilət] 명 조종사, 비행사
- **realistic**[rì:əlístik] 형 진짜 같은, 사실적인
- **realize**[rí:əlàiz] 동 깨닫다
- **ruin**[rú:in] 동 망치다, 파산시키다
- **save**[seiv] 동 구하다
- **scholar**[skálər] 명 학자
- **since**[sins] 접 ~이기 때문에, ~한 이래로
- **social studies** 사회
- **solve**[sɑlv] 동 해결하다, 풀다
- **strange**[streindʒ] 형 낯선, 모르는
- **Sudan**[su:dǽn] 명 수단 (민주 공화국)
- **truth**[tru:θ] 명 진실, 사실
- **village**[vílidʒ] 명 마을, 농촌
- **whenever**[hwenévər] 접 ~할 때마다, ~하면
- **whisper**[hwíspər] 동 속삭이다, (사람·일에 대하여) 소곤소곤 이야기하다
- **wonder**[wʌ́ndər] 동 궁금하다
- **wooden**[wúdn] 형 나무로 된, 목재의
- **would**[wəd] 동 (과거에 있어서의 습관·습성·반복적 동작) ~(하곤) 했다

Key Expressions

- **ask for**: 청구하다, 청하다
- **at that moment**: 그 순간에
- **at this hour**: 이 시간에
- **be used to (동)명사**: ~하는 데 익숙하다
- **behind one's back**: ~ 몰래, ~의 등 뒤에서
- **by 동사ing**: ~함으로써
- **devote one's life to 명사**: ~에 일생을 바치다
- **hear of[about]** ~: ~에 대해 듣다
- **instead of**: ~ 대신에

- **Is it okay if I** ~?: 제가 ~해도 될까요?
- **It is said that 주어+동사** ~: (사람들이) ~라고 한다
- **keep a secret**: 비밀을 지키다
- **make an arrangement**: ~을 결정하다
- **so+형용사/부사+that 주어+동사**: 너무 ~해서 …하다
- **take a look at** ~: ~을 보다
- **try on**: 입어 보다, 신어 보다
- **yell at**: ~에게 고함치다, ~에게 호통치다

Word Power

※ 명사형 어미 -age(~하는 행위, 상태)

- □ **marry**(결혼하다)+**-age**(~의 상태) → **marriage**(결혼)
- □ **pack**(싸다)+**-age**(~한 것) → **package**(꾸러미, 하나로 묶음)
- □ **use**(사용하다)+**-age**(법) → **usage**(사용법)
- □ **cour**(마음)+**-age**(~의 상태) → **courage**(용기, 용감)
- □ 라틴어 **damnum**(손해)+**-age**(상태, 요금) → **damage**(손해, 손상)
- □ 라틴어 **ab**(~으로)+**ante**(앞)+**-age**(상태) → **advantage**(우위, 우세)

※ 부사형 접미어 -ward(s)(방향, ~쪽으로)

- □ **after**(뒤에, 후에)+**-ward**(~쪽으로) → **afterwards**(후에, 나중에)
- □ **back**(뒤)+**-ward**(~쪽으로) → **backwards**(뒤로)
- □ **up**(위)+**-ward**(~쪽으로) → **upwards**(위로)
- □ **fore**(앞)+**-ward**(~쪽으로) → **forwards**(앞으로)
- □ **in**(안)+**-ward**(~쪽으로) → **inward**(안으로)
- □ **out**(바깥에)+**-ward**(~쪽으로) → **outward**(밖으로)

English Dictionary

□ **article** 기사
→ a piece of writing about a particular subject that is published in a newspaper or magazine
신문이나 잡지에 발행되는 특정한 주제에 대해 쓴 글

□ **biography** 자서전, 전기
→ a book that someone writes about someone else's life
누군가가 다른 누군가의 삶에 대해 쓴 책

□ **chest** 서랍장, 큰 상자, 장롱
→ a large strong heavy box used for storing things
물건을 보관하기 위해 사용되는 크고 무거운 상자

□ **female** 여자의, 여성의
→ relating to women or girls
여자나 여자아이와 관련된

□ **fortress** 요새
→ a large strong building used for defending an important place
중요한 장소를 방어하기 위해 사용되는 크고 튼튼한 건물

□ **fortune** 재산
→ a very large amount of money
매우 많은 돈

□ **general** 장군
→ an officer of very high rank in the army or air force
육군이나 공군에서 높은 계급을 가진 장교

□ **include** ~을 포함하다
→ to contain someone or something as a part
사람이나 사물을 어떤 것의 일부로 내포하다

□ **independence** 독립
→ freedom from control by another country or organization
다른 나라나 조직에 의한 통제로부터 벗어난 자유

□ **merchant** 상인
→ someone who buys and sells goods in large quantities
많은 양의 물건을 사고파는 사람

□ **movement** (정치적 · 사회적) 운동
→ a gradual development or change of an attitude, opinion, or policy
태도, 의견 또는 정책의 점진적인 발전 또는 변화

□ **ruin** 망치다, 파산시키다
→ to make someone lose all their money or power
누군가로 하여금 그들의 돈이나 권력을 모두 잃게 만들다

□ **scholar** 학자
→ someone who studies a particular subject and knows a lot about it, especially a subject that is not scientific
특히 과학적인 주제가 아닌 특정 주제에 대해 공부하고 많이 아는 사람

□ **save** 구하다
→ to make someone or something safe from danger, harm, or destruction
위험, 해로움, 또는 파괴로부터 사람이나 사물을 안전하게 만들다

[01~02] 다음 밑줄 친 부분과 바꿔 쓸 수 있는 말을 고르시오.

01
> We were <u>rescued</u> from the sinking ship by a passing fishing boat.

① trapped　② protected　③ saved
④ rushed　⑤ searched

02
> Buffett made <u>a lot of money</u> through intelligent investments.

① a move　② a result　③ a chance
④ a fortune　⑤ a poverty

03 중요 다음 밑줄 친 부분의 의미로 알맞지 <u>않은</u> 것은?

① He is a writer rather than a <u>scholar</u>. (학자)
② She was clearly speaking the <u>truth</u>. (진실)
③ The soldiers were ready to defend the <u>fortress</u>. (요새)
④ Have you ever been to the War <u>Memorial</u> Museum of Korea? (기념관)
⑤ He was recently promoted to <u>general</u>. (일반적인 것)

04 다음 빈칸에 들어갈 말을 고르시오.

> It was really _____ to find all our money stolen.

① terrific　② confident　③ boring
④ horrible　⑤ exciting

05 다음 제시된 단어를 사용하여 자연스러운 문장을 만들 수 <u>없는</u> 것은? (형태 변화 가능)

> hear　make　take　try

① Let's _____ an arrangement of our destination.
② She said she would _____ her life to public service.
③ Do you have any jackets I could _____ on?
④ It's an interesting place. Do you want to _____ a look around?
⑤ Have you _____ about the garage sale?

06 서답형 두 문장이 같은 의미가 되도록 빈칸을 채우시오. (주어진 철자로 시작할 것)

> You should talk to Karen because she's the one responsible for it.
> = You should talk to Karen s_____ she's the one responsible for it.

07 중요 다음 영영풀이가 나타내는 말을 고르시오.

> a gradual development or change of an attitude, opinion, or policy

① movement　② culture
③ model　④ volunteer
⑤ activity

01 우리말 해석에 맞게 주어진 단어를 알맞게 배열하시오.

(1) 그는 새로운 안경에 익숙해지려고 노력하면서 늙은이처럼 걸었다.

➡ He walked like an old man _____ _____. (glasses, be, to, trying, to, new, used)

(2) 사람들은 그녀가 전 세계를 다녀왔다고 말한다.

➡ _____ (that, all, said, world, she, is, the, been, over, it, has)

(3) 나는 그의 등 뒤에서 이렇게 얘기하는 것을 싫어한다.

➡ _____ (talking, behind, like, back, his, hate, this, I)

(4) 내가 사진을 찍어도 괜찮을까요?

➡ _____ (a, okay, picture, I, if, it, take, is)

02 빈칸에 적절한 말을 주어진 단어를 변형하여 채우시오.

> She took part in the March 1st Movement for Korea's _____. (depend)

03 두 문장이 같은 의미가 되도록 주어진 단어를 이용하여 빈칸을 채우시오.

> He was strong enough to lift it.
> = He was _____ strong _____ _____ lift it. (can)

04 다음 제시된 의미에 맞는 단어를 주어진 철자로 시작하여 빈칸에 쓰고, 알맞은 것을 골라 문장을 완성하시오.

> • i_____ : to contain someone or something as a part
> • r_____ : to make someone lose all their money or power
> • s_____ : to make someone or something safe from danger, harm, or destruction

(1) Some say spoilers _____ the story.
(2) Wearing a seat belt can help _____ your life.
(3) The price for the hotel _____s breakfast.

05 다음 빈칸에 공통으로 들어갈 말을 쓰시오.

> • The building was destroyed _____ fire in 2004.
> • She earns extra money _____ babysitting.

06 다음 우리말에 맞도록 빈칸에 알맞은 말을 쓰시오.

(1) LA Times에 직장 내 괴롭힘에 대한 흥미로운 기사가 있었다.

➡ There was an interesting _____ in the LA Times about bullying at work.

(2) 우리는 자주 저녁 산책을 하곤 했다.

➡ We _____ often have a walk of an evening.

① 알고 있는 내용 진술하기

A: Wasn't Jeong Yakyong a scholar in the Joseon Dynasty?

정약용이 조선왕조 때의 학자가 아니었나요?

B: Yeah, but it is said that he was also a detective.

네, 하지만 그는 또한 탐정이었다는 말이 있어요.

■ 'It is said that 주어+동사 ~.'는 '(사람들이) ~라고 한다.'라는 뜻으로 that절의 내용에 대해 진술할 때 사용한다. 'is said'가 수동태 형태임에 주의한다.

■ 'It is said that 주어+동사 ~.'는 말하는 사람이 구체적으로 정해져 있지 않고 '(사람들이) ~라고 말했다'라는 의미로 사용하므로, 일반인인 'they[people]'를 주어로 'They[People] say that 주어+동사'.로 바꿔 쓸 수 있다.

알고 있는 내용 진술하기

- It is said that 주어+동사 ~. (~라고 한다.)
- It is believed that 주어+동사 ~. (~라고 믿어진다.)
- It is thought that 주어+동사 ~. (~라고 생각된다.)
- They[People] say (that) 주어+동사 ~. (사람들이 ~라고 말한다.)

핵심 Check

1. 우리말과 일치하도록 주어진 단어를 알맞게 배열하여 문장을 만드시오.

> A: _____ in front of the City Hall this weekend.
> (that, is, will, a, said, it, there, be, festival, big)
> B: I'm interested in that. How about going there?

2. 다음 문장과 같은 의미가 되도록 주어진 단어를 이용하여 쓰시오.

> They say that he is a liar.

➡ _____ (said)

3. 다음 우리말과 일치하도록 빈칸에 알맞은 말을 쓰시오.

보라색은 클레오파트라가 가장 좋아하는 색이었다고 한다.

➡ _____ a favorite color of Cleopatra.

② 허락 요청하기

> A: Is it okay if I take pictures in the museum? 박물관에서 사진을 찍어도 괜찮나요?
> B: Sure. Go ahead. 물론이죠. 그렇게 하세요.

- 'Is it okay if I ~?'는 '제가 ~해도 될까요?'라는 뜻으로 어떤 행동을 하기 전에 허가를 요청할 때 사용하는 표현이다. if 다음에는 허락을 구하는 내용을 쓴다.

- 허가를 묻는 다른 표현으로 'Can I ~?', 'Are we allowed to 동사원형 ~?', I'm wondering if I ~. 등이 있다.

허락 요청하기

- Is it okay if I ~?
- Can[May] I ~?
- Would it be all right if I ~?
- Is it possible that I ~?
- I'm wondering if I ~.
- Are we allowed to 동사원형 ~?

허락을 요청하는 질문에 답하기

〈허락하기〉
- Sure.   • Of course.   • Certainly.   • Why not?   • No problem.

〈거절하기〉
- I'm sorry, but you can't[may not]
- I'm afraid not.
- You're not allowed to 동사원형.
- You can't do that.
- I'm afraid you can't.
- No way!
- You're not permitted to do that.
- Not right now.

핵심 Check

4. 다음 우리말과 일치하도록 주어진 말을 이용해 빈칸을 완성하시오.

> A: _____ (okay, if, the guitar) (제가 기타를 연습해도 될까요?)
> B: OK, but you're not allowed to practice after 10 p.m.

5. 우리말과 일치하도록 주어진 단어를 배열하여 영작하시오.

> A: _____ (okay, to, it, you, if, is, next, sit, I)
> (내가 당신 옆에 앉아도 될까요?)
> B: No problem.

 Listen & Talk 1 A-1

M: Lisa, ❶what are you reading?

W: I'm reading a ❷biography of Gwon Giok.

M: ❸I haven't heard about her. Who is she?

W: She was the first ❹female pilot in Korea. ❺It is said that she had over 7,000 hours of flying time.

M: Wow, I didn't know that.

| |
| M: Lisa, 너 뭐 읽고 있니? |
| W: 권기옥의 전기를 읽고 있어. |
| M: 그녀에 대해 들어본 적이 없어. 그녀는 누구니? |
| W: 그녀는 한국의 첫 번째 여성 조종사야. 그녀는 비행시간이 7,000 시간이 넘는다고 해. |
| M: 와, 난 몰랐어. |

❶ 무엇을 읽고 있는지 현재진행형(be동사+동사-ing)을 이용해 질문하고 있다.

❷ biography: 자서전, 전기

❸ hear about ～: ～에 대해 듣다

❹ female: 여자; 여자의, 여성의 pilot: 조종사, 비행사

❺ 'It is said that 주어+동사 ～.'는 '(사람들이) ～라고 한다.'라는 뜻으로 that절의 내용에 대해 진술할 때 사용한다. over: ～을 넘어, ～보다 많은

Check(√) True or False

(1) Lisa is reading a novel about Gwon Giok.   T ☐ F ☐

(2) The man didn't know who Gwon Giok was.   T ☐ F ☐

(3) Gwon Giok was the first female pilot in Korea.   T ☐ F ☐

 Listen & Talk 2 A-1

W: Excuse me, you ❶can't take your backpack ❷inside the museum.

M: Oh, I didn't know that. Is it okay if I ❸bring in my water bottle?

W: ❹Yes, that's fine. You can ❺leave your bag in the locker.

M: Okay, thank you.

| |
| W: 죄송합니다만, 박물관에 가방을 가지고 들어갈 수 없어요. |
| M: 아, 몰랐어요. 물병은 가지고 들어가도 괜찮나요? |
| W: 네, 그건 괜찮아요. 가방은 라커에 두시면 돼요. |
| M: 알았어요. 감사합니다. |

❶ 어떤 일이 가능한지 묻고 답할 때 조동사 can을 사용할 수 있다.

❷ inside: ～ 안에

❸ bring in: 들여가다

❹ 'that's fine.'은 '그것은 괜찮다.'라는 의미로 상대방이 허락을 구하는 말을 했을 때 허락하는 표현이다. 이외의 허락의 표현에는 'Of course.', 'Certainly.', 'No problem.' 등이 있다.

❺ leave: 남기다, 맡기다

Check(√) True or False

(4) The museum allows people to take their backpack inside it.   T ☐ F ☐

(5) The woman can't bring in her water bottle.   T ☐ F ☐

Listen & Talk 1 B

W: Hey, Mark, ❶do you know about Father Lee Taeseok?

M: Yeah, ❷I've heard of him. Why?

W: ❸Take a look at this article. He is going to ❹be included in the social studies textbook in South Sudan.

M: Wow, that's great.

W: Yeah, he helped the children ❺by building a clinic and a school. ❻It is said that such stories will be included in the textbook.

M: It is good to hear ❼that students will learn about such a great person.

W: 어이, Mark, 너 이태석 신부에 대해 아니?

M: 응, 그에 대해 들어본 적이 있어. 왜?

W: 이 기사를 봐. 그는 남수단의 사회 교과서에 실릴 거야.

M: 와, 그거 대단하구나.

W: 그래. 그는 병원과 학교를 지어 아이들을 도와주었어. 그런 이야기들이 교과서에 실릴 거라고 해.

M: 학생들이 그토록 훌륭한 사람에 대해 배울 거라는 말을 들으니 좋군.

❶ 'Do you know about ~?'은 '~에 대해서 알고 있어?'라는 의미로 상대방에게 알고 있는지 묻는 표현이다. 'Have you heard about ~?'이나 'Are you aware of ~?'로 바꿔 쓸 수 있다.

❷ 'I've heard of[about] ~'은 '~에 대해 들었다'라는 뜻으로 알고 있거나 들은 것에 대해 말할 때 쓰는 표현이다. 일반적으로 현재완료의 형태로 쓰지만 'I heard of[about] ~'라고 할 수도 있다

❸ take a look at ~: ~을 보다 article: 기사 ❹ include: ~을 포함하다 ❺ by 동사ing: ~함으로써

❻ 'It is said that 주어+동사 ~.'는 말하는 사람이 구체적으로 정해져 있지 않고 '(사람들이) ~라고 말한다'라는 의미로 사용하므로, 일반인인 'they[people]'를 주어로 'They[People] say that 주어+동사 ~.'로 바꿔 쓸 수 있다. (= They[People] say that such stories will be included in the textbook.)

❼ 동사 hear 뒤에 명사절을 이끄는 접속사 that이 사용되고 있다.

Check(√) True or False

(6) The woman read the article about how to be a great person. T ☐ F ☐

(7) Mark wasn't aware of Father Lee Taeseok. T ☐ F ☐

Communication Step B

A: This ❶is called the *Geojunggi*.

B: Wow, this ❷looks interesting.

A: This is a machine ❸that moves heavy objects. It is said that ❹it helped to build the Hwaseong Fortress only in 28 months.

B: How amazing! Is it okay if I take a closer look at it?

A: Sure.

A: 이것은 거중기라고 불려.

B: 와, 이거 흥미 있어 보이는데.

A: 이것은 무거운 물체들을 옮기는 기계야. 그것은 화성 요새를 겨우 28개월 만에 짓는 데 도움이 되었다고 해.

B: 정말 놀랍다! 그걸 더 자세히 봐도 괜찮겠니?

A: 물론이지.

❶ call이 5형식으로 사용하여 '[사람·물건을] (어떤 이름으로) 부르다, 이름을 붙이다'로 쓰일 수 있다. 원래는 'People call this the *Geojunggi*.'인 문장을 수동태로 바꾼 것이다.

❷ look+형용사: ~하게 보이다 / interesting은 현재분사형의 형용사로 '~하게 하는'의 뜻으로 감정을 유발하는 대상에 쓰인다.

❸ that은 주격 관계대명사로 which와 바꿔 쓸 수 있다. 주격 관계대명사는 생략할 수 없다.

❹ help (to+) 동사원형: ~ 하는 데 도움이 되다

Check(√) True or False

(8) They are looking at the *Geojunggi*. T ☐ F ☐

(9) *B* is interested in *Geojunggi*. T ☐ F ☐

Listen & Talk 1 Get Ready

A: Kim Deuksin was a painter.

B: ❶No! I read a book and ❷it is said that he was a scholar.

C: Don't fight. You are ❸both right.

❶ 다음에 'He was not a painter.'가 생략되어 있다.
❷ scholar: 학자 ❸ both: 둘 다

Listen & Talk 1 A-2

M: I watched an interesting movie yesterday. Jeong Yakyong was a ❶detective in it.

W: Jeong Yakyong? Wasn't he a scholar in the Joseon ❷Dynasty?

M: Yeah, but it is said that he was also a detective. He ❸solved ❹about 90 cases.

W: Oh, I didn't know that he was also a detective.

❶ detective: 형사, 탐정. in it에서 it은 남자가 어제 본 영화를 의미한다.
❷ Dynasty: 왕조 ❸ solve: 해결하다, 풀다
❹ 숫자 앞의 about은 '대략, 약'의 의미를 가진다.

Listen & Talk 2 A-2

W: Hi, ❶welcome to the National Museum. How can I help you?

M: Hi, is it okay if I ❷take pictures in the museum?

W: Yes, but please ❸don't use a flash.

M: Oh, I see. Thank you.

❶ welcome to 장소: (장소에) 오신 것을 환영합니다
❷ take pictures: 사진 찍다
❸ 명령문은 동사로 시작한다. 하지 말라고 할 때는 그 앞에 'Don't'를 붙인다.
flash: (카메라) 플래시

Listen & Talk 2 B

M: Hello, Ms. Jackson. How was your tour of the *Hanok Village*?

W: It was wonderful. The houses were really beautiful.

M: That's great.

W: Actually, I didn't ❶get the chance to have dinner. Is it okay if I cook in the kitchen at this hour?

M: Yes, but please remember ❷that the kitchen ❸closes at 10 p.m.

W: Okay. The kitchen is on the 5th floor, right?

M: Yes, it is. ❹Let me know if you need anything.

❶ get a chance: 기회를 가지다(= have a chance) 'to have dinner'는 앞의 the chance를 수식하는 형용사적 용법이다. ❷ that은 remember의 목적어인 명사절을 이끄는 접속사이다. ❸ 반복되는 사실에 대해서 현재시제를 사용할 수 있다. ❹ 상대방에게 어떤 일을 나에게 알려 달라고 부탁할 때 'let me know'를 이용해 말할 수 있다. let은 사역동사이므로 목적격보어 자리에 동사원형인 know를 사용한다.

Wrap Up 1

W: James, ❶what are you watching?

M: Oh, I'm watching a video about Yi Sunsin.

W: Isn't he the one ❷that saved Joseon from Japan?

M: Right. It is said that he won the war only with twelve wooden ships.

W: Wow, ❸how can that be possible?

M: He was a wise general who made creative plans.

❶ 무엇을 읽는 중인지 현재진행형(be동사+ing)을 사용하여 질문하고 있다.
❷ 주격 관계대명사(= who) ❸ '그것이 어떻게 가능하겠어요?'의 의미로 놀람을 나타내는 표현이며, 여기서는 가능하게 된 이유를 물어보고 있다.

● 다음 우리말과 일치하도록 빈칸에 알맞은 말을 쓰시오.

Listen & Talk 1 Get Ready

A: Kim Deuksin _____ a painter.

B: No! I _____ a book and _____ _____ _____ that he was a scholar.

C: Don't fight. You are _____ right.

해석

A: 김득신은 화가였어.
B: 아니야! 내가 책을 읽었는데 그는 학자였다고 해.
C: 싸우지 마. 너희 둘 다 옳아.

Listen & Talk 1 A-1

M: Lisa, _____ are you _____?

W: I'm reading a _____ of Gwon Giok.

M: I _____ _____ about her. Who is she?

W: She was _____ _____ _____ pilot in Korea. _____ _____ _____ she had _____ 7,000 hours of flying time.

M: Wow, I didn't know that.

M: Lisa, 너 뭐 읽고 있니?
W: 권기옥의 전기를 읽고 있어.
M: 그녀에 대해 들어본 적이 없어. 그녀는 누구니?
W: 그녀는 한국의 첫 번째 여성 조종사야. 그녀는 비행시간이 7,000 시간이 넘는다고 해.
M: 와, 난 몰랐어.

Listen & Talk 1 A-2

M: I watched an _____ movie yesterday. Jeong Yakyong was a _____ in it.

W: Jeong Yakyong? Wasn't he a _____ in the Joseon Dynasty?

M: Yeah, _____ _____ _____ _____ _____ _____ _____ a detective. He _____ about 90 cases.

W: Oh, I _____ _____ _____ he was also a detective.

M: 난 어제 흥미 있는 영화를 보았어. 그 영화에서 정약용이 탐정이었어
W: 정약용? 그는 조선 왕조의 학자 아니었니?
M: 응, 하지만 그는 탐정이기도 했다고 해. 그는 약 90개의 사건을 해결했어.
W: 아, 그가 또한 탐정이었다는 건 몰랐어.

Listen & Talk 1 B

W: Hey, Mark, do you _____ _____ Father Lee Taeseok?

M: Yeah, I've _____ of him. Why?

W: _____ _____ _____ _____ this article. He is going _____ _____ _____ in the social studies textbook in South Sudan.

M: Wow, that's great.

W: Yeah, he _____ the children _____ _____ _____ _____ and a school. It is said _____ _____ _____ will _____ the textbook.

M: It is good _____ hear that students will learn about _____ a great person.

W: 어이, Mark, 너 이태석 신부에 대해 아니?
M: 응, 그에 대해 들어본 적이 있어. 왜?
W: 이 기사를 봐. 그는 남수단의 사회 교과서에 실릴 거야.
M: 와, 그거 대단하구나.
W: 그래, 그는 병원과 학교를 지어 아이들을 도와주었어. 그런 이야기들이 교과서에 실릴 거라고 해.
M: 학생들이 그토록 훌륭한 사람에 대해 배울 거라는 말을 들으니 좋군.

Listen & Talk 2 A-1

W: Excuse me, you _____ _____ your backpack inside the _____.

M: Oh, I didn't know that. _____ _____ _____ if I bring in my water bottle?

W: Yes, that's fine. You can _____ your bag _____ the locker.

M: Okay, thank you.

해석

W: 죄송합니다만, 박물관에 가방을 가지고 들어갈 수 없어요.

M: 아, 몰랐어요. 물병은 가지고 들어가도 괜찮나요?

W: 네, 그건 괜찮아요. 가방은 라커에 두시면 돼요.

M: 알았어요. 감사합니다.

Listen & Talk 2 A-2

W: Hi, welcome _____ the National Museum. _____ can I help you?

M: Hi, _____ _____ _____ _____ _____ _____ _____ _____ the museum?

W: Yes, but please _____ use a flash.

M: Oh, I see. Thank you.

W: 안녕하세요, 국립박물관에 오신 걸 환영합니다. 무엇을 도와드릴까요?

M: 안녕하세요, 박물관에서 사진을 찍어도 괜찮나요?

W: 네, 하지만 플래시는 사용하지 마세요.

M: 아, 알겠습니다. 감사합니다.

Listen & Talk 2 B

M: Hello, Ms. Jackson. _____ _____ your tour of the *Hanok Village*?

W: It was wonderful. The houses _____ really beautiful.

M: That's great.

W: Actually, I didn't _____ _____ _____ _____ have dinner. Is it _____ _____ cook in the kitchen at this hour?

M: Yes, but please _____ _____ the kitchen closes _____ 10 p.m.

W: Okay. The kitchen is _____ the 5th floor, right?

M: Yes, it is. _____ _____ _____ _____ you need anything.

M: 안녕하세요. Jackson 씨. 한옥 마을 관광은 어땠어요?

W: 굉장했어요. 집들이 정말 아름다웠습니다.

M: 대단하네요.

W: 사실 전 저녁식사를 할 기회가 없었어요. 이 시간에 부엌에서 요리해도 괜찮나요?

M: 네, 하지만 부엌이 오후 10시에 문을 닫는 걸 기억하세요.

W: 알겠습니다. 부엌은 5층에 있죠, 맞나요?

M: 네, 그래요. 무언가 필요하시면 제게 말씀해 주세요.

Communication Step A

M: All right, everyone! This way, please. Now, we _____ _____ _____ the Joseon Dynasty. _____ _____ _____ _____, there were _____ interesting _____. This one _____ the *Jagyeongnu*.

W: Is it a _____ _____?

M: Actually, this is a water clock. _____ _____ _____ the oldest and the _____ water clock in Korea.

W: _____ amazing! _____ _____ _____ _____ I take a picture of it?

M: Sure.

M: 좋아요, 여러분! 이쪽으로 오세요. 이제, 우리는 조선 왕조로 옮겨갑니다. 보시다시피, 많은 흥미 있는 발명품들이 있습니다. 이것은 자격루라고 불립니다.

W: 그것은 악기인가요?

M: 사실은 이것은 물시계입니다. 그것은 한국에서 가장 오래되고, 가장 큰 물시계라고 합니다.

W: 정말 놀랍군요. 그것을 사진 찍어도 괜찮나요?

M: 물론입니다.

Wrap Up 1

W: James, _____ are you watching?

M: Oh, I'm _____ a video about Yi Sunsin.

W: _____ _____ the one that saved Joseon from Japan?

M: Right. _____ _____ _____ _____ _____ _____ the war only with twelve wooden ships.

W: Wow, _____ can that be _____?

M: He was a wise _____ _____ _____ _____ plans.

W: James, 뭘 보고 있니?

M: 아, 이순신에 관한 비디오를 보고 있어.

W: 그는 일본으로부터 조선을 구한 사람 아니니?

M: 맞아. 그는 겨우 12척의 목선으로 전쟁에 이겼다고 해.

W: 와, 그게 어떻게 가능할 수 있지?

M: 그는 창의적인 계획을 세운 현명한 장군이었어.

Wrap Up 2

W: Excuse me, sir. _____ _____ _____ _____ have curry or *bibimbap*?

M: _____ _____ _____ have *bibimbap*, please.

W: _____ you are.

M: Thank you. Oh, _____ _____ _____ I use the bathroom now?

W: Sure, but _____ the seat light is _____, you should _____ in your seat.

M: Okay, thank you.

W: 실례합니다, 선생님. 카레를 드시겠어요 아니면 비빔밥을 드시겠어요?

M: 비빔밥을 먹고 싶습니다.

W: 여기 있습니다.

M: 고마워요. 아, 지금 화장실을 이용해도 괜찮나요?

W: 그럼요, 하지만 좌석 불이 켜져 있으면 선생님 좌석에 있으셔야 합니다.

M: 알았어요, 감사합니다.

01 주어진 문장 이후에 올 대화의 순서를 바르게 배열한 것을 고르시오.

> Lisa, what are you reading?

> (A) Wow, I didn't know that.
> (B) She was the first female pilot in Korea. It is said that she had over 7,000 hours of flying time.
> (C) I'm reading a biography of Gwon Giok.
> (D) I haven't heard about her. Who is she?

① (B) – (A) – (C) – (D)　　② (B) – (C) – (A) – (D)
③ (C) – (A) – (B) – (D)　　④ (C) – (B) – (A) – (D)
⑤ (C) – (D) – (B) – (A)

[02~03] 다음 대화를 읽고 물음에 답하시오.

> W: Hi, welcome to the National Museum. How can I help you?
> M: Hi, is it okay (A)_____ I take pictures in the museum?
> W: (B)_____, but please don't use a flash.
> M: Oh, I see. Thank you.

02 빈칸 (A)에 알맞은 말을 고르시오

① that　　　　② if　　　　③ while
④ what　　　　⑤ though

03 빈칸 (B)에 알맞은 말을 <u>모두</u> 고르시오.

① No, you can't　　② Okay　　③ Of course not
④ Sure, go ahead　　⑤ Yes

04 밑줄 친 우리말을 주어진 단어를 이용해 영작하시오.

> A: 내가 창문을 열어도 되나요?
> B: Sorry, you can't.

➡ _____ (if, okay)

[01~02] 다음 대화를 읽고 물음에 답하시오.

M: I watched an interesting movie yesterday. (①) Jeong Yakyong was a (A)_____ in it. (②)
W: Jeong Yakyong? (③)
M: Yeah, but it is said that he was also a (B)_____. (④) <u>He solved about 90 cases.</u> (⑤)
W: Oh, I didn't know that he was also a (C)_____.

 01 위 대화의 ①~⑤ 중 주어진 문장이 들어갈 알맞은 곳은?

> Wasn't he a scholar in the Joseon Dynasty?

①   ②   ③   ④   ⑤

02 밑줄 친 부분을 근거로 (A)~(C)에 알맞은 말을 고르시오.

① diplomat   ② detective
③ reporter   ④ victim
⑤ painter

[03~04] 다음 대화를 읽고 물음에 답하시오.

M: Lisa, what are you reading? (①)
W: I'm reading a biography of Gwon Giok. (②)
M: I haven't heard about her. (③)
W: She was the first female pilot in Korea. (④) It is said that she had over 7,000 hours of flying time.
M: Wow, I didn't know that. (⑤)

03 위 대화의 ①~⑤ 중 주어진 문장이 들어갈 알맞은 곳은?

> Who is she?

①   ②   ③   ④   ⑤

 04 위 대화를 읽고 답할 수 없는 질문을 모두 고르시오.

① What kind of book is Lisa reading?
② How many hours of flying time did Gwon Giok have?
③ Who was the first male pilot in Korea?
④ Why is Lisa reading the book about Gwon Giok?
⑤ Has the man heard about Gwon Giok?

05 다음 중 짝지어진 대화가 어색한 것은?

① A: Is it okay if I turn on the air conditioning?
   B: I'm afraid not. I feel so cold now.
② A: You didn't hand in the homework?
   B: I'm sorry. Is it okay if I submit it tomorrow?
③ A: May I turn on the heater?
   B: Sure. Go ahead.
④ A: Is it possible that I use your cellphone?
   B: Certainly. I didn't bring it today.
⑤ A: Is it okay if I go out and play?
   B: I'm sorry, but it's too late.

06 대화가 자연스럽게 연결되도록 (A)~(D)를 순서대로 가장 적절하게 배열한 것은?

> M: Hello, Ms. Jackson. How was your tour of the *Hanok Village*?
> W: _____
> M: _____
> W: _____
> M: _____
> W: Okay. The kitchen is on the 5th floor, right?
> M: Yes, it is. Let me know if you need anything.

> (A) That's great.
> (B) Actually, I didn't get the chance to have dinner. Is it okay if I cook in the kitchen at this hour?
> (C) It was wonderful. The houses were really beautiful.
> (D) Yes, but please remember that the kitchen closes at 10 p.m.

① (B) – (A) – (C) – (D)
② (B) – (C) – (A) – (D)
③ (C) – (A) – (B) – (D)
④ (C) – (B) – (A) – (D)
⑤ (C) – (D) – (B) – (A)

[07~09] 다음 대화를 읽고 물음에 답하시오.

> W: Hey, Mark, (A)_____
> M: Yeah, I've heard of him. (①) Why?
> W: (B)_____ a look at this article. (②) He is going to be included in the social studies textbook in South Sudan. (③)
> M: Wow. that's great. (④)
> W: Yeah, he helped the children by building a clinic and a school. (⑤)
> M: It is good to hear that students will learn about such a great person.

 07 위 대화의 ①~⑤ 중 주어진 문장이 들어갈 알맞은 곳은?

> It is said that such stories will be included in the textbook.

①   ②   ③   ④   ⑤

08 빈칸 (A)에 알맞지 <u>않은</u> 말을 <u>모두</u> 고르시오.

① what do you think about Father Lee Taeseok?
② do you know about Father Lee Taeseok?
③ are you reading about Father Lee Taeseok?
④ have you heard of Father Lee Taeseok?
⑤ do you know who Father Lee Taeseok is?

09 빈칸 (B)에 알맞은 말을 고르시오.

① Take   ② See   ③ Make
④ Stay   ⑤ Find

10 빈칸 (A)에 알맞지 <u>않은</u> 말을 <u>모두</u> 고르시오.

> A: Do you know who Kim Deuksin is?
> B: Yes. Isn't he a scholar from the Joseon Dynasty?
> A: Right. I saw a TV show and it is (A)_____ that he read one book over 10,000 times.

① said   ② allowed
③ thought   ④ possible
⑤ believed

[01~02] 다음 대화를 읽고 물음에 답하시오.

A: Do you know (A)_____?
B: Yes. Isn't she an artist from the Joseon Dynasty?
A: Right. I saw a TV show and (B)_____. (that, painted, so, paintings, gathered, were, birds, is, the, that, realistic, her, tree, said, around, it)

01 Who is Shin Saimdang?을 빈칸 (A)에 어법에 맞게 써 넣으시오.

➡ _____

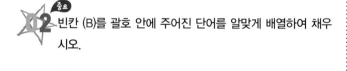 빈칸 (B)를 괄호 안에 주어진 단어를 알맞게 배열하여 채우시오.

➡ _____
_____

[03~04] 다음 대화를 읽고 물음에 답하시오.

W: Hi, welcome to the National Museum. How can I help you?
M: Hi, is it okay (A)_____ I take pictures in the museum?
W: (B)_____, but please don't use a flash.
M: Oh, I see. Thank you.

03 빈칸 (A)에 알맞은 말을 쓰시오.

➡ _____

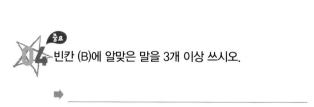 빈칸 (B)에 알맞은 말을 3개 이상 쓰시오.

➡ _____

[05~07] 다음 대화를 읽고 물음에 답하시오.

W: Hey, Mark, do you know about Father Lee Taeseok?
M: Yeah, I've heard of him. Why?
W: Take a look at this article. He is going to be included in the social studies textbook in South Sudan.
M: Wow. that's great.
W: Yeah, he helped the children (A)_____ building a clinic and a school. It is said that (B)_____ stories will be included in the textbook.
M: It is good to hear that students will learn about (C)_____ a great person.

05 빈칸 (A)에 알맞은 전치사를 쓰시오.

➡ _____

06 빈칸 (B)와 (C)에 공통으로 들어갈 말을 쓰시오.

➡ _____

07 위 대화의 내용에 맞게 빈칸에 알맞은 말을 쓰시오.

Father Lee Taeseok's story that he _____ a clinic and a school to help the children _____ _____ _____ in the social studies textbook in _____ _____.

08 밑줄 친 우리말과 일치하도록 주어진 단어를 이용하여 영작하시오.

A: 내가 너의 모자를 써 보아도 될까?
B: Yes, go ahead.

➡ _____ (okay, try, on)

Grammar

① 접속사 if

> • I was not sure **if** he was telling the truth. 나는 그가 진실을 말하고 있는지 확신할 수 없었다.
>
> • I don't know **if** Sarah will like the idea. 사라가 그 아이디어를 좋아할지 모르겠어요.

■ '~인지 (아닌지)'라는 의미의 접속사로 어떠한 사실의 여부를 확인하거나 불확실함을 나타낼 때 쓰이며, 주로 ask, find out, know, see, tell, wonder, be not sure 등의 동사의 목적어 역할을 하는 명사절을 이 끈다. if 뒤에 오는 절은 의문사가 없는 간접의문문으로 'if[whether]+주어+동사'의 어순으로 쓴다.

• I asked him **if** I could borrow his car. 나는 그에게 차를 빌려 달라고 부탁했다.

• I wonder **if** he is at home. 그가 집에 있을지 모르겠다.

• I can't tell **if** it will rain or not. 비가 올지 안 올지 모르겠다.

• I'm not sure. + Can I ask this kind of question?

→ I'm not sure **if** I can ask this kind of question. 이런 질문해도 될까 모르겠네요.

■ if가 명사절을 이끄는 접속사로 그 명사절이 문장 내에서 동사의 목적어로 쓰일 때는 whether로 바꿔 쓸 수 있다. whether가 이끄는 절이 주어 역할을 할 경우에는 if로 바꿔 쓸 수 없으며, whether 다음에는 or not을 바로 붙여 쓸 수 있지만, if는 바로 붙여 쓸 수 없다.

• When they asked me **if** I wanted the job, I said yes. 그들이 나에게 그 직장을 원하느냐고 물었을 때 난 그렇다 고 대답했다. [목적어]

= When they asked me **whether** I wanted the job, I said yes.

• **Whether** it's true or not doesn't matter. 그것이 진실이든 아니든 중요하지 않다. [주어]

= If it's true or not doesn't matter. (✗)

• It's questionable **whether** or not that will be true. 그게 사실일지 어쩔지는 의심스럽다.

= It's questionable if or not that will be true. (✗)

cf. if가 조건의 부사절을 이끌 때는 '만약 ~라면'이라는 의미로 쓰이며, whether가 부사절을 이끌 경우에 는 '~이든 (아니든)'이라는 '양보'의 의미로 쓰인다.

• **If** anyone calls, tell them I'm not at home. 누구든 전화하면 나 집에 없다고 해. [조건]

• I'm going **whether** you like it or not. 네가 좋아하든 안 하든 난 갈 거야. [양보]

핵심 Check

1. 다음 〈보기〉에서 알맞은 말을 골라 빈칸을 채우시오.

> ┤ 보기 ├
>
> whether, if

(1) I wonder _____ he is at home.

(2) Tell me _____ or not you are willing to believe it.

(3) I don't know _____ you can help me.

② 과거완료

> • When I was sixteen years old, my family **had** already **made** an arrangement for me to marry him. 내가 열여섯 살 때 나의 가족은 이미 내가 그와 결혼하기로 합의했다.
>
> • I was in a hotel, and I **had** just **finished** shaving. 전 그때 호텔에 있었는데 막 면도를 끝냈어요.

■ 과거완료는 과거 이전에 일어난 일이 과거의 어느 시점까지 영향을 미칠 때 쓰며, 'had+과거분사'의 형태로 쓴다. 과거완료도 현재완료처럼 완료, 경험, 계속, 결과의 용법이 있다. 또한 과거의 어느 시점보다 먼저 일어난 일이나 상태를 나타낼 때도 쓰이며 이것을 보통 '대과거'라고 한다.

• A young businessman **had** just **started** his own firm. (한 젊은 사업가가 막 자신의 회사를 열었다.) 〈완료〉

• He **had** never **learned** to read and write. (그는 읽고 쓰기를 전혀 배우지 못했다.) 〈경험〉

• She **had written** the letter for two hours. (그녀는 2시간 동안 그 편지를 쓰고 있었다.) 〈계속〉

• He **had gone** to America leaving his family in Korea. (그는 가족을 한국에 남겨 두고 미국으로 가버렸다.) 〈결과〉

• She wasn't recognizable after she **had had** plastic surgery. (성형 수술 후 그녀를 알아볼 수 없었다.) 〈대과거〉

■ 한 문장에 두 가지 과거의 일이 나올 때, 두 동작이 거의 동시에 일어났거나 시간차가 거의 없이 연속적으로 일어났을 경우에는 단순과거로 표현한다. 또, 접속사 after나 before가 쓰여 두 동작의 전후 관계가 명백할 때도 단순과거로 표현할 수 있다.

• He **closed** the door and **went** away. (그는 문을 닫고 가버렸다.) 〈시간차가 거의 없는 연속 동작〉

• His father **died** before he **was** born. (그의 아버지는 그가 태어나기 전에 돌아가셨다.) 〈전후 관계가 명백함〉

핵심 Check

2. 괄호 안에서 알맞은 말을 고르시오.

(1) She couldn't believe what she (has just heard / had just heard).

(2) Their friends knew that they (had lost / lost) their son a week before.

(3) His face grew dark after he (has heard / heard) the news.

01 다음 빈칸에 들어갈 말로 알맞은 것은?

> He remembered that he _____ them onto the table.

① toss   ② tosses   ③ tossed
④ has tossed   ⑤ had tossed

02 다음 괄호 안에서 알맞은 말을 고르시오.

(1) When I arrived at the station, the train (already left / had already left).

(2) He confessed to me that he (broke / had broken) the vase.

(3) I don't know (if / that) he will be able to come.

(4) Decide (if / whether) or not the answer is correct.

03 다음 빈칸에 알맞은 것은?

> I asked her _____ she was ready to go, and she nodded.

① that   ② what   ③ which
④ if   ⑤ unless

04 다음 우리말에 맞게 주어진 어휘를 바르게 배열하시오.

(1) 제 딸은 그때까지 아팠던 적이 한 번도 없어요.

(my daughter, been, then, sick, had, until, never)

➡ _____

(2) 잠이 막 들었을 때 누군가가 문을 노크했다. (I로 시작할 것)

(I, someone, the door, asleep, fallen, knocked, had, when, just, at)

➡ _____

(3) 그녀는 자신이 미래에 돌아올지 여부에 대해 확신하지 못한다.

(she, she, the future, will, is, return, sure, not, if, in)

➡ _____

01 다음 중 어법상 어색한 것은?

① I was so excited because I had never played yut before.

② When she arrived at the station, the first train already left.

③ They described a bear that had threatened them.

④ Tom has lived in LA for 12 years.

⑤ This was the first gold medal that Korea had ever won.

02 다음 중 어법상 바르지 않은 것은?

① I am not sure if he had lunch already.

② I asked her if she wanted to join our meeting.

③ If my guess is right, he must be about forty.

④ He asked her nicely that he could see her license.

⑤ Let your friends know that Thursday's the deadline.

03 다음 빈칸에 알맞은 말이 바르게 짝지어진 것은?

> • I wonder _____ my child expresses himself well in English.
> • I came across a pen that I _____ last week.

① if – had lost

② because – had lost

③ if – lost

④ because – lost

⑤ whether – have lost

04 다음 괄호 안에서 알맞은 말을 고르시오.

(1) She was the most remarkable woman he had ever (encounters / encountered).

(2) I walked the dog which Dad (had bought / bought) for me.

(3) Sartre (had practiced / practiced) playing the piano since childhood.

(4) Please tell me (whether / that) he is at home.

(5) Carol wants to know (if / that) the seat is vacant.

(6) We're debating (whether / if) or not to go skiing this winter.

05 주어진 문장의 틀린 부분을 찾아, 올바르게 고친 것을 고르시오.

> When Dave got there, Juliet already entered the theater by herself.

① When Dave got there, Juliet already enters the theater by herself.

② When Dave got there, Juliet has already entered the theater by herself.

③ When Dave got there, Juliet had already entered the theater by herself.

④ When Dave had got there, Juliet already entered the theater by herself.

⑤ When Dave had got there, Juliet already had entered the theater by herself.

06 다음 문장의 밑줄 친 부분 중 어법상 어색한 것은?

> I ⓐhave been, I ⓑthought, a ⓒbalanced reporter ⓓfor ⓔ26 years.

① ⓐ   ② ⓑ   ③ ⓒ
④ ⓓ   ⑤ ⓔ

07 빈칸 (A)와 (B)에 알맞은 것으로 바르게 짝지어진 것은?

> Sara wanted to know ___(B)___ the bag ___(A)___ away or not.

	(A)	(B)
①	whether	was thrown
②	that	was thrown
③	if	has been thrown
④	that	had been thrown
⑤	if	had been thrown

08 〈보기〉에서 알맞은 접속사를 골라 다음 빈칸을 채우시오. (한 번씩만 쓸 것.)

> ┌─ 보기 ┤
>
> whether, though, if, when, unless

(1) We will go on a picnic _____ it rains.

(2) She will forgive you _____ you apologize to her.

(3) Cross the road carefully _____ there is no car coming.

(4) Alicia put on a mask _____ working as a spy.

(5) They have never decided _____ or not he was killed.

[09~10] 다음 문장의 빈칸에 알맞은 말을 고르시오.

09

> When I got back home, my parents _____ out for a walk.

① goes   ② went   ③ going
④ has gone   ⑤ had gone

10

> I wonder _____ this soup will keep till tomorrow.

① since   ② unless   ③ if
④ after   ⑤ though

11 다음 우리말을 바르게 영작한 것을 고르시오.

> 그 일을 끝냈는지 물어봐도 될까요?

① May I ask though you finished the work?
② May I ask if you finished the work?
③ May I ask unless you finished the work?
④ May I ask as you finished the work?
⑤ May I ask since you finished the work?

12 다음 두 문장을 한 문장으로 바꿔 쓰고자 한다. 빈칸에 들어갈 알맞은 말을 쓰시오.

> • Cathy started to play the violin when she was 6.
> • Cathy played the violin successfully at the contest yesterday.
> = Cathy played the violin successfully at the contest yesterday as she _____ it since she was 6.

13 다음 밑줄 친 과거완료의 용법이 〈보기〉와 같은 것은?

> ─┤ 보기 ├─
> Kim <u>had been</u> ill for a couple of years.

① He <u>had</u> just <u>arrived</u> from the countryside.
② It was the best chicken soup I <u>had</u> ever <u>had</u>.
③ When you hired him, how long <u>had</u> he <u>practiced</u> law?
④ The people <u>had lost</u> faith in their politicians and faith in their government.
⑤ He realized that it <u>had been</u> a bad decision on his part.

서답형

14 다음 문장에서 어법상 어색한 것을 바르게 고쳐 다시 쓰시오.

(1) Please tell me what your sister is in her room.

➡ _____

(2) If he wants or not isn't that important.

➡ _____

(3) I suddenly remembered that I left the windows open.

➡ _____
_____

(4) I had never been to the big city ago.

➡ _____

(5) I found out that someone broke the lamp.

➡ _____

[15~16] 다음 우리말에 맞게 영작한 것을 고르시오.

15

> 그는 내게 고전 음악을 좋아하느냐고 물었다.

① He asked me that I liked classic music.
② He asked me what I liked classic music.
③ He asked me which I liked classic music.
④ He asked me if I liked classic music.
⑤ He asked me if or not I liked classic music.

16

> 나는 네게 얘기했던 카메라를 샀다.

① I bought the camera that I told you about.
② I bought the camera that I told you.
③ I bought the camera that I have told you about.
④ I bought the camera that I had told you.
⑤ I bought the camera that I had told you about.

중요

17 다음 중 어법상 어색한 것을 고르시오. (2개)

① He asked me if or not the book was boring.
② I remembered that I turned the stove on.
③ He had never been to any foreign countries.
④ When I arrived at the theater, the movie had already begun.
⑤ John wants to ask if you are going to go on a world tour this year.

01 시간 흐름에 따른 사건 전개에 맞게 빈칸을 채워 문장을 완성하시오.

> (1) My boy friend bought a ring for me the day before. → Yesterday I lost the ring.
>
> (2) Clare received flowers last Saturday. → Today her little brother threw them away.

(1) Yesterday I lost the ring that my boy friend ＿＿＿＿＿＿ the day before.

(2) Today Clare's little brother threw away the flowers that ＿＿＿＿＿＿ last Saturday.

02 다음을 when을 이용하여 한 문장으로 연결할 때 빈칸을 알맞게 채우시오. (시제에 유의할 것.)

(1) I went to the restaurant to have lunch with my friends. I arrived there. I remembered that I did not lock the door.
　→ When I arrived at the restaurant to have lunch with my friends, I remembered that I ＿＿＿＿＿＿ the door.

(2) I was supposed to meet Harry at the library. I went there very late. He already went back to his home. So, I couldn't meet him.
　→ When I got to the library to meet Harry, ＿＿＿＿＿＿ back to his home.

03 다음 우리말에 맞게 주어진 단어를 바르게 배열하시오.

(1) 이 음식들이 입맛에 맞으실지 모르겠군요. (I, your taste, these dishes, suit, wonder, will, if)
　➡ ＿＿＿＿＿＿＿＿＿＿＿＿

(2) 그가 집에 있는지 사무실에 있는지 모른다. (I, he, at the office, at home, is, don't, know, whether, or)
　➡ ＿＿＿＿＿＿＿＿＿＿＿＿

(3) 우리는 우리가 같은 학교에 다녔다는 걸 알게 되었다. (we, we, school, found, been, had, the, that, same, out, at)
　➡ ＿＿＿＿＿＿＿＿＿＿＿＿
　＿＿＿＿＿＿＿＿＿＿＿＿

(4) 내가 파리에 한 번도 못 가 보았다는 것에 그녀가 몹시 놀라는 눈치였다. (I, she, Paris, had, astonished, seemed, been, that, never, to)
　➡ ＿＿＿＿＿＿＿＿＿＿＿＿
　＿＿＿＿＿＿＿＿＿＿＿＿

04 다음 문장에서 잘못된 것을 알맞게 고치시오.

(1) If you said so or not doesn't matter now.
　➡ ＿＿＿＿＿＿＿＿＿＿

(2) This approach may be useful in assessing if or not the programme was of value.
　➡ ＿＿＿＿＿＿＿＿＿＿

(3) I couldn't decide if to have pizza or a hamburger.
　➡ ＿＿＿＿＿＿＿＿＿＿

05 그림을 보고, 주어진 어휘를 이용하여 빈칸을 알맞게 채우시오.

(1) The elderly man was afraid of skiing because he _____ skiing before. (never, learn)

(2) He wonders _____ about the appointment. (she, forgot)

06 알맞은 접속사를 이용하여 주어진 두 문장을 하나의 문장으로 쓰시오.

(1) • The man isn't sure.
　　• He can help her.
　　➡ _____

(2) • They don't know.
　　• Will he be promoted?
　　➡ _____

(3) • Would you tell me?
　　• He needs surgery or not.
　　➡ _____
　　_____

07 다음 두 문장을 because를 사용하여 한 문장으로 연결하시오. (두 사건의 시간차가 드러나도록 할 것.)

(1) • He won the contest.
　　• He practiced a lot for the contest.
　　➡ _____
　　_____

(2) • I couldn't take the class.
　　• The class was canceled.
　　➡ _____
　　_____

08 다음 문장에서 어법상 어색한 것을 바르게 고쳐 다시 쓰시오.

(1) He told me that he stole the money the other day.
　　➡ _____
　　_____

(2) No computer won even one game against a human player until then.
　　➡ _____

(3) I found my bag that I lost on the bus.
　　➡ _____

(4) I asked the lady that I could use the bathroom.
　　➡ _____

(5) I'm not sure if Santa gives me a nice gift or not.
　　➡ _____

(6) I couldn't decide if to buy it.
　　➡ _____

The Secret of My Father

In 1946, a strange man visited me and asked, "Are you Mr. Kim Yonghwan's daughter?"

For me, this was an odd question because I was more used to being
= Are you Mr. Kim Yonghwan's daughter?   be used to ~ing: ~하는 데 익숙하다
called the daughter of a *parakho*.

"I'm your father's friend. You may wonder if it is true, but your
= whether
father...," the man said.

At that moment, I was expecting disappointing news since I did not
disappointed(×)   이유를 나타내는 접속사
have good memories of my father.

Back in the 1920's, whenever people saw me in the village, they
과거 1920년대에
would say, "There goes the *parakho*'s daughter."
과거의 불규칙적 습관을 나타내는 조동사(~하곤 했다)
My father was a son from a very rich family. Instead of living the life
~하는 대신에   동명사
of a *seonbi*, he was always at the gambling house. That is why he was
because(×)
called a *parakho*, which means someone who ruins his family's fortune.
계속적 용법의 관계대명사(= and it)   = that
"Your father has gambled away all of the money, and now he's asking
gamble away: 도박으로 ~을 다 날리다[잃다]   요청하다
for more. Go and tell him that we have no more money left," my
더 이상 돈이 남아 있지 않다
mother would tell me whenever she sent me to the gambling house.
과거의 불규칙적 습관을 나타내는 조동사(~하곤 했다)
Then, my father would yell at me angrily, "Why did you come empty-
주격 보어로 쓰인 유사분사(명사+ed)
handed? Bring me more money!"

확인문제

● 다음 문장이 본문의 내용과 일치하면 T, 일치하지 않으면 F를 쓰시오.

1 The writer was more used to being called the daughter of a *parakho* than Mr. Kim Yonghwan's daughter. ☐

2 The writer was expecting terrific news though she did not have good memories of her father. ☐

3 The writer's father lived the life of a *seonbi*. ☐

---

strange 이상한, 낯선
odd 이상한
moment 순간
disappointing 실망스러운
back 돌아가서, 과거로 거슬러
whenever ~할 때마다
instead of ~하는 대신에
gambling 도박
ruin 망치다, 파산시키다
fortune 재산
yell 소리치다
angrily 화가 나서
empty-handed 빈손으로

When I was sixteen years old, my family had already made an arrangement for me to marry Mr. Seo. As part of the wedding tradition, Mr. Seo's family sent my family some money to buy a new chest for clothes.

Right before the wedding day, my mother came into my room and said, "Your father has taken the money for the chest."

I asked angrily, "How could he do such a horrible thing? What should we do now?"

"We have no choice. You'll have to take your aunt's old chest," my mother said.

"How embarrassing for the family," people would whisper behind my back.

Since the first day of marriage, life at my husband's house had been difficult for me.

"Your father, my dear friend...," my father's friend continued his story. "He was not a gambler. Your father sent the family money to the independence fighters in Manchuria. He made himself look like a gambler to keep this a secret from the Japanese officers."

At first, I was not sure if he was telling the truth. But afterwards, I found out the truth about my father and I realized that I had been wrong about him. Ever since that moment, I have been proud to be the daughter of a *parakho* who had devoted his life to the independence movement.

arrangement	협의, 합의
wedding	결혼, 결혼식
tradition	전통
chest	상자, 장롱
horrible	지긋지긋한, 끔찍한
choice	선택
embarrassing	난처한, 당혹스러운
behind one's back	~ 몰래, ~의 등 뒤에서
whisper	속삭이다
continue	계속하다
officer	경찰관
at first	처음에
truth	사실
afterwards	나중에, 그 후에
realize	깨닫다, 알아차리다

확인문제

● 다음 문장이 본문의 내용과 일치하면 T, 일치하지 <u>않으면</u> F를 쓰시오.

1 Mr. Seo's family sent the writer's family some money to buy a new chest for clothes. ☐

2 The writer's father sent the family money to the independence fighters in Manchuria. ☐

3 The writer's father devoted his life to gambling. ☐

● 우리말을 참고하여 빈칸에 알맞은 말을 쓰시오.

1 The _____ of My Father

2 In 1946, _____ _____ _____ visited me and asked, "Are you Mr. Kim Yonghwan's daughter?"

3 For me, this was _____ _____ _____ because I _____ _____ _____ _____ _____ _____ _____ the daughter of a *parakho*.

4 "I'm _____ _____ _____.

5 You may _____ _____ it is true, but your father...," the man said.

6 At that moment, I was expecting _____ news since I did not have _____ _____ of my father.

7 _____ in the 1920's, _____ people saw me in the village, they would say, "_____ _____ the *parakho*'s daughter."

8 My father was a son _____ a very rich family.

9 _____ _____ _____ the life of a *seonbi*, he was always at the gambling house.

10 _____ _____ _____ he was called a *parakho*, _____ means someone who _____ his family's fortune.

11 "Your father _____ _____ _____ all of the money, and now he's asking for more.

12 Go and tell him that we _____ _____ _____ _____ _____," my mother _____ tell me _____ she sent me to the gambling house.

13 Then, my father _____ _____ _____ me angrily, "Why did you come _____?

14 _____ me more money!"

---

1 아버지의 비밀

2 1946년에, 낯선 남자가 나를 찾아와 물었다. "당신이 김용환 씨의 딸입니까?"

3 나는 파락호의 딸이라고 불리는 것이 더 익숙했으므로 나에게 이것은 이상한 질문이었다.

4 "나는 당신 아버지의 친구입니다.

5 당신은 이것이 사실인지 의아하겠지만, 당신의 아버지는…,"이라고 그 남자는 말했다.

6 나는 내 아버지에 대해 좋은 기억을 가지고 있지 않았으므로 그 순간에 실망스러운 소식을 예상하고 있었다.

7 1920년대에 마을에서 사람들이 나를 볼 때마다 그들은 "저기에 파락호의 딸이 가네."라고 말하곤 했다.

8 나의 아버지는 매우 부유한 집안의 아들이었다.

9 선비의 삶을 사는 대신, 아버지는 항상 도박장에 계셨다.

10 그것이 그가 집안의 재산을 탕진하는 사람이라는 뜻의 파락호로 불린 이유이다.

11 "네 아버지는 도박으로 모든 돈을 써 버리고 지금 더 요구하고 계신다.

12 가서 더 이상 남아 있는 돈이 없다고 말씀드려라."라고 나의 어머니는 나를 도박장으로 보낼 때마다 말씀하시곤 했다.

13 그러면, 아버지는 나에게 화를 내시며 소리치셨다. "왜 빈손으로 왔니?

14 돈을 더 가져와!"

15 When I was sixteen years old, my family _____ _____ _____ _____ _____ for me to marry Mr. Seo.

16 _____ _____ _____ the wedding tradition, Mr. Seo's family sent my family some money to buy _____ _____ _____ _____ _____.

17 _____ _____ the wedding day, my mother came into my room and said, "Your father _____ _____ _____ _____ for the chest."

18 I asked angrily, "How could he do _____ _____ _____ _____?

19 _____ should we do now?"

20 "We have _____ _____.

21 _____ _____ _____ _____ your aunt's old chest," my mother said.

22 "_____ _____ for the family," people would whisper _____ .

23 Since the first day of marriage, life at my husband's house _____ _____ _____ _____ _____.

24 "Your father, my dear friend...," my father's friend _____ _____ _____.

25 "He was not _____ _____.

26 Your father sent the family money to the _____ _____ in Manchuria.

27 He _____ _____ look like a gambler to _____ _____ _____ _____ _____ the Japanese officers."

28 At first, I was not sure _____ he was telling the truth.

29 But _____, I found out the truth about my father and I realized that I _____ _____ _____ about him.

30 Ever since that moment, I have been proud to be the daughter of a *parakho* who _____ _____ _____ _____ _____ the independence movement.

---

15 내가 16살이 되었을 때, 나의 가족은 나를 서 씨와 결혼시키기로 이미 결정을 했었다.

16 결혼 풍습이 일부로, 서 씨네 가족은 새 장롱을 사라고 우리 가족에게 돈을 보냈다.

17 결혼식 바로 전날, 나의 어머니는 내 방에 들어오셔서 말씀하셨다. "네 아버지가 장롱을 살 돈을 가져 버렸다."

18 나는 화가 나서 물었다 "어떻게 그리 끔찍한 일을 하실 수 있나요?

19 우린 이제 어떡해요?"

20 "우리에게 선택권은 없구나.

21 큰어머니의 옛 장롱을 가져가야겠구나."라고 어머니가 말씀하셨다.

22 "가문에 부끄러운 일이야."라고 사람들이 내 뒤에서 속삭이곤 했다.

23 결혼 첫날부터, 남편의 집에서의 생활은 나에게 힘겨웠다.

24 "당신의 아버지, 나의 친애하는 친구…," 나의 아버지의 친구분은 그의 이야기를 이어가셨다.

25 "그는 도박꾼이 아니었어요.

26 당신의 아버지는 가족의 돈을 만주에 있는 독립운동가들에게 보냈답니다.

27 그는 이것을 일본 순사들에게 비밀로 하기 위해 그 자신을 도박꾼처럼 보이게 했어요."

28 처음엔, 나는 그분이 사실을 얘기하시는 건지 확신할 수 없었다.

29 그러나 나중에, 나는 나의 아버지에 대한 진실을 알게 되었고 내가 아버지에 관해 오해하고 있었다는 것을 깨달았다.

30 그 순간부터, 나는 독립운동에 그의 인생을 헌신하신 파락호의 딸인 것이 자랑스러웠다.

● 우리말을 참고하여 본문을 영작하시오.

1 아버지의 비밀
➡ _____

2 1946년에, 낯선 남자가 나를 찾아와 물었다. "당신이 김용환 씨의 딸입니까?"
➡ _____

3 나는 파락호의 딸이라고 불리는 것이 더 익숙했으므로 나에게 이것은 이상한 질문이었다. .
➡ _____

4 "나는 당신 아버지의 친구입니다.
➡ _____

5 당신은 이것이 사실인지 의아하겠지만, 당신의 아버지는…,"이라고 그 남자는 말했다.
➡ _____

6 나는 내 아버지에 대해 좋은 기억을 가지고 있지 않았으므로 그 순간에 실망스러운 소식을 예상하고 있었다.
➡ _____

7 1920년대에 마을에서 사람들이 나를 볼 때마다 그들은 "저기에 파락호의 딸이 가네."라고 말하곤 했다.
➡ _____
_____

8 나의 아버지는 매우 부유한 집안의 아들이었다.
➡ _____

9 선비의 삶을 사는 대신, 아버지는 항상 도박장에 계셨다.
➡ _____

10 그것이 그가 집안의 재산을 탕진하는 사람이라는 뜻의 파락호로 불린 이유이다.
➡ _____

11 "네 아버지는 도박으로 모든 돈을 써 버리고 지금 더 요구하고 계신다.
➡ _____

12 가서 더 이상 남아 있는 돈이 없다고 말씀드려라."라고 나의 어머니는 나를 도박장으로 보낼 때마다 말씀하시곤 했다.
➡ _____
_____

13 그러면, 아버지는 나에게 화를 내시며 소리치셨다. "왜 빈손으로 왔니?
➡ _____

14 돈을 더 가져와!"
➡ _____

15 내가 16살이 되었을 때, 나의 가족은 나를 서 씨와 결혼시키기로 이미 결정을 했었다.
➡ _____

16 결혼 풍습의 일부로, 서 씨네 가족은 새 장롱을 사라고 우리 가족에게 돈을 보냈다.
➡ _____

17 결혼식 바로 전날, 나의 어머니는 내 방에 들어오셔서 말씀하셨다. "네 아버지가 장롱을 살 돈을 가져가 버렸다."
➡ _____

18 나는 화가 나서 물었다 "어떻게 그리 끔찍한 일을 하실 수 있나요?
➡ _____

19 우린 이제 어떡해요?"
➡ _____

20 "우리에게 선택권은 없구나.
➡ _____

21 큰어머니의 옛 장롱을 가져가야겠구나."라고 어머니가 말씀하셨다.
➡ _____

22 "가문에 부끄러운 일이야."라고 사람들이 내 뒤에서 속삭이곤 했다.
➡ _____

23 결혼 첫날부터, 남편의 집에서의 생활은 나에게 힘겨웠다.
➡ _____

24 "당신의 아버지, 나의 친애하는 친구…," 나의 아버지의 친구분은 그의 이야기를 이어가셨다.
➡ _____

25 "그는 도박꾼이 아니었어요.
➡ _____

26 당신의 아버지는 가족의 돈을 만주에 있는 독립운동가들에게 보냈답니다.
➡ _____

27 그는 이것을 일본 순사들에게 비밀로 하기 위해 그 자신을 도박꾼처럼 보이게 했어요."
➡ _____

28 처음엔, 나는 그분이 사실을 얘기하시는 건지 확신할 수 없었다.
➡ _____

29 그러나 나중에, 나는 나의 아버지에 대한 진실을 알게 되었고 내가 아버지에 관해 오해하고 있었다는 것을 깨달았다.
➡ _____

30 그 순간부터, 나는 독립운동에 그의 인생을 헌신하신 파락호의 딸인 것이 자랑스러웠다.
➡ _____
_____

[01~03] 다음 글을 읽고 물음에 답하시오.

In 1946, a strange man visited me and asked, "Are you Mr. Kim Yonghwan's daughter?"

For me, ⓐthis was a(n) (A)[familiar / odd] question because I was more used to (B)[be / being] called the daughter of a *parakho*.

"I'm your father's friend. You may wonder (C)[if / that] it is true, but your father...," the man said.

At that moment, I was expecting disappointing news ⓑsince I did not have good memories of my father.

서답형

01 위 글의 밑줄 친 ⓐthis가 가리키는 것을 본문에서 찾아 쓰시오.

➡ _____

서답형

02 위 글의 괄호 (A)~(C)에서 문맥이나 어법상 알맞은 낱말을 골라 쓰시오.

➡ (A)_____ (B)_____ (C)_____

03 위 글의 밑줄 친 ⓑsince와 같은 의미로 쓰인 것을 모두 고르시오.

① She's been off work since Tuesday.
② Since you're already here, you might as well stay.
③ We've lived here since 1994.
④ Since then, I had wondered where he lived.
⑤ Since we're not very busy just now, I can get away from the office.

[04~05] 다음 글을 읽고 물음에 답하시오.

"Your father, my dear friend...," my father's friend continued his story. "He was not a gambler. Your father sent the family money to the independence fighters in Manchuria. He made himself look like a gambler to keep this a secret from the Japanese officers."

At first, I was not sure ⓐif he was telling the truth. But afterwards, I found out the truth about my father and I realized that I had been wrong about him. Ever since that moment, I have been proud to be the daughter of a *parakho* who had devoted his life to the independence movement.

04 위 글의 밑줄 친 ⓐif와 문법적 쓰임이 같은 것을 모두 고르시오.

① If necessary, I can come at once.
② If you run all the way, you'll get there in time.
③ I don't care if you agree with me.
④ He asked me if I knew Spanish.
⑤ I will tell him if he comes.

중요

05 위 글을 읽고 알 수 없는 것을 고르시오.

① Was the writer's father a gambler?
② To whom did the writer's father send the family money?
③ Why did the writer's father make himself look like a gambler?
④ How much money did the writer's father send to the independence fighters?
⑤ How did the writer find out the truth about her father?

[06~08] 다음 글을 읽고 물음에 답하시오.

Back in the 1920's, whenever people saw me in the village, they would say, "There goes the *parakho*'s daughter." (①)

My father was a son from a very rich family. (②) That is why he was called a *parakho*, which means someone who ruins his family's fortune. (③)

"Your father has gambled away all of the money, and now he's asking ____ⓐ____ more. (④) Go and tell him that we have no more money left," my mother would tell me whenever she sent me to the gambling house. (⑤)

Then, my father would yell ____ⓑ____ me angrily, "Why did you come empty-handed? Bring me more money!"

06 위 글의 빈칸 ⓐ와 ⓑ에 들어갈 전치사가 바르게 짝지어진 것은?

ⓐ	ⓑ		ⓐ	ⓑ
① for	at		② in	to
③ in	for		④ on	at
⑤ for	for			

07 위 글의 흐름으로 보아, 주어진 문장이 들어가기에 가장 적절한 곳은?

Instead of living the life of a *seonbi*, he was always at the gambling house.

① ② ③ ④ ⑤

08 According to the passage, which is NOT true?

① The writer's father was a son from a very rich family.

② The writer's father lived the life of a *seonbi*.

③ A *parakho* means someone who ruins his family's fortune.

④ The writer's father gambled away all of the money.

⑤ The writer's family had no more money left.

09 주어진 글 다음에 이어질 글의 순서로 가장 적절한 것은?

"Your father, my dear friend...," my father's friend continued his story.

(A) "He was not a gambler. Your father sent the family money to the independence fighters in Manchuria. He made himself look like a gambler to keep this a secret from the Japanese officers."

(B) Ever since that moment, I have been proud to be the daughter of a *parakho* who had devoted his life to the independence movement.

(C) At first, I was not sure if he was telling the truth. But afterwards, I found out the truth about my father and I realized that I had been wrong about him.

① (A)–(C)–(B)   ② (B)–(A)–(C)

③ (B)–(C)–(A)   ④ (C)–(A)–(B)

⑤ (C)–(B)–(A)

[10~12] 다음 글을 읽고 물음에 답하시오.

When I was sixteen years old, my family had (A)[already / yet] made an arrangement for me to marry Mr. Seo. ⓐAs part of the wedding tradition, Mr. Seo's family sent my family some money to buy a new chest for clothes.

Right before the wedding day, my mother came into my room and said, "Your father has taken the money for the chest."

I asked angrily, "How could he do such a horrible thing? (B)[How / What] should we do now?"

"We have no choice. You'll have to take your aunt's old chest," my mother said.

(C)[For / Since] the first day of marriage, life at my husband's house had been difficult for me.

10 위 글의 괄호 (A)~(C)에서 어법상 알맞은 낱말을 골라 쓰시오.

➡ (A)_____ (B)_____ (C)_____

11 위 글의 밑줄 친 ⓐAs와 같은 의미로 쓰인 것을 고르시오.

① She came up as I was speaking.
② Her anger grew as she talked.
③ This is twice as large as that.
④ Leave it as it is.
⑤ This box will be used as a table.

12 Which question CANNOT be answered after reading the passage?

① Whom did the writer's family make an arrangement for the writer to marry?
② Why did Mr. Seo's family send the writer's family some money?
③ Could the writer buy a new chest for clothes?
④ Where did the writer's father spend the money for the chest?
⑤ Was the writer's life at Mr. Seo's house easy for her?

[13~15] 다음 글을 읽고 물음에 답하시오.

Back in the 1920's, whenever people saw me in the village, they would say, "There goes ①the *parakho*'s daughter."

My father was a son from a very rich family. __ⓐ__ living the life of a *seonbi*, ②he was always at the gambling house. That is why he was called a *parakho*, which means someone who ruins ③his family's fortune.

"Your father has gambled away all of the money, and now he's asking for more. Go and tell ④him that we have no more money left," my mother ⓑwould tell me whenever she sent me to the gambling house.

Then, my father would yell at me angrily, "Why did you come empty-handed? Bring ⑤me more money!"

13 위 글의 빈칸 ⓐ에 들어갈 알맞은 말을 고르시오.

① In spite of   ② Because of
③ As well as   ④ Instead of
⑤ In addition to

14 밑줄 친 ①~⑤ 중에서 가리키는 대상이 나머지 넷과 다른 것은?

①   ②   ③   ④   ⑤

15 위 글의 밑줄 친 ⓑwould와 문법적 쓰임이 같은 것을 고르시오.

① He said he would be here at eight o'clock.
② Would you open the door for me, please?
③ I would rather come with you.
④ When my parents were away, my grandmother would take care of me.
⑤ Would you like a sandwich?

[16~17] 다음 글을 읽고 물음에 답하시오.

"Your father, my dear friend...," my father's friend continued his story. "He was not a gambler. Your father sent the family money to the independence fighters in Manchuria. He made himself look like a gambler to keep this a secret from the Japanese officers."

At first, ⓐ그분이 사실을 얘기하시는 건지 확신할 수 없었다. But afterwards, I found out the truth about my father and I realized that I had been wrong about him. Ever since that moment, I have been proud to be the daughter of a *parakho* who had devoted his life to the independence movement.

서답형

16 위 글의 밑줄 친 ⓐ의 우리말에 맞게 한 단어를 보충하여, 주어진 어휘를 알맞게 배열하시오.

> the truth / not / telling / was / sure / I / was / he

➡ _____

중요

17 위 글의 제목으로 알맞은 것을 고르시오.

① The Miserable Life of a *Parakho*
② Not a *Parakho* But a Secret Independence Fighter
③ The Secret Independence Fighters in Manchuria
④ History of Independence Movement
⑤ The Life as a Daughter of a *Parakho*

[18~21] 다음 글을 읽고 물음에 답하시오.

Back in the 1920's, whenever people saw me in the village, they (A)[should / would] say, "There goes the *parakho*'s daughter."

My father was a son from a very rich family. Instead of living the life of a *seonbi*, he was always at the gambling house. That is ⓐ he was called a *parakho*, ⓑwhich means someone who (B)[increases / ruins] his family's fortune.

"Your father has gambled away all of the money, and now he's asking for more. Go and tell him that ⓒ우리는 더 이상 남아 있는 돈이 없다," my mother would tell me whenever she sent me to the gambling house.

Then, my father would yell at me angrily, "Why did you come (C)[empty-hand / empty-handed]? Bring me more money!"

18 위 글의 빈칸 ⓐ에 들어갈 알맞은 말을 모두 고르시오.

① how   ② the reason
③ why   ④ when
⑤ where

서답형

19 위 글의 괄호 (A)~(C)에서 문맥이나 어법상 알맞은 낱말을 골라 쓰시오.

➡ (A) _____ (B) _____ (C) _____

서답형

20 위 글의 밑줄 친 ⓑ를 접속사를 사용하여 두 단어로 바꿔 쓰시오.

➡ _____

서답형

21 위 글의 밑줄 친 ⓒ의 우리말에 맞게 주어진 어휘를 이용하여 6 단어로 영작하시오.

> more, left

➡ _____

[01~03] 다음 글을 읽고 물음에 답하시오.

Back in the 1920's, (A)whenever people saw me in the village, they would say, "There goes the *parakho*'s daughter."

My father was a son from a very rich family. Instead of living the life of a *seonbi*, he was always at the gambling house. (B)That is why he was called a *parakho*, which means someone who ruins his family's fortune.

"Your father has gambled away all of the money, and now he's asking for more. Go and tell him that we have no more money ⓐ_____," my mother would tell me whenever she sent me to the gambling house.

Then, my father would yell at me angrily, "Why did you come empty-handed? Bring me more money!"

01 위 글의 빈칸 ⓐ에 leave를 알맞은 형태로 쓰시오.

➡ _____

02 위 글의 밑줄 친 (A)whenever와 바꿔 쓸 수 있는 말을 쓰시오.

➡ _____

03 위 글의 밑줄 친 (B)That이 가리키는 것을 본문에서 찾아 쓰시오.

➡ _____
_____

[04~07] 다음 글을 읽고 물음에 답하시오.

"Your father, my dear friend...," my father's friend continued his story. "He was not a gambler. (A)Your father sent the family money to the independence fighters in Manchuria. He made himself look like a gambler to keep this a secret from the Japanese officers."

(B)At first, I was not sure if he was telling the truth. But afterwards, I found out the truth about my father and I realized that I had been wrong about him. Ever since that moment, I have been proud to be the daughter of a *parakho* who ⓐ_____ his life to the independence movement.

04 위 글의 빈칸 ⓐ에 devote를 알맞은 형태로 쓰시오.

➡ _____

05 위 글의 밑줄 친 (A)를 4형식 문장으로 고치시오.

➡ _____
_____

06 위 글의 밑줄 친 (B)를 다음과 같이 바꿔 쓸 때 빈칸에 들어갈 알맞은 단어를 쓰시오.

➡ At first, I was not sure _____ he was telling the truth.

07 다음 빈칸 (A)와 (B)에 알맞은 단어를 넣어 필자가 아버지에 대해 오해한 내용을 완성하시오.

The writer mistook her father for a *parakho* but in fact he sent the family money to the (A)_____ _____ in Manchuria and made himself look like a gambler to keep this (B)_____ _____ from the Japanese officers.

[08~10] 다음 글을 읽고 물음에 답하시오.

When I was sixteen years old, my family had already made an arrangement for me to marry Mr. Seo. As ⓐpart of the wedding tradition, Mr. Seo's family sent my family some money to buy a new chest for (A)[cloths / clothes].

Right before the wedding day, my mother came into my room and said, "Your father has taken the money for the chest."

I asked angrily, "How could he do such a (B)[horrible / terrific] thing? What should we do now?"

"We have no choice. You'll have to take your aunt's old chest," my mother said.

"How (C)[embarrassing / embarrassed] for the family," people would whisper behind my back.

Since the first day of marriage, life at my husband's house had been difficult for me.

08 다음 빈칸에 알맞은 말을 넣어 위 글의 밑줄 친 ⓐ에 대한 설명을 완성하시오.

> The family of the bridegroom sent (A)_____ _____ to buy a (B)_____ _____ for clothes to the family of the bride.

09 위 글의 괄호 (A)~(C)에서 문맥이나 어법상 알맞은 낱말을 골라 쓰시오.

➡ (A) _____ (B) _____ (C) _____

10 주어진 영영풀이에 해당하는 단어를 본문에서 찾아 쓰시오.

> a large, heavy box used for storing things

➡ _____

[11~13] 다음 글을 읽고 물음에 답하시오.

Back in the 1920's, whenever people saw me in the village, they would say, "ⓐ저기에 파락호의 딸이 간다."

My father was a son from a very rich family. Instead of living the life of a *seonbi*, he was always at the gambling house. ⓑThat is why he was called a *parakho*, that means someone who ruins his family's fortune.

"Your father has gambled away all of the money, and now he's asking for more. Go and tell him that we have no more money left," my mother would tell me whenever she sent me to the gambling house.

Then, my father would yell at me angrily, "Why did you come empty-handed? Bring me more money!"

11 위 글의 밑줄 친 ⓐ의 우리말에 맞게 주어진 어휘를 알맞게 배열하시오.

> there / the *parakho*'s daughter / goes

➡ _____

12 위 글의 밑줄 친 ⓑ에서 어법상 틀린 부분을 찾아 고치시오.

➡ _____

13 다음 빈칸 (A)와 (B)에 알맞은 단어를 넣어 글쓴이의 아버지에 대한 소개를 완성하시오.

> The writer's father was called a (A)_____ because he (B)_____ away his family's fortune.

교과서

구석구석

Grammar in Real Life A

해석

Mary Jane, your fans have many questions about your plans.

1. Are you going to release a new song this month?

2. Are you interested in various music genres?
= a variety of

3. Do you have any plans to work with other artists?
부정사의 형용사적 용법

4. Are you going to go on a world tour this year?

구문해설 • release: 발표[발매]하다 • genre: 유형(類型), 양식, 장르

Mary Jane, 너의 팬들은 너의 계획에 대해 많은 질문들을 가지고 있어.

1. 넌 이 달에 새 노래를 발표할 거니?

2. 넌 다양한 음악 장르에 관심이 있니?

3. 넌 다른 아티스트들과 일할 계획을 가지고 있니?

4. 넌 금년에 월드 투어를 떠날 거니?

Grammar in Real Life B

When I got back home, my parents had gone out for a walk. The house was
때를 나타내는 접속사   대과거

dark and quiet, but it seemed a little bit strange. I remembered that I had left
                                          strangely(×)   대과거

the door in my room open. I saw that someone had broken the lamp. I found
                                                              대과거

out that someone had eaten my cookies on the table. At last I knew who did it!
              대과거   간접의문문

I found small footprints of my dog, Lucy, and the cat next door.
                                                    (footprints of) the cat

구문해설 • a little bit: 조금 (a bit에 little이 붙은 말; 뜻은 a bit과 같음) • at last: 마침내
• next door: 옆집에

내가 집에 돌아왔을 때 나의 부모님은 산보를 나가셨다. 집은 어둡고 조용했지만, 조금 이상해 보였다. 나는 내 방 문을 열어둔 것이 기억났다. 나는 누군가가 램프를 깨뜨린 것을 알았다. 나는 누군가가 식탁 위에 있던 내 쿠키를 먹은 것을 알아냈다. 마침내 나는 누가 그런 일을 했는지 알았다! 나는 내 개 Lucy와 옆집 고양이의 작은 발자국들을 발견했다.

After You Read: Read and Write A

The Secret of My Father

I thought my father was ...

My father was known as a *parakho*. He was born into a rich family but he
            be known as: ~로 알려지다

gambled away all of the money. He even took the money for a new chest for
노름으로 모든 돈을 탕진했다

clothes.
cloth의 복수: 의복

Actually my father was ...

My father was not a gambler. He sent the family money to the independence
                                              send는 to를 사용하여 3형식으로 고친다.

fighters in Manchuria. He made himself look like a gambler to keep this a
                              him(×)   to부정사의 부사적 용법(목적)

secret from the Japanese officers.

구문해설 • secret: 비밀 • gamble away: 도박으로 ~을 다 날리다 • chest: 궤 • gambler: 노름꾼
• independence fighter: 독립 운동가 • keep+O+O.C.+from A: A로부터 ~을 …로 지키다

나의 아버지의 비밀
나는 아버지가 …라고 생각했다.
나의 아버지는 '파락호'라고 알려져 있었다. 그는 부잣집에 태어났지만, 모든 돈을 노름으로 날렸다. 그는 심지어 새 장롱을 살 돈도 가져갔다.

사실 나의 아버지는 …이었다.
나의 아버지는 노름꾼이 아니었다. 그는 가족의 돈을 만주에 있는 독립 운동가들에게 보냈다. 그는 일본 경찰들로부터 이것을 비밀로 지키려고 스스로를 노름꾼처럼 보이게 했다.

영역별 핵심문제

01 다음 밑줄 친 부분의 의미로 알맞지 <u>않은</u> 것을 <u>모두</u> 고르시오.

① The <u>odd</u> thing was that he didn't recognize me. (이상한)

② The country has made great advances since <u>independence</u>. (독립)

③ He followed the impressionist <u>movement</u>. (이동)

④ Did you <u>leave</u> the kids with Grandma on Saturday? (떠나다)

⑤ Don't <u>whisper</u> with your neighbors. (속삭이다)

02 다음 짝지어진 두 단어의 관계가 같도록 빈칸에 알맞은 말을 쓰시오.

solve : solution = marry : _____

[03~04] 다음 빈칸에 공통으로 들어갈 말을 쓰시오.

03

• Have you ever heard _____ a band called Big Star?

• Could I have tuna instead _____ ham?

04

• Most humans are not very good at _____ secrets.

• Paul was _____ awake by drinking lots of strong black coffee.

[05~07] 다음 대화를 읽고 물음에 답하시오.

A: This (A)[called / is called] the *Geojunggi*.

B: Wow, this looks interesting.

A: This is a machine that moves heavy objects. It is said that it helped to build the Hwaseong Fortress only in 28 months.

B: How amazing! Is it okay (B)[that / if / what] I take a closer look at it?

A: Sure.

05 위 대화의 괄호 (A)와 (B)에서 적절한 것을 골라 쓰시오.

➡ (A) _____, (B) _____

06 위 대화에서 다음 영영풀이에 해당하는 단어를 찾아 쓰시오.

a large strong building used for defending an important place

➡ _____

07 위 대화의 내용과 일치하는 것은 <u>모두</u> 몇 개인지 고르시오.

ⓐ *Geojunggi* was used for building the Hwaseong Fortress.

ⓑ *B* wants to watch Hwaseong Fortress closely.

ⓒ Hwaseong Fortress was built in 28 months.

ⓓ *Geojunggi* is a kind of machine.

ⓔ *A* knows about what *Geojunggi* is.

① 1개 ② 2개 ③ 3개 ④ 4개 ⑤ 5개

[08~09] 다음 대화를 읽고 물음에 답하시오.

M: Hello, Ms. Jackson. (①)
W: It was wonderful. (②) The houses were really beautiful.
M: That's great.
W: Actually, I didn't get the chance ⓐ_____ have dinner. (③) Is it okay ⓑ_____ I cook in the kitchen at this hour?
M: Yes, but please remember ⓒ_____ the kitchen closes ⓓ_____ 10 p.m. (④)
W: Okay. The kitchen is on the 5th floor, right? (⑤)
M: Yes, it is. Let me know ⓔ_____ you need anything.

08 ①~⑤ 중 주어진 문장이 들어갈 곳은?

> How was your tour of the *Hanok Village*?

①   ②   ③   ④   ⑤

09 빈칸 ⓐ~ⓔ에 들어가지 <u>않는</u> 말을 고르시오.

① for   ② at   ③ if   ④ that   ⑤ to

[10~12] 다음 대화를 읽고 물음에 답하시오.

W: James, what are you watching?
M: Oh, I'm watching a video about Yi Sunsin.
W: Isn't he the one that saved Joseon from Japan?
M: (A)[No, he isn't. / Right.] It is said that he won the war only with twelve (a)_____(wood) ships.
W: Wow, how can that be possible?
M: He was a wise general (B)[who / which] (C)[made / is made] creative plans.

10 괄호 안의 단어를 문맥에 맞게 고쳐 빈칸 (a)에 쓰시오.

➡ _____

11 위 대화의 괄호 (A)~(C)에서 적절한 것을 골라 쓰시오.

➡ (A)_____ (B)_____ (C)_____

12 위 대화에서 다음 영영풀이에 해당하는 단어를 찾아 쓰시오.

> an officer of very high rank in the army or air force

➡ _____

Grammar

13 다음 밑줄 친 부분과 바꿔 쓸 수 있는 것은?

> You were the one who asked me <u>if</u> I had anything to say.

① unless   ② that   ③ what
④ which   ⑤ whether

14 다음 문장 중에서 어법상 <u>어색한</u> 문장을 고르시오.

① When I got home, Mom had already prepared our dinner.
② I found out that someone had eaten my cookies on the table.
③ Cathy lost the necklace that I had bought for her.
④ When Megan had arrived at the station, the train already left for London.
⑤ He had gone out for a walk when I arrived at his home.

15 다음 그림을 보고 주어진 어휘를 이용하여 빈칸을 알맞게 채우시오.

➡ A man visited his teacher, and asked him

_____ .

(his fault, forgive, will)

16 다음 ⓐ~ⓖ 중 어법상 옳은 것을 <u>모두</u> 고르시오.

> ⓐ The movie has been over when I arrived at the theater.
> ⓑ I realized that I had been wrong about him.
> ⓒ I had eaten the sandwich which Mom made the night before.
> ⓓ David would like to know if you have any plans to work with other artists.
> ⓔ Can you tell me if she's a new student in our class?
> ⓕ Let me ask you which you want to buy something nice.
> ⓖ I wonder that the dress looks good on me.

➡ _____

17 다음 문장의 빈칸에 들어갈 수 <u>없는</u> 말은?

> When Scott arrived at the station, _____
> _____ .

① the train had already left for London
② the train had just arrived at the platform
③ he had already his lunch
④ he remembered that he had left his smart phone at the restaurant
⑤ Lily had already gone

18 다음 두 문장을 한 문장으로 쓰시오.

(1) • I was not sure.
   • He was telling the truth.
   ➡ _____

(2) • Rob wants to know.
   • More men than women like gardening.
   ➡ _____
   _____

(3) • I asked her.
   • I could have a drink.
   ➡ _____

19 다음 빈칸에 들어갈 말이 <u>다른</u> 하나는?

① Try this food and see _____ you like it.
② I wonder _____ the movie is still showing on the theater.
③ Lucy wants to know _____ you are going to release a new song this month.
④ I am not sure _____ Rachel can play the cello.
⑤ I can't believe _____ it will be New Year's Day soon.

Reading

[20~21] 다음 글을 읽고 물음에 답하시오.

Back in the 1920's, whenever people saw me in the village, they would say, "There goes the *parakho*'s daughter."

ⓐMy father was a son from a very rich family. Instead of living the life of a *seonbi*, he was always at the gambling house. ⓑThat is because he was called a *parakho*, which means someone who ruins his family's fortune.

"Your father has gambled away all of the money, and now he's asking for more. Go and tell him that we have no more money left," my mother would tell me whenever she sent me to the gambling house.

Then, my father would yell at me angrily, "Why did you come empty-handed? Bring me more money!"

20 위 글의 ⓐMy father에 관한 내용으로 옳지 <u>않은</u> 것은?

① He was born into a rich family.
② He didn't live the life of a *seonbi*.
③ He was always at the gambling house.
④ He was called a *parakho*.
⑤ He won a lot of money by gambling.

21 위 글의 밑줄 친 ⓑ에서 흐름상 <u>어색한</u> 부분을 찾아 고치시오.

➡ _____

[22~24] 다음 글을 읽고 물음에 답하시오.

When I was sixteen years old, my family had already made an arrangement for me to marry Mr. Seo. (①)

ⓐRight before the wedding day, my mother came into my room and said, "Your father has taken the money for the chest." (②) I asked angrily, "How could he do such a horrible thing? (③) What should we do now?" (④)

"We have no choice. (⑤) You'll have to take your aunt's old chest," my mother said.

"How embarrassing for the family," people would whisper behind my back.

Since the first day of marriage, life at my husband's house had been difficult for me.

22 위 글의 흐름으로 보아, 주어진 문장이 들어가기에 가장 적절한 곳은?

As part of the wedding tradition, Mr. Seo's family sent my family some money to buy a new chest for clothes.

①　　②　　③　　④　　⑤

23 위 글의 밑줄 친 ⓐRight과 같은 의미로 쓰인 것을 고르시오.

① What gives you the <u>right</u> to do that?
② The bus came <u>right</u> on time.
③ You were quite <u>right</u> to criticize him.
④ Next time we'll get it <u>right</u>.
⑤ I don't feel quite <u>right</u> today.

24 본문의 내용과 일치하도록 다음 빈칸 (A)와 (B)에 알맞은 단어를 쓰시오.

The writer got married to Mr. Seo, but because of (A)_____ _____, she couldn't buy a (B)_____ _____ for clothes.

[25~27] 다음 글을 읽고 물음에 답하시오.

"Your father, my dear friend...," my father's friend continued his story. "He was not a gambler. Your father sent the family money to the independence fighters in Manchuria. He made (A)[him / himself] look like a gambler to (B)[keep / stop] this a secret from the Japanese officers."

(C)[At first / For the first time], I was not sure if he was telling the truth. But afterwards, I found out the truth about my father and I realized that I had been wrong about him. Ever since that moment, I @have been proud to be the daughter of a *parakho* who had devoted his life to the independence movement.

25 위 글의 괄호 (A)~(C)에서 문맥이나 어법상 알맞은 낱말을 골라 쓰시오.

➡ (A)_____ (B)_____ (C)_____

26 위 글의 밑줄 친 @have been과 현재완료 용법이 <u>다른</u> 것을 <u>모두</u> 고르시오.

① I have worn these jeans for 3 years.
② I have never met a student like him.
③ How long has Jim been here?
④ She has gone to Paris.
⑤ He hasn't eaten his hamburger yet.

27 위 글에서 알 수 있는 아버지에 대한 'I'의 심경 변화로 가장 알맞은 것을 고르시오.

① ashamed → surprised
② respectful → satisfied
③ bored → disappointed
④ ashamed → respectful
⑤ surprised → proud

[28~30] 다음 글을 읽고 물음에 답하시오.

Have you heard of Nam Jahyun? She was a female independence fighter. When her husband died during the war, she decided to fight for independence. In 1919, Nam Jahyun moved to Manchuria. Then, she built schools and educated women there. When she was arrested by the Japanese in 1933, she had tried to kill Japanese officers. After she @_____ in prison for six months, she was released and died shortly after. In 1962, to honor her work fighting for independence, the government gave her an award.

28 위 글의 빈칸 @에 be동사를 알맞은 형태로 쓰시오.

➡ _____

29 위 글의 종류로 알맞은 것을 고르시오.

① e-mail   ② biography
③ diary   ④ article
⑤ autobiography

30 위 글의 남자현에 관한 내용으로 옳지 <u>않은</u> 것은?

① 여성 독립 운동가였다.
② 그녀의 남편이 죽은 뒤에 만주로 갔다.
③ 만주에서 학교를 세우고 여성들을 가르쳤다.
④ 일본 경찰에 체포된 뒤에 감옥에서 죽었다.
⑤ 1962년 정부가 그녀에게 상을 주었다.

단원별 예상문제

01 접미사 -ward(s)를 붙여 부사로 만들 수 <u>없는</u> 것을 고르시오.

① in ② over ③ after
④ back ⑤ fore

02 다음 빈칸에 알맞은 단어를 〈보기〉에서 골라 쓰시오.

┌─── 보기 ────┐
any most so some such
└────────────┘

(1) Everything has changed _____ much that I can hardly recognize the place.

(2) He came to _____ a sudden stop that we almost hit him.

03 빈칸 (A)와 (B)에 들어갈 말로 알맞은 것끼리 짝지어진 것을 고르시오.

```
• He's always unwilling to ask (A)_____
  anyone's help.
• She announced that she would devote her
  life (B)_____ art.
```

　(A) (B) 　　(A) (B)
① out – for ② out – to
③ for – for ④ for – to
⑤ around – for

04 다음 주어진 우리말에 맞게 빈칸을 채우시오. (철자가 주어진 경우 주어진 철자로 시작할 것.)

(1) 그녀는 포기하지 않고 유명한 중국 장군을 만나러 갔다.
　➡ She did not give up and went to see a famous Chinese g_____.

(2) 너무 많은 결혼들이 이혼으로 끝난다.
　➡ Too many _____ end in divorce.

(3) 하늘에 이상한 물체가 있다.
　➡ There's a strange o_____ in the sky.

(4) 내가 휴가 갈 것이기 때문에, 그 회의에 참석할 수 없을 것 같다.
　➡ I won't be able to attend the meeting s_____ I'll be on vacation.

[05~07] 다음 대화를 읽고 물음에 답하시오.

```
W: Excuse me, sir. (①)
M: I'd like to have bibimbap, please. (②)
W: Here you are. (③)
M: Thank you. (④) Oh, 지금 화장실을 이용해도 될
   까요?
W: Sure, but if the seat light is on, you should
   stay in your seat. (⑤)
M: Okay, thank you.
```

05 ①~⑤ 중 주어진 문장이 들어갈 곳은?

```
Would you like to have curry or bibimbap?
```

① ② ③ ④ ⑤

06 Where is this conversation taking place?

① bus ② train ③ hotel
④ airplane ⑤ factory

07 밑줄 친 우리말과 일치하도록 주어진 단어를 이용해 문장을 만드시오.

➡ _____

(okay, bathroom, use)

[08~10] 다음 대화를 읽고 물음에 답하시오.

M: Lisa. (A)_____

W: I'm reading a biography of Gwon Giok.

M: I haven't heard about her. (B)_____

W: She was the first ⓐ[male / female] pilot in Korea. It ⓑ[says / said / is said] ⓒ[which / what / that] she had over 7,000 hours of flying time.

M: Wow, I didn't know that.

출제율 95%

08 위 대화의 빈칸 (A)와 (B)에 알맞은 것을 〈보기〉에서 골라 쓰시오.

┤ 보기 ├
- Is it okay if I take a picture of it?
- Who is she?
- Why did she become a pilot?
- What are you reading?
- How was your reading?
- How can it be possible?

➡ (A) _____
   (B) _____

출제율 90%

09 위 대화의 괄호 ⓐ~ⓒ에서 적절한 것을 골라 쓰시오.

➡ ⓐ_____ ⓑ_____ ⓒ_____

출제율 90%

10 위 대화에서 다음 영영풀이에 해당하는 단어를 찾아 쓰시오.

a book that someone writes about someone else's life

➡ _____

[11~12] 다음 대화를 읽고 물음에 답하시오.

M: All right, everyone! This way, please. Now, we are moving onto the Joseon Dynasty. (A)_____, there were many interesting (B)_____(invent). This one is called the *Jagyeongnu*.

W: Is it a musical instrument?

M: Actually, this is a water clock. It is said that it is the oldest and the largest water clock in Korea.

W: How amazing! Is it okay if I take a picture of it?

M: Sure.

출제율 95%

11 빈칸 (A)에 알맞은 말을 고르시오.

① Besides   ② However
③ Instead   ④ As it is
⑤ As you can see

출제율 95%

12 괄호 안의 단어를 문맥에 맞게 고쳐 빈칸 (B)에 쓰시오.

➡ _____

출제율 95%

13 다음 그림을 보고 주어진 어휘를 사용하여 빈칸을 알맞게 채우시오.

Jonathan asked Bells _____

_____ with him. (go, she, can, out)

14 출제율 95%
다음 중 밑줄 친 if의 쓰임이 다른 하나는?

① It does not matter if you answer yes or no.

② I'm not sure if I'm well prepared.

③ I asked him if he was sorry for what he had done.

④ Please let me know if he comes.

⑤ You may wonder if it is true or not.

15 출제율 100%
다음 중 어법상 적절한 문장은?

① I had told the story that I have read in the book.

② I couldn't find the pen which Dad had gave to me.

③ After she was in prison for 6 months, she had been released and died short after.

④ I couldn't meet him because he had left the town when I got back.

⑤ It was proved that the officials took bribes from him months before.

[16~17] 다음 글을 읽고 물음에 답하시오.

Back in the 1920's, whenever people saw me in the village, they would say, "There goes the *parakho*'s daughter."

My father was a son from a very rich family. Instead of ⓐliving the life of a *seonbi*, he was always at the gambling house. That is why he was called a *parakho*, which means someone who ruins his family's fortune.

"Your father has gambled away all of the money, and now he's asking for more. Go and tell him that we have no more money left," my mother would tell me whenever she sent me to the gambling house.

Then, my father would yell at me angrily, "Why did you come empty-handed? Bring me more money!"

16 출제율 100%
위 글의 밑줄 친 ⓐliving과 문법적 쓰임이 다른 것을 모두 고르시오.

① He is good at playing tennis.

② We enjoy swimming after school.

③ She is cooking in the kitchen.

④ They stopped eating the food.

⑤ They sat studying in the room.

17 출제율 90%
Why was the writer's father called a *parakho*? Fill in the blanks below with suitable words. (2 words)

Because he was always at the _____ _____ instead of living the life of a *seonbi*.

[18~20] 다음 글을 읽고 물음에 답하시오.

ⓐWhen I was sixteen years old, my family has already made an arrangement for me to marry Mr. Seo. As part of the wedding tradition, Mr. Seo's family sent my family some money to buy a new chest for clothes.

Right before the wedding day, my mother came into my room and said, "Your father has taken the money for the chest."

I asked angrily, "How could he do ⓑ그런 끔찍한 일? What should we do now?"

"We have no choice. You'll have to take your aunt's old chest," my mother said.

"How embarrassing for the family," people would whisper ⓒ나 몰래.

Since the first day of marriage, life at my husband's house had been difficult for me.

18 출제율 95%
위 글의 밑줄 친 ⓑ와 ⓒ의 우리말에 맞게 주어진 어휘를 이용하여, 각각 4 단어와 3 단어로 영작하시오.

ⓑ horrible ⓒ back

➡ ⓑ _____ ⓒ _____

19 위 글의 밑줄 친 ⓐ에서 어법상 **틀린** 부분을 찾아 고치시오.

➡ _____

20 According to the passage, which is NOT true?

① The writer's husband's family name was Seo.

② As part of the wedding tradition, the writer received some money from Mr. Seo's family.

③ The money that Mr. Seo's family sent was for buying a new chest for clothes.

④ The writer's father took the money for the chest on the wedding day.

⑤ The writer had to take her aunt's old chest.

[21~23] 다음 글을 읽고 물음에 답하시오.

"Your father, my dear friend...," my father's friend continued his story. "He was not a gambler. Your father sent the family money to the independence fighters in Manchuria. He made himself look like a gambler (A)to keep this a secret ⓐ the Japanese officers."

At first, I was not sure if he was telling the truth. But afterwards, I found out (B)the truth about my father and I realized that I had been wrong about him. Ever since that moment, I have been proud to be the daughter of a parakho who had devoted his life ⓑ the independence movement.

21 위 글의 빈칸 ⓐ와 ⓑ에 들어갈 전치사가 바르게 짝지어진 것은?

	ⓐ	ⓑ			ⓐ	ⓑ
①	from	on		②	to	at
③	to	on		④	for	to
⑤	from	to				

22 위 글의 밑줄 친 (A)to keep과 to부정사의 용법이 **다른** 것을 **모두** 고르시오.

① I don't have any friends to talk with.

② He went to Africa in 1990, never to return.

③ He can't be rich to ask me for some money.

④ She encouraged me to try once again.

⑤ She came here to ask a question.

23 다음 빈칸 (A)와 (B)에 알맞은 단어를 넣어 (B)the truth에 대한 설명을 완성하시오.

The writer's father was not a *parakho* but he made himself (A)_____ _____ a gambler to keep the fact that he sent the family money to the independence fighters in Manchuria a secret from the (B)_____ _____.

[24~25] 다음 글을 읽고 물음에 답하시오.

I thought my father was ...

My father was known as a *parakho*. He was born into a rich family but he gambled away all of the money. He even took the money for a new chest for clothes.

Actually my father was ...

My father was not a gambler. He sent the family money to the independence fighters in Manchuria. ⓐHe made himself to look a gambler to keep ⓑthis a secret from the Japanese officers.

24 위 글의 밑줄 친 ⓐ에서 어법상 **틀린** 부분을 찾아 고치시오.

➡ _____

25 위 글의 밑줄 친 ⓑthis가 가리키는 것을 본문에서 찾아 쓰시오.

➡ _____
_____

서술형 실전문제

[01~02] 다음 대화를 읽고 물음에 답하시오.

> W: Hey, Mark, do you know about Father Lee Taeseok?
>
> M: Yeah, I've heard of him. ⓐWho?
>
> W: ⓑTake a look at this article. ⓒHe is going to include in the social studies textbook in South Sudan.
>
> M: Wow. that's great.
>
> W: Yeah, ⓓhe helped the children by building a clinic and a school. 사람들이 그러한 이야기들이 교과서에 포함된다고 말했어.
>
> M: ⓔIt is bad to hear that students will learn about such a great person.

01 밑줄 친 ⓐ~ⓔ 중 문맥상 또는 어법상 어색한 것을 모두 골라 바르게 고치시오.

➡ _____
_____
_____
_____

02 밑줄 친 우리말을 주어진 단어를 이용하여 영작하시오.

➡ _____
_____ (say, it)

➡ _____
_____ (people)

03 주어진 단어를 이용하여 빈칸에 알맞은 말을 쓰시오.

(1) I remembered that I _____ the door of my room open. (leave)

(2) The library _____ when I got there. (closed)

04 밑줄 친 우리말을 주어진 단어를 이용하여 영작하시오.

> W: Excuse me, you can't take your backpack inside the museum.
>
> M: Oh, I didn't know that. 물병을 가지고 들어가도 될까요?
>
> W: Yes, that's fine. You can leave your bag in the locker.
>
> M: Okay, thank you.

➡ _____ (okay)

➡ _____ (can)

05 다음 문장에서 틀린 것을 고쳐 다시 쓰시오.

(1) It was the most interesting game that I ever played.

➡ _____
_____

(2) His wife was surprised to learn that he was already fired without any warning.

➡ _____
_____

(3) He could not decide that this was a fairy tale or a nightmare.

➡ _____
_____

(4) I'm considering if to accept his offer.

➡ _____

52 Lesson 3. For the Love of Our Country

06 다음 우리말을 주어진 어휘를 이용하여 영작하시오.

(1) 나는 그가 그녀에게 추천서를 줄 수 있는지 알고 싶다. (give her a recommendation, 11 단어)

➡ _____

_____

(2) 그녀는 열쇠를 학교에 두고 왔기 때문에 문을 열 수가 없었다. (at school, leave, the door, the key, because, open, 14 단어)

➡ _____

_____

[07~08] 다음 글을 읽고 물음에 답하시오.

Back in the 1920's, whenever people saw me in the village, they would say, "There goes the *parakho*'s daughter."

My father was a son from a very rich family. ⓐInstead of living the life of a *seonbi*, he was always at the gambling house. That is why he was called a *parakho*, which means someone who ruins his family's fortune.

"Your father has gambled away all of the money, and now he's asking for more. Go and tell him that we have no more money left," my mother would tell me whenever she sent me to the gambling house.

Then, my father would yell at me angrily, "Why did you come empty-handed? ⓑBring me more money!"

07 위 글의 밑줄 친 ⓐ를 다음과 같이 바꿔 쓸 때 빈칸에 들어갈 알맞은 단어를 쓰시오.

➡ He did _____ live the life of a *seonbi*, _____ he was always at the gambling house.

08 위 글의 밑줄 친 ⓑ를 3형식 문장으로 고치시오.

➡ _____

[09~11] 다음 글을 읽고 물음에 답하시오.

ⓐWhen I was sixteen years old, my family had already made an arrangement for me to marry with Mr. Seo. As part of the wedding tradition, Mr. Seo's family sent my family some money to buy a new chest for clothes.

Right before the wedding day, my mother came into my room and said, "Your father has taken the money for the chest."

I asked angrily, "How could he do ⓑsuch a horrible thing? What should we do now?"

"We have no choice. You'll have to take your aunt's old chest," my mother said.

"How embarrassing for the family," people would whisper behind my back.

Since the first day of marriage, life at my husband's house had been difficult for me.

09 위 글의 밑줄 친 ⓐ에서 어법상 틀린 부분을 찾아 고치시오.

➡ _____

10 위 글의 밑줄 친 ⓑsuch a horrible thing이 가리키는 내용을 우리말로 쓰시오.

➡ _____

11 Why did people whisper behind the writer's back that it was very embarrassing for the family? Fill in the blanks below with suitable words.

Because _____ _____ took the _____ for the chest.

창의사고력 서술형 문제

01 그림을 보고 허락을 요청하는 말을 이용해 문장을 완성하시오. 괄호 안에 주어진 말을 이용하시오.

A: _____
_____
(borrow, 2개 이상)
B: _____
(sorry, broken)

02 그림을 참고하고, 주어진 어휘를 이용하여 대화를 완성하시오.

(1)    (2)

(1) A: Do you know _____ a comic book? (she, read)

B: I'm not sure, but she likes to read comic books.

(2) A: How was your play yesterday?

B: It was terrible. I forgot the lines that I _____ during our practice.
(memorize)

03 다음 내용을 바탕으로 독립운동가 남자현의 전기문을 쓰시오.

> Biography of Nam Jahyun, a female independence fighter
> 1873: born in Yeongyang
> 1919: Her husband died during the war.
> • moved to Manchuria • built schools and educated women there
> 1919: decided to fight for independence
> 1924~1933: tried to kill Japanese officers
> 1933: • arrested by the Japanese • had been in prison for six months
> • died on Aug 22nd
> 1962: The government gave her an award.

> Have you heard of Nam Jahyun? She was a (A)_____. When her husband died during the war, she decided (B)_____. In 1919, Nam Jahyun moved to Manchuria. Then, she (C)_____ there. When she was arrested by the Japanese in 1933, she had tried to kill Japanese officers. After she had been in prison for (D)_____, she was released and died shortly after. In 1962, to honor her work fighting for independence, the government gave her (E)_____.

단원별 모의고사

01 다음 문장 중 자연스럽지 <u>않은</u> 것을 찾아 고치시오.

ⓐ The road surface became so hot that it melted.
ⓑ Children are used to spend much of their free time watching TV.
ⓒ I wanted to buy a new car by selling my house.

➡ _____

02 다음 빈칸에 공통으로 들어갈 말을 고르시오.

• Right _____ that moment, you came up to me and issued a ticket without giving me a chance to explain.
• Don't yell _____ me like that!

03 다음 빈칸을 〈보기〉에 있는 어휘를 이용하여 채우시오.

┌─ 보기 ─┐
biography detective female locker
└──────┘

(1) I have read a _____ of Abraham Lincoln.
(2) Oh Eun-sun is a Korean _____ mountaineer.
(3) Where can I get a key for my _____?
(4) The _____ found some evidence.

04 다음 우리말에 맞도록 빈칸에 알맞은 말을 쓰시오. (철자가 주어진 경우 주어진 철자로 시작할 것.)

(1) 미국의 많은 가정, 호텔, 학교에서 이 운동에 참여했습니다.
➡ Many American families, hotels, and schools participated in this _____.
(2) 그의 많은 발명품 덕분에 그는 많은 돈을 벌었습니다.
➡ He made a lot of money thanks to his many _____.
(3) 그는 일찍 일어나는 데 익숙하다.
➡ He is used to _____ up early.

[05~06] 다음 대화를 읽고 물음에 답하시오.

W: Excuse me, you can't ⓐ_____ your backpack inside the museum.
M: Oh, I didn't ⓑ_____ that. Is it okay if I ⓒ_____ in my water bottle?
W: Yes, that's fine. You can ⓓ_____ your bag in the locker.
M: Okay, thank you.

05 빈칸 ⓐ~ⓔ에 들어가지 <u>않는</u> 말을 고르시오.

① know   ② help   ③ leave
④ bring   ⑤ take

06 위 대화를 읽고 답할 수 <u>없는</u> 질문을 고르시오.

① Can the man carry the water bottle inside the museum?
② Where is the man now?
③ Is there a locker in the museum?
④ Can the man take pictures inside the museum?
⑤ Can the man take his backpack inside the museum?

[07~09] 다음 대화를 읽고 물음에 답하시오.

M: All right, everyone! This way, please. Now, we are moving onto the Joseon Dynasty. As you can see, there were many interesting inventions. This one (A)[called / is called] the *Jagyeongnu*.
W: Is it a musical instrument?
M: (a)Actually, this is a water clock. (b)그것은 한국에서 가장 오래되고 가장 큰 물시계라고 합니다.
W: How amazing! Is it okay if I take a picture of (B)[it / them]?
M: Sure.

07 위 대화의 괄호 (A)와 (B)에서 적절한 것을 고르시오.

➡ (A)_____ (B)_____

08 밑줄 친 (a)Actually와 바꿔 쓸 수 있는 말을 고르시오.

① However   ② Rather
③ In fact   ④ In the end
⑤ On the other hand

09 밑줄 친 (b)의 우리말과 일치하도록 주어진 단어를 이용하여 영작하시오.

➡ _____

_____

(large, say, in, old)

[10~13] 다음 대화를 읽고 물음에 답하시오.

M: I watched an interesting movie yesterday. (①)
W: Jeong Yakyong? (②) Wasn't he a scholar in the Joseon Dynasty? (③)
M: Yeah, but (A)그는 또한 탐정이었다고 한다. (④) He solved about 90 cases. (⑤)
W: Oh, I didn't know (B)_____ he was also a detective.

10 ①~⑤ 중 주어진 문장이 들어갈 곳은?

Jeong Yakyong was a detective in it.

①   ②   ③   ④   ⑤

11 위 대화에서 다음 영영풀이에 해당하는 단어를 찾아 쓰시오.

someone who studies a particular subject and knows a lot about it, especially a subject that is not scientific

➡ _____

12 밑줄 친 (A)의 우리말과 일치하도록 영작하시오. (9 단어)

➡ _____

13 빈칸 (B)에 알맞은 말을 고르시오.

① how   ② what   ③ which
④ that   ⑤ if

14 Which is grammatically WRONG?

① The woman wants to know if there is a bank near here.
② I want to ask Wendy if she likes ice cream or not.
③ Try this food and see if or not you like it.
④ Can you tell me whether you will go shopping tonight?
⑤ I'm not sure whether Mina can join the picnic or not.

15 다음 두 문장을 한 문장으로 바꿔 쓸 때 빈칸에 알맞은 말을 쓰시오.

(1) • I want to know.
   • Is the school lunch delicious?
   ➡ I want to know _____

   _____ .

(2) • I'll ask Sarah.
   • It's all right to sit next to her.
   ➡ I'll ask Sarah _____

   _____ .

(3) • Jim didn't feel hungry.
   • Jim ate lunch already.
   ➡ Jim didn't feel hungry because he

   _____ lunch.

16 다음 문장에서 어법상 어색한 것을 바르게 고쳐 다시 쓰시오.

(1) Would you please check that I filled out this card right?

   ➡ _____

   _____

(2) I don't know that my mom likes potato pizza.

   ➡ _____

   _____

(3) I am not sure that Mike will meet Judy at 3 o'clock.

   ➡ _____

   _____

(4) He insisted that he never heard a girl crying that night.

   ➡ _____

   _____

(5) I decided to come home earlier than I planned.

   ➡ _____

17 다음 중 어법상 어색한 문장을 고르시오.

① I knew that Mike had won first prize at the singing contest.
② Lisa doesn't know whether I can ride a bike.
③ Whether Juliet likes Romeo is not certain.
④ Lily wonders if you are interested in various music genres.
⑤ I'm not sure if or not she made a mistake.

18 다음 두 문장의 뜻이 같도록 빈칸에 알맞은 말을 쓰시오.

(1) I went to the store, but all the flowers were sold out.
   = All the flowers _____
   when I went to the store.

(2) I didn't know who she was. I never met her.
   = I didn't know who she was since I
   _____ her.

[19~20] 다음 글을 읽고 물음에 답하시오.

In 1946, a strange man visited me and asked, "Are you Mr. Kim Yonghwan's daughter?"

For me, this was an odd question because I was more used to ⓐbeing called the daughter of a *parakho*.

"I'm your father's friend. You may wonder if it is true, but your father...," the man said.

At that moment, I was expecting disappointing news since I did not have good memories of my father.

19 위 글의 밑줄 친 ⓐbeing과 문법적 쓰임이 같은 것을 <u>모두</u> 고르시오.

① His hobby is <u>collecting</u> stamps.
② <u>Playing</u> the piano is fun.
③ I finished <u>doing</u> my homework.
④ Kirl was <u>playing</u> chess.
⑤ Look at the <u>smiling</u> girl.

20 When the writer heard the man's words, why was she expecting disappointing news? Fill in the blanks below with suitable words. (2 words)

> Because she did not have _____ _____ of her father.

21 위 글의 밑줄 친 ⓐ를 능동태로 고치시오.

➡ _____

22 아래 〈보기〉에서 위 글의 밑줄 친 ⓑwho와 문법적 쓰임이 <u>다른</u> 것의 개수를 고르시오.

> ─┤ 보기 ├─
> ① Anyone <u>who</u> wants to come is welcome.
> ② There's a student <u>who</u> wants to see you.
> ③ This is the person <u>who</u> made me a kite yesterday.
> ④ Nobody knew <u>who</u> he was.
> ⑤ He was the only one <u>who</u> trusted me.

① 1개 ② 2개 ③ 3개 ④ 4개 ⑤ 5개

[21~22] 다음 글을 읽고 물음에 답하시오.

Back in the 1920's, whenever people saw me in the village, they would say, "There goes the *parakho*'s daughter."

My father was a son from a very rich family. Instead of living the life of a *seonbi*, he was always at the gambling house. That is why ⓐhe was called a *parakho*, which means someone ⓑwho ruins his family's fortune.

"Your father has gambled away all of the money, and now he's asking for more. Go and tell him that we have no more money left," my mother would tell me whenever she sent me to the gambling house.

Then, my father would yell at me angrily, "Why did you come empty-handed? Bring me more money!"

[23~24] 다음 글을 읽고 물음에 답하시오.

When I was sixteen years old, my family (A)<u>had</u> already <u>made</u> an arrangement for me to marry Mr. Seo. As part of the wedding tradition, Mr. Seo's family sent my family some money to buy a new chest for clothes.

Right before the wedding day, my mother came into my room and said, "Your father has taken the money for the chest."

I asked angrily, "How could he do such a horrible thing? What should we do now?"

"We have no choice. You'll have to take your aunt's old chest," my mother said.

"How ⓐ for the family," people would whisper behind my back.

Since the first day of marriage, life at my husband's house had been difficult for me.

23 위 글의 빈칸 ⓐ에 들어갈 알맞은 말을 고르시오.

① exciting ② satisfying
③ boring ④ embarrassing
⑤ amazing

24 위 글의 밑줄 친 (A)had made와 과거완료의 용법이 같은 것을 모두 고르시오.

① I found that I had lost my watch.
② When she came, I had not finished my homework yet.
③ When I called on her, she had been ill for two weeks.
④ The train had just left when he got to the station.
⑤ I did not tell him at first, for I had never seen him before.

25 밑줄 친 ⓐhim을 알맞은 형으로 고치시오.

➡ _____

26 빈칸 ⓑ에 알맞은 것은?

① In ② At
③ For ④ With
⑤ From

27 위 글의 밑줄 친 ⓒ의 우리말에 맞게 주어진 어휘를 이용하여 9 단어로 영작하시오.

had devoted, life, movement

➡ _____
_____

[25~28] 다음 글을 읽고 물음에 답하시오.

"Your father, my dear friend...," my father's friend continued his story. "He was not a gambler. Your father sent the family money to the independence fighters in Manchuria. He made ⓐhim look like a gambler to keep this a secret from the Japanese officers."

___ⓑ___ first, I was not sure if he was telling the truth. But afterwards, I found out the truth about my father and I realized that I had been wrong about him. Ever since that moment, I have been proud to be the daughter of a *parakho* ⓒ독립운동에 그의 인생을 헌신하신.

28 According to the passage, which is NOT true?

① The writer's father was not a gambler.
② The writer's father sent the family money to the independence fighters in Manchuria.
③ The writer's father wanted to look like a gambler to keep his secret identity from the independence fighters.
④ The writer realized that she had been wrong about her father.
⑤ The writer's father was a *parakho* who had devoted his life to the independence movement.

MEMO

Lesson

4

Music to My Ears!

 의사소통 기능

- 상대방의 의견 묻기

  A: **Do you find it** helpful to listen to music before you swim?

  B: Yes, it helps me focus.

- 앞으로의 계획 묻기

  A: **Are you planning to** perform at the talent show?

  B: Yeah, I am.

 언어 형식

- 분사

  They played instruments **made** out of garbage.

- it(가목적어) ~ to부정사(진목적어)

  I found **it** possible **to inspire** people by music.

교과서
Words & Expressions

Key Words

- **anchor** [ǽŋkər] 명 (뉴스 등의) 진행자
- **attention** [əténʃən] 명 관심, 주목
- **background** [bǽkgraund] 명 배경
- **balloon** [bəlúːn] 명 풍선
- **beat** [biːt] 명 울림, 맥박 동 때리다, 두드리다
- **broadcast** [brɔ́ːdkæst] 동 방송하다
- **choir** [kwaiər] 명 합창단
- **compete** [kəmpíːt] 동 (경기 등에) 출전하다
- **concentrate** [kánsəntrèit] 동 집중하다
- **conductor** [kəndʌ́ktər] 명 지휘자
- **congratulation** [kəngrætʃuléiʃən] 명 축하
- **consider** [kənsídər] 동 ～이라고 여기다, 생각하다
- **deliver** [dilívər] 동 전하다
- **endless** [éndlis] 형 끝없는, 무한한
- **entirely** [intáiərli] 부 완전히, 전부
- **environmental** [invàiərənméntl] 형 환경의, 환경과 관련된
- **famous** [féiməs] 형 유명한
- **garbage** [gáːrbidʒ] 명 쓰레기
- **imagine** [imǽdʒin] 동 상상하다
- **index finger** 집게손가락
- **instrument** [ínstrəmənt] 명 악기
- **local** [lóukəl] 형 현지의, 지역의
- **mostly** [móustli] 부 주로, 대부분
- **musical** [mjúːzikəl] 형 음악의
- **musician** [mjuːzíʃən] 명 음악가
- **nail** [neil] 명 손톱

- **notice** [nóutis] 동 ～을 알아차리다
- **orchestra** [ɔ́ːrkəstrə] 명 오케스트라, 관현악단
- **pain** [pein] 명 고통, 아픔
- **perform** [pərfɔ́ːrm] 동 공연하다, 수행하다
- **picker** [píkər] 명 줍는 사람, 채집자
- **positive** [pázətiv] 형 긍정적인
- **pure** [pjuər] 형 깨끗한, 순수한
- **quickly** [kwíkli] 부 빠르게
- **recommend** [rèkəménd] 동 추천하다
- **recycle** [riːsáikl] 동 재활용하다
- **return** [ritə́ːrn] 동 돌아오다
- **review** [rivjúː] 동 재검토하다, 복습하다
- **serious** [síəriəs] 형 심각한
- **share** [ʃɛər] 동 나누다
- **shiny** [ʃáini] 형 빛나는, 반짝거리는
- **shocked** [ʃɑkt] 형 충격을 받은
- **solo** [sóulou] 명 독주, 독창
- **talented** [tǽləntid] 형 재능이 있는
- **tank** [tæŋk] 명 (물, 기름 등의) 저장 통
- **thumb** [θʌm] 명 엄지손가락
- **title** [táitl] 명 제목
- **touch** [tʌtʃ] 동 감동시키다
- **treasure** [tréʒər] 명 보물, 보물 같은 것
- **water pipe** 수도관
- **worthless** [wə́ːrθlis] 형 쓸모없는, 가치 없는

Key Expressions

- **add ～ to ...** ～을 …에 추가하다
- **as long as** ～하는 한
- **be eager to** ～하고 싶어 하다
- **be filled with** ～로 가득 차다
- **be similar to** ～와 비슷하다
- **bring ～ to one's attention** ～에 …가 주목하게 하다
- **calm down** 진정하다
- **draw on** ～을 활용하다
- **in harmony with** ～와 조화를 이루어

- **in the beginning** 처음에, 초반에
- **keep a journal** 일기를 쓰다
- **keep ～ awake** ～을 깨어 있게 하다
- **put one's heart into** ～에 정열을 쏟다, ～에 열중하다
- **send back** ～을 돌려주다
- **sign up for** ～을 신청하다, ～에 가입하다
- **stand on one's head** 물구나무서다
- **Where are you off to?** 어디 가니?
- **work out** 운동하다

Word Power

※ 서로 비슷한 뜻을 가진 어휘
- □ **concentrate** 집중하다 – **focus** 집중하다
- □ **entirely** 완전히, 전부 – **totally** 전적으로
- □ **mostly** 주로, 대부분 – **largely** 주로
- □ **touch** 감동시키다 – **move** 감동을 주다

- □ **consider** ~이라고 여기다 – **regard** ~이라고 여기다
- □ **garbage** 쓰레기 – **waste** 쓰레기
- □ **positive** 긍정적인 – **affirmative** 긍정적인
- □ **worthless** 쓸모없는 – **useless** 쓸모없는

※ 서로 반대의 뜻을 가진 어휘
- □ **positive** 긍정적인 ↔ **negative** 부정적인
- □ **worthless** 가치 없는 ↔ **worthwhile** 가치 있는

- □ **pure** 깨끗한, 순수한 ↔ **impure** 순수하지 못한
- □ **entirely** 전부 ↔ **partly** 부분적으로

※ re+동사
- □ **re-+cycle = recycle** (재활용하다)
- □ **re-+view = review** (재검토하다)
- □ **re-+play = replay** (재생하다, 다시 보다)

- □ **re-+turn = return** (되돌아오다, 돌아오다)
- □ **re-+form = reform** (다시 만들다, 개선하다)

※ 명사 – 형용사
- □ **environment** 환경 – **environmental** 환경의
- □ **music** 음악 – **musical** 음악의
- □ **nature** 자연 – **natural** 자연스러운

- □ **nation** 국가 – **national** 국가의, 국가 소유의
- □ **culture** 문화 – **cultural** 문화적인, 문화의
- □ **magic** 마술 – **magical** 마술의

※ 동사 – 명사
- □ **arrive** 도착하다 – **arrival** 도착
- □ **rehears** 연습하다 – **rehearsal** 리허설, 예행 연습
- □ **approve** 승인하다 – **approval** 승인

- □ **propose** 제안하다 – **proposal** 제안
- □ **remove** 제거하나 – **removal** 세기
- □ **survive** 살아남다 – **survival** 생존

English Dictionary

- □ **conductor** 지휘자
  → a person who directs the performance of an orchestra or choir
  오케스트라나 합창단의 공연을 지휘하는 사람

- □ **endless** 끝없는, 무한한
  → having no end
  끝이 없는

- □ **garbage** 쓰레기
  → things that are no longer useful and that have been thrown out
  더 이상 쓸모가 없어 버려지는 것들

- □ **instrument** 악기
  → a device that is used to make music
  음악을 하기 위하여 사용되는 도구

- □ **picker** 줍는 사람, 채집자
  → a person or machine that gathers something
  무언가를 모으는 사람이나 기계

- □ **positive** 긍정적인
  → giving cause for hope and confidence
  희망이나 자신감의 원인을 제공하는

- □ **recycle** 재활용하다
  → to use something again for a different purpose
  다른 목적으로 무언가를 다시 사용하다

- □ **shiny** 빛나는, 반짝거리는
  → having a smooth, shining, bright appearance
  매끄럽고, 반짝거리고, 밝은 겉모습을 가진

- □ **talented** 재능이 있는
  → having a special ability to do something well
  어떤 것을 잘하는 특별한 능력을 가진

- □ **tank** (물, 기름 등의) 저장 통
  → a container for holding a liquid or gas
  액체나 기체를 담는 용기

- □ **treasure** 보물, 보물 같은 것
  → a very valuable object
  매우 소중한 물건

- □ **worthless** 쓸모없는, 가치 없는
  → having no real value or use
  실제적인 가치나 쓸모가 없는

서답형
01 다음 짝지어진 단어의 관계가 같도록 빈칸에 알맞은 말을 쓰시오.

> pure : impure = _____ : negative

02 다음 영영풀이가 가리키는 것을 고르시오.

> a person who directs the performance of an orchestra or choir

① conductor   ② anchor
③ picker   ④ treasure
⑤ solo

03 다음 주어진 문장의 밑줄 친 beat과 같은 의미로 쓰인 것은?

> I like this rap song because of the strong beats.

① I heard several loud beats on the drum.
② Have you heard somebody beating at the door?
③ My brother used to beat the window when he didn't have a key.
④ I saw the thief beat the car with a baseball bat.
⑤ My child beat on the table with his chopsticks.

04 다음 밑줄 친 부분의 의미로 알맞지 않은 것은?

① Is he learning an instrument? (악기)
② The decision is entirely yours. (부분적으로)
③ He asked us to imagine a world without poverty or war. (상상하다)
④ You didn't notice that I got my hair cut. (알아차리다)
⑤ She put on the silky dress, white stockings, and shiny black boots. (빛나는, 반짝거리는)

서답형
05 다음 문장의 빈칸에 들어갈 말을 〈보기〉에서 골라 쓰시오.

> ─┤ 보기 ├─
> thumb / shocked / pure / treasure / recommend

(1) On Christmas, I used to play _____ hunt with my brother.
(2) I was _____ when I listened to the news.
(3) Henry hit his _____ by mistake.
(4) I brought a bottle of _____ water.
(5) Would you _____ an interesting novel?

서답형
06 다음 우리말에 맞게 주어진 단어를 활용하여 영작하시오.

(1) 우리는 현지 식당에서 저녁을 먹었다. (had, dinner, at)
➡ _____
(2) 그는 체리 채집자로서 근무했다. (as, cherry, pick)
➡ _____
(3) 내 삶은 음악이 없다면 가치 없을 것이다. (would, without, worth)
➡ _____

01 다음 짝지어진 단어의 관계가 같도록 빈칸에 알맞은 말을 쓰시오.

clean : dirty = _____ : narrow

02 다음 우리말에 맞게 빈칸에 알맞은 말을 주어진 철자로 시작하여 쓰시오.

(1) 나의 형에게 대학을 가지 않은 것은 심각한 실수였다.
➡ For my brother, not going to college was a s_____ mistake.

(2) 그는 정오에 연설을 할 것이다.
➡ He will d_____ the speech at noon.

(3) 그 책은 국가적 관심을 이끌었다.
➡ The book has attracted national a_____.

(4) 시험을 보기 전에 노트를 복습하도록 노력해라.
➡ Try to r_____ your notes before you take a test.

(5) 중세시대의 보물은 박물관에 보관된다.
➡ The t_____ from the Middle Ages is kept in the museum.

03 다음 우리말을 주어진 단어를 활용하여 영작하시오.

(1) 은행에 끝없는 줄이 있었다. (end)
➡ _____

(2) 모든 구성원들은 독특하고 재능이 있다. (talent)
➡ _____

(3) 미세 먼지는 환경 재난이다. (fine dust, environment)
➡ _____

04 다음 문장의 빈칸에 들어갈 말을 〈보기〉에서 골라 쓰시오.

┤ 보기 ├
as long as / eager to / in harmony with / calm down / draw on

(1) You can _____ your imagination.
(2) I think this color is _____ the background.
(3) I told him to _____ and not to be so excited.
(4) Mike is _____ become the ace of the team.
(5) We'll go on a picnic _____ the weather is good.

05 우리말과 일치하도록 주어진 단어를 모두 배열하여 영작하시오.

(1) 지문 감식기 위에 집게손가락을 올려놓으세요.
(finger / your / the / on / scanner / place / index / finger)
➡ Please _____
_____.

(2) 그 노인은 멋진 구두를 만드는 것에 그의 열정을 쏟는다.
(nice / the / shoes / old / into / man / puts / heart / his / making)
➡ _____
_____

(3) 우리는 그들이 그 문제에 주목하게 해야 한다.
(the / to / their / attention / we / bring / should / matter)
➡ _____

Conversation

① 상대방의 의견 묻기

> **A:** Do you find it helpful to listen to music before you swim?
> 너는 수영하기 전에 음악을 듣는 것이 도움이 된다고 생각하니?
>
> **B:** Yes, it helps me focus. 물론이지. 그것은 집중하도록 도와줘.

- 경험한 일을 바탕으로 하여 상대방의 의견이나 감정을 물을 때는 'Do you find it ~?(너는 ~가 …하다고 생각하니?)'를 사용한다. 주로 'find it+형용사+to부정사'의 형태로, 여기에 사용되는 it은 가목적어이고, 그 다음에는 다양한 형용사가 나올 수 있다. 예를 들어, 친구가 기타를 연주할 줄 아는데 기타를 연주하는 것이 쉬운지 어려운지 친구의 의견을 묻고 싶으면, 'Do you find it easy/hard to play the guitar?(너는 기타 연주하는 것이 쉽다고/어렵다고 생각하니?)'와 같이 말한다.

- 상대방의 의견을 물어보는 표현으로 'Would you find it easy/hard to play the guitar if you had the chance to play it?(만약 네가 기타를 연주할 기회가 있다면 너는 그것을 연주하는 것이 쉽다고/어렵다고 생각하니?)'를 사용할 수 있고, think를 사용하여 'Do you think it is easy/hard to play the guitar?(너는 기타 치는 것이 쉽다고/어렵다고 생각하니?)'와 같이 물어볼 수 있다.

- 막연하게 상대방의 의견을 물어보는 표현일 때는 'How do you feel about ~?(~에 대하여 어떻게 생각하니?)', 'What do you think about ~?(~에 대하여 어떻게 생각하니?)', 'What's your opinion about ~?(~에 대한 의견이 무엇이니?)'와 같이 물어볼 수 있다.

상대방의 의견 묻기

- Would you find it easy/hard to ~ if you had the chance to ~? (만약 네가 ~할 기회가 있다면 너는 ~을 쉽다고/어렵다고 생각하니?)
- Do you think it is easy/hard to ~? (너는 ~하는 것을 쉽다고/어렵다고 생각하니?)
- How do you feel about ~? (~에 대하여 어떻게 생각하니?)
- What do you think about ~? (~에 대하여 어떻게 생각하니?)
- What's your opinion about ~? (~에 대한 의견이 무엇이니?)

핵심 Check

1. 주어진 단어를 포함하여, 다음 우리말과 일치하도록 빈칸에 알맞은 말을 쓰시오.

> **M:** Hi, Sally. Where are you off to?
>
> **W:** I'm going to the music room. I have choir practice.
>
> **M:** Oh, yeah. I forgot that you've joined the choir. _____
> _____ (it, find, interesting) (너는 합창단에서 노래하는 것이 재미있다고 생각하니?)
>
> **W:** Yeah, it's great to sing in harmony with others.

❷ 앞으로의 계획 묻기

> **A:** Are you planning to perform at the talent show? 너는 장기 자랑에서 공연할 계획이니?
> **B:** Yeah, I am. 응. 그래.

■ 상대방에게 앞으로의 계획을 물을 때 'Are you planning to ~?(너는 ~할 계획이니?)'를 사용할 수 있다. 예를 들어, 방학 동안 해외여행을 갈 계획을 하고 있는지 알고 싶을 때, 'Are you planning to travel abroad during the vacation?(너는 여름 방학 동안 해외여행을 갈 계획이니?)'와 같이 물을 수 있다.

■ 앞으로의 계획을 물어볼 때는 'be going to ~(~할 것이다, ~할 예정이다)'를 사용하여 'Are you going to ~?(너는 ~할 거니?)'라고 할 수 있고, 'Do you have plans to ~?(너는 ~할 계획을 가지고 있니?)' 또는 'Do you intend to ~?(너는 ~할 의도이니?)'와 같이 물어볼 수 있다.

■ 상대방이 계획하는 일에 대하여서 아는 바가 없이 막연하게 앞으로의 계획이 무엇인지를 물어볼 때는 'What are you going to do?(너는 무엇을 할 거니?)', 'What are you planning to do?(너는 무엇을 할 계획이니?)', 'What's your plan?(네 계획이 무엇이니?)' 등으로 물어볼 수 있다.

■ 계획이 무엇인지를 묻는 말에 대한 대답은 'will', 'be going to', 'plan to부정사' 등을 사용하여 'I will ~.(나는 ~할 것이다.)', 'I am going to ~.(나는 ~할 예정이다)', 'I am planning to ~.(나는 ~할 계획이다)', 'I have a plan to ~.(나는 ~할 계획을 가지고 있다.)' 등으로 대답할 수 있다.

앞으로의 계획 묻기

- Are you planning to ~? (너는 ~할 계획이니?)
- Are you going to ~? (너는 ~할 거니?)
- Do you have plans to ~? (너는 ~할 계획을 가지고 있니?)
- Do you intend to ~? (너는 ~할 의도이니?)
- What are you going/planning to do? (너는 무엇을 할 거니?)
- What's your plan? (네 계획이 무엇이니?)

핵심 Check

2. 다음 대화를 자연스러운 순서로 배열하시오.

> **W:** Hey, Tommy. When is the last day to sign up for the talent show?
> (A) How cool! What are you going to do?
> (B) Yeah, I'm going to perform with a couple of people.
> (C) This Friday. Are you planning to sign up for it, Megan?
> **W:** We will play K-pop music with the violin and cello.

➡  _____

Listen and Talk 1-B

Sujin: Hi, Jason. Great to see you again. I've heard the new rap song, *Young and Wild*, ❶that you recorded. It's really cool.

Jason: Oh, thanks.

Sujin: I really like your songs. ❷Do you find it easy to write them?

Jason: Well, it was hard ❸in the beginning, but now it's getting easier. I ❹draw on my experiences and ❺keep a journal.

Sujin: Wow! As they say, "No pain, no gain." Best of luck with your new song!

Jason: Thank you.

Sujin: 안녕하세요, Jason. 다시 만나서 반갑습니다. 녹음하신 새로운 랩 노래, '젊고 무모한(Young and Wild)'을 들었어요. 정말 멋지던데요.
Jason: 오, 고마워요.
Sujin: 당신 노래들은 정말 좋아요. 곡을 쓰는 일이 쉬우세요?
Jason: 글쎄요, 처음에는 어려웠어요. 하지만 지금은 쉬워지고 있어요. 저는 제 경험을 활용해서 일기를 쓰고 있거든요.
Sujin: 와! '고통 없이는 얻는 것도 없다.'라는 말이 있잖아요. 새 노래가 잘 되길 바랍니다!
Jason: 고마워요.

❶ 목적격 관계대명사로 which로 바꾸어 쓸 수 있다.
❷ 상대방의 의견을 묻는 표현으로 'find it+형용사+to부정사"의 형태로, 여기에 사용되는 it은 가목적어이다.
❸ in the beginning: 처음에, 초반에 ❹ draw on: ~을 활용하다 ❺ keep a journal: 일기를 쓰다

Check(√) True or False

(1) It was difficult for Jason to write the song in the beginning.　　　　T ☐ F ☐

(2) Jason recommended keeping a journal to write a song to Sujin.　　　　T ☐ F ☐

Communication

Emma: Hey, Anthony. ❶Can you help me with something?

Anthony: Sure, what's up?

Emma: I'm going to a concert at the Arts Center, but I don't know ❷which seat I should choose.

Anthony: ❸Are you planning to go to the orchestra concert?

Emma: Yes. I'm going to watch the orchestra concert.

Anthony: Then, you should get the seats on the second floor. You can hear the beautiful sounds of various ❹musical instruments better.

Emma: Oh, do you find it better to hear the performance from the second floor?

Anthony: Yes. I find it better than from other seats.

Emma: 저기, Anthony. 나 뭐 좀 도와줄래?
Anthony: 물론, 무슨 일이야?
Emma: 예술 회관에서 하는 공연에 가려고 하는데, 어떤 좌석을 골라야 할지 모르겠어.
Anthony: 오케스트라 공연에 갈 계획이니?
Emma: 응. 나는 오케스트라 공연을 보려고 해.
Anthony: 그럼, 너는 2층 좌석을 얻는 게 좋아. 다양한 악기들의 아름다운 소리를 더 잘 들을 수 있거든.
Emma: 오, 2층에서 공연을 듣는 것이 더 낫다는 거니?
Anthony: 응. 다른 좌석들보다 더 낫다고 생각해.

❶ 도움을 요청하는 표현으로 'Can you give me a hand?' 등으로 바꾸어 표현할 수 있다.
❷ 간접의문문 어순으로 '의문사+주어+동사'의 순서로 이어진다.
❸ 상대방에게 앞으로의 계획을 묻는 표현으로 'Are you going to go to the orchestra concert?'로 바꾸어 표현할 수 있다.
❹ musical instrument: 악기

Check(√) True or False

(3) Emma had a difficulty choosing the seat for the orchestra concert.　　　　T ☐ F ☐

(4) Anthony had a plan to watch the concert at the second floor.　　　　T ☐ F ☐

Listen and Talk 1-A-1

W: Hey, Jake. I saw ❶you won the swimming ❷competition yesterday. Congratulations!

M: Thanks, Anna.

W: You always seem to listen to music before you compete. ❸Do you find it helpful to listen to music before you swim?

M: Yes, it ❹keeps me awake and it helps me focus.

❶ 목적어 역할을 하는 명사절을 이끄는 접속사 that이 생략되어 있다.

❷ competition: 대회

❸ 상대방의 의견을 묻는 표현으로 'Do you think it is helpful to listen to music before you swim?' 등으로 바꾸어 표현할 수 있다.

❹ keep ~ awake: ~을 깨어 있게 하다

 Listen and Talk 1-A-2

M: Hi, Sally. ❶Where are you off to?

W: I'm going to the music room. I have ❷choir practice.

M: Oh, yeah. I forgot that you've joined the choir. Do you find it interesting to sing in the choir?

W: Yeah, it's great to sing ❸in harmony with others.

❶ Where are you off to?: 어디 가니?

❷ choir: 합창단 ❸ in harmony with: ~와 조화를 이루어

 Listen and Talk 2-A-1

W: Hey, Tommy. When is the last day to ❶ sign up for the talent show?

M: This Friday. Are you planning to sign up for ❷it, Megan?

W: Yeah, ❸I'm going to perform with a couple of people.

M: How cool! What are you going to do?

W: We will play K-pop music with the violin and cello.

❶ sign up for: ~을 신청하다, ~에 가입하다

❷ it은 the talent show를 가리킨다.

❸ 앞으로의 계획을 설명하는 표현으로 'I have a plan to perform with a couple of people.'로 바꾸어 쓸 수 있다.

 Listen and Talk 2-A-2

W: Hello, ❶I'd like to sign up for a drum class.

M: Okay. ❷Are you planning to take the class during the week or during the weekend?

W: I'm planning to take a weekday class. When do you offer them?

M: There is a class on Tuesday and ❸another one on Thursday. Both classes start at 6 o'clock.

W: Great. I'd like to sign up for the Tuesday class.

❶ I'd like to ~. = I would like to ~.: ~하고 싶다. ❷ Are you planning to ~? = Are you going to ~?: 너는 ~할 거니? ❸ another one = another class

 Listen and Talk 2-B

W: Are you planning to learn a musical instrument? I'd like to recommend the *kalimba*, a small African musical instrument. The sound ❶it makes ❷is similar to ❸that of a music box. Playing the *kalimba* is very easy. You can learn to use your ❹thumb nails to play beautiful music in just one lesson!

❶ it은 *kalimba*를 가리킨다. ❷ be similar to ~: ~와 비슷하다

❸ that은 the sound를 가리킨다. ❹ thumb: 엄지손가락

Wrap Up

M: Hey, Alice.

W: Hi, Sam. ❶How have you been?

M: Great. Actually, ❷I've read a lot of pop news from your blog.

W: Oh, have you? Thanks for visiting my blog!

M: Do you find it interesting to post ❸the latest pop news?

W: Yes, I love to spread news to people.

❶ '어떻게 지냈니?'라고 안부를 묻는 표현이다.

❷ 'have + p.p.' 형태의 현재완료 시제이다. ❸ the latest ~: 가장 최근의 ~

● 다음 우리말과 일치하도록 빈칸에 알맞은 말을 쓰시오.

Listen & Talk 1 A-1

W: Hey, Jake. I saw you _____ the swimming _____ yesterday. _____!

M: Thanks, Anna.

W: You always seem to listen to music before you _____. Do you _____ _____ _____ to listen to music before you swim?

M: Yes, it _____ me _____ and it helps me focus.

Listen & Talk 1 A-2

M: Hi, Sally. Where are you _____ to?

W: I'm going to the music room. I have _____ _____.

M: Oh, yeah. I _____ that you've joined the _____. Do you _____ it _____ to sing in the choir?

W: Yeah, it's great to sing _____ _____ _____ others.

Listen & Talk 1-B

W: Hi, Jason. Great to see you again. I've heard the new rap song, *Young and Wild*, that _____ _____. It's really cool.

M: Oh, thanks.

W: I really like your songs. Do you _____ _____ _____ _____ _____ _____?

M: Well, it was hard in the _____, but now it's getting easier. I _____ _____ my experiences and _____ _____ _____.

W: Wow! As they say, "_____ _____, _____ _____." Best of luck with your new song!

M: Thank you.

Listen & Talk 2 A-1

W: Hey, Tommy. When is the last day to _____ _____ _____ the talent show?

M: This Friday. _____ _____ _____ _____ sign up for it, Megan?

W: Yeah, I'm going to _____ with a couple of people.

M: How cool! What are you going to do?

W: We will play K-pop music with the _____ and _____.

W: 안녕, Jake. 어제 수영 대회에서 네가 이긴 것을 봤어. 축하해!

M: 고마워, Anna.

W: 너는 경기하기 전에 항상 음악을 듣는 것 같더라. 수영하기 전에 음악을 듣는 게 도움이 되니?

M: 응, 그것은 나를 깨어 있게 하고 집중하는 데 도움을 줘.

M: 안녕, Sally. 어디 가는 길이야?

W: 음악실에 가는 중이야. 합창단 연습이 있거든.

M: 오, 그래. 네가 합창단에 들어간 걸 잊고 있었어. 합창단에서 노래하는 것은 재미있니?

W: 응, 다른 사람들과 조화를 이루어 노래하는 게 좋아.

W: 안녕하세요, Jason. 다시 만나서 반갑습니다. 녹음하신 새로운 랩 노래, '젊고 무모한(Young and Wild)'을 들었어요. 정말 멋지던데요.

M: 오, 고마워요.

W: 당신 노래들은 정말 좋아요. 곡을 쓰는 일이 쉬우세요?

M: 글쎄요, 처음에는 어려웠어요, 하지만 지금은 쉬워지고 있어요. 저는 제 경험을 활용해서 일기를 쓰고 있거든요.

W: 와! '고통 없이는 얻는 것도 없다.'라는 말이 있잖아요. 새 노래가 잘 되길 바랍니다!

M: 고마워요.

W: 안녕, Tommy. 장기 자랑 등록 마감이 언제야?

M: 이번 주 금요일이야. 너 그거 등록할 계획이니, Megan?

W: 응, 나는 몇 사람과 함께 공연할 거야.

M: 정말 멋지다! 무엇을 할 거야?

W: 우리는 케이팝 음악을 바이올린과 첼로로 연주할 거야.

Listen & Talk 2 A-2

W: Hello, I'd like to _____ _____ _____ a drum class.

M: Okay. Are you planning to _____ _____ _____ during the week or during the weekend?

W: I'm _____ to take a weekday class. When do you _____ them?

M: There is a class on Tuesday and _____ _____ on Thursday. _____ classes start at 6 o'clock.

W: Great. I'd like to _____ _____ for the Tuesday class.

Listen & Talk 2-B

W: Are you planning to learn a _____ _____? I'd like to _____ the *kalimba*, a small African musical instrument. The sound it makes _____ _____ _____ that of a music box. _____ the *kalimba* is very easy. You can learn to use your _____ _____ to play beautiful music in just one lesson!

Communication

W: Hey, Anthony. Can you help me with _____?

M: Sure, what's _____?

W: I'm going to a concert at the Arts Center, but I don't know _____ _____ _____ _____.

M: Are you planning to go to the _____ concert?

W: Yes. I'm going to watch the _____ concert.

M: Then, you should _____ _____ _____ on the second floor. You can hear the beautiful sounds of _____ _____ _____ better.

W: Oh, do you find it better to hear the performance _____ _____ _____ _____?

M: Yes. I _____ _____ _____ than from other seats.

Wrap Up

M: Hey, Alice.

W: Hi, Sam. How have you _____?

M: Great. Actually, _____ _____ a lot of pop news from your blog.

W: Oh, _____ _____? Thanks _____ _____ my blog!

M: Do you _____ it interesting to _____ the _____ pop news?

W: Yes, I love to _____ news to people.

해석

W: 안녕하세요, 드럼 수업에 등록하고 싶은데요.

M: 알겠습니다. 수업을 주중에 들으실 건가요, 주말에 들으실 건가요?

W: 주중 수업을 들을 계획이에요. 수업이 언제 있나요?

M: 화요일 수업이 하나 있고 또 하나는 목요일에 있어요. 두 수업 모두 6시 정각에 시작합니다.

W: 좋아요. 화요일 수업에 등록할게요.

W: 악기를 배울 계획인가요? 아프리카의 작은 악기인 '칼림바'를 추천하고 싶습니다. 그 악기가 내는 소리는 음악 상자의 소리와 비슷합니다. '칼림바'를 연주하는 것은 아주 쉬워요. 단 한 번의 수업으로 엄지손톱을 사용해 아름다운 음악을 연주하는 걸 배울 수 있어요!

W: 저기, Anthony. 나 뭐 좀 도와줄래?

M: 물론, 무슨 일이야?

W: 예술 회관에서 하는 공연에 가려고 하는데, 어떤 좌석을 골라야 할지 모르겠어.

M: 오케스트라 공연에 갈 계획이니?

W: 응. 나는 오케스트라 공연을 보려고 해.

M: 그럼, 너는 2층 좌석을 얻는 게 좋아. 다양한 악기들의 아름다운 소리를 더 잘 들을 수 있거든.

W: 오, 2층에서 공연을 듣는 것이 더 낫다는 거니?

M: 응. 다른 좌석들보다 더 낫다고 생각해.

M: 안녕, Alice.

W: 안녕, Sam. 어떻게 지내?

M: 좋아. 사실, 네 블로그에서 팝 소식을 많이 읽었어.

W: 오, 그랬어? 내 블로그를 방문해 줘서 고마워!

M: 최신 팝 소식을 올리는 게 재미있니?

W: 응, 사람들에게 소식을 전하는 게 좋아.

01 다음 대화의 빈칸에 들어갈 말을 〈보기〉에 주어진 단어들을 모두 배열하여 영작하시오.

> Minho: Hi, Sally. Where are you off to?
>
> Sally: I'm going to the music room. I have choir practice.
>
> Minho: Oh, yeah. I forgot that you've joined the choir. _____
>
> Sally: Yeah, it's great to sing in harmony with others.

> ┤ 보기 ├
>
> in / you / it / do / to / sing / the / find / choir / interesting / ?

➡ _____

02 다음 대화의 내용과 일치하지 않는 것은?

> Chris: Hi, Julie. Where are you going?
>
> Julie: Hi, Chris. I'm going to my guitar lesson. Our band has a concert at the hospital this Sunday.
>
> Chris: This Sunday? Are you planning to perform at the Happy Children's Hospital?
>
> Julie: Yes. How do you know about the concert?
>
> Chris: Oh, my sister is going to play the piano there, so I'm going to the concert, too.
>
> Julie: Great. Come and watch our performance!

① Julie는 기타 수업에 가는 길이다.

② Julie의 밴드는 이번 주 일요일에 병원에서 공연을 할 것이다.

③ Julie는 Happy 아동 병원에서 공연을 할 계획이다.

④ Chris의 여동생은 공연에서 피아노를 연주할 것이다.

⑤ Julie는 Chris의 여동생을 공연에 초대했다.

03 다음 대화가 자연스럽게 이어지도록 순서대로 배열하시오.

> (A) How cool! What are you going to do?
>
> (B) We will play K-pop music with the violin and cello.
>
> (C) Yeah, I'm going to perform with a couple of people.
>
> (D) This Friday. Are you planning to sign up for it, Megan?
>
> (E) Hey, Tommy. When is the last day to sign up for the talent show?

➡ _____

[01~02] 다음 대화를 읽고 물음에 답하시오.

Sujin: Hi, Jason. Great to see you again. I've heard the new rap song, *Young and Wild*, that you recorded. It's really cool.
Jason: Oh, thanks.
Sujin: I really like your songs. (A)_____
Jason: Well, it was hard in the beginning, but now it's getting easier. I draw on my experiences and keep a journal.
Sujin: Wow! As they say, "No pain, no gain." Best of luck with your new song!
Jason: Thank you.

서답형

01 위 대화의 빈칸 (A)에 들어갈 말을 <보기>에 주어진 단어들을 배열하여 영작하시오.

┌─ 보기 ┤
you / it / do / to / write / them / find / easy / ?
└─

➡ _____

02 위 대화의 내용과 일치하지 <u>않는</u> 것은?

① 수진은 Jason을 처음 만났다.
② 수진은 Jason의 새로운 노래를 정말 좋아한다.
③ Jason은 경험을 활용해 일기를 쓰고 있다.
④ '젊고 무모한(*Young and Wild*)'은 Jason의 새로운 랩 노래이다.
⑤ Jason은 곡을 쓰는 일이 처음에는 어려웠지만 지금은 점점 쉬워지고 있다.

[03~04] 다음 대화를 읽고 물음에 답하시오.

Anna: Hey, Jake. I saw you ⓐ<u>won</u> the swimming competition yesterday. ⓑ <u>Congratulations!</u>
Jake: Thanks, Anna.

Anna: You always seem to listen to music before you ⓒ<u>competing</u>. Do you find it ⓓ<u>helpful</u> to listen to music before you swim?
Jake: Yes, it keeps me ⓔ<u>awake</u> and it helps me focus.

03 위 대화의 밑줄 친 ⓐ~ⓔ 중 어법상 <u>틀린</u> 것을 찾아 바르게 고치시오.

➡ _____

04 위 대화의 내용과 일치하지 <u>않는</u> 것은?

① Jake took part in the swimming competition yesterday.
② Jake won the swimming competition yesterday.
③ Jake always listens to music before he competes.
④ It is helpful for Jake to listen to music to keep awake.
⑤ It is necessary for Jake to swim to focus on his work.

[05~06] 다음 대화를 읽고 물음에 답하시오.

Megan: Hey, Tommy. When is the last day to sign up for the talent show?
Tommy: This Friday. Are you planning to sign up for it, Megan?
Megan: Yeah, I'm going to perform with a couple of people.
Tommy: How cool! What are you going to do?
Megan: We will play K-pop music with the violin and cello.

서답형

05 Until when should Megan sign up for the talent show?

➡ _____

서답형

06 What is Megan's plan for the talent show? Use the words 'people', 'play', and 'violin and cello'.

➡ _____

_____

[07~09] 다음 글을 읽고 물음에 답하시오.

> W: Are you planning to learn a musical instrument? I'd like to recommend the *kalimba*, a small African musical instrument. The sound it makes is similar to that of a music box. Playing the *kalimba* is very easy. You can learn to use your thumb nails to play beautiful music in just one lesson!

서답형

07 What is the *kalimba*?

➡ _____

서답형

08 What is the sound the *kalimba* makes similar to?

➡ _____

서답형

09 What should you use to play the *kalimba*?

➡ _____

10 다음 짝지어진 대화가 어색한 것은?

① A: Do you find it helpful to listen to music before you swim?

　B: Yes, it helps me focus.

② A: Are you planning to perform at the talent show?

　B: Yeah, I am.

③ A: Do you find it interesting to learn how to cook?

　B: Yes, I am. It's so interesting.

④ A: Do you think it is fun to play baseball?

　B: No, I don't. How about you?

⑤ A: Are you planning to visit Jejudo this summer?

　B: Well, I'm not sure yet.

[11~12] 다음 대화를 읽고 물음에 답하시오.

> Sue: (A) Hello, I'd like to sign up for a drum class.
>
> Mike: (B) Okay. Are you planning to take the class during the week or during the weekend?
>
> Sue: (C) When do you offer them?
>
> Mike: (D) There is a class on Tuesday and another one on Thursday. Both classes start at 6 o'clock.
>
> Sue: (E) Great. I'd like to sign up for the Tuesday class.

11 위 대화의 (A)~(E) 중 주어진 문장이 들어가기에 적절한 곳은?

> I'm planning to take a weekday class.

① (A)　② (B)　③ (C)　④ (D)　⑤ (E)

12 위 대화의 내용과 일치하지 않는 것을 고르시오.

① Sue는 드럼 수업에 등록하고 싶다.

② Sue는 주중 수업을 들을 계획이다.

③ 주중 드럼 수업은 화요일과 목요일에 있다.

④ 주중 드럼 수업 시간은 서로 다르다.

⑤ Sue는 화요일 수업에 등록하고 싶다.

[01~02] 다음 대화를 읽고 물음에 답하시오.

Megan: Hey, Tommy. When is the last day to sign up for the talent show?

Tommy: This Friday. (A)너 그거 등록할 계획이니?(it, planning, sign), Megan?

Megan: Yeah, I'm going to perform with a couple of people.

Tommy: How cool! What are you going to do?

Megan: We will play K-pop music with the violin and cello.

01 위 대화의 밑줄 친 (A)의 우리말을 주어진 어휘를 이용하여 8 단어로 영작하시오.

➡ _____

02 What kind of musical instruments is Megan's team going to play?

➡ _____

[03~04] 다음 글을 읽고 물음에 답하시오.

W: (A)악기를 배울 계획인가요?(musical, planning) I'd like to recommend the *kalimba*, a small African musical instrument. The sound it makes (B)_____(be) similar to that of a music box. (C)_____(play) the *kalimba* is very easy. You can learn to use your thumb nails to play beautiful music in just one lesson!

03 위 글의 밑줄 친 (A)의 우리말을 주어진 어휘를 이용하여 영작하시오.

➡ _____

04 위 글의 빈칸 (B)와 (C)에 괄호 안에 주어진 단어를 알맞은 형태로 쓰시오.

➡ (B) _____ (C) _____

05 다음 대화의 내용과 일치하도록 빈칸을 완성하시오.

Anna: Hey, Jake. I saw you won the swimming competition yesterday. Congratulations!

Jake: Thanks, Anna.

Anna: You always seem to listen to music before you compete. Do you find it helpful to listen to music before you swim?

Jake: Yes, it keeps me awake and it helps me focus.

⬇

Anna congratulated Jake on (A)_____ _____ competition yesterday. She wanted to know why Jake always listens to music before (B)_____. Jake told her that (C)_____ _____.

06 다음 대화의 밑줄 친 (A)의 우리말을 주어진 어구를 배열하여 영작하시오.

Sam: Hey, Alice.

Alice: Hi, Sam. How have you been?

Sam: Great. Actually, I've read a lot of pop news from your blog.

Alice: Oh, have you? Thanks for visiting my blog!

Sam: (A)최근 팝 소식을 올리는 게 재미있니?

Alice: Yes, I love to spread news to people.

┤ 보기 ├
the / it / you / to / pop news / post / interesting / do / find / latest

➡ _____

Grammar

① 분사(현재분사·과거분사)

> • They played instruments **made** out of garbage. 그들은 쓰레기로 만들어진 악기를 연주했다.
> • She soothed the **crying** baby by patting it on the back.
> 그녀는 우는 아기를 토닥거리며 달랬다.

■ 분사는 동사의 활용형으로, 동사의 성격을 지니면서 형용사의 역할을 할 수 있게 변형한 것을 말한다. 분사는 명사의 앞이나 뒤에서 명사를 꾸며주며, 현재분사는 '능동'이나 '진행'의 의미가 있고, 과거분사는 '수동'이나 '완료'의 의미가 있다.

- Do you know the baby **sleeping** in the cradle? (너는 요람에서 자고 있는 아기를 아니?: 뒤에서 수식하는 현재분사 '진행')
- I put the **sleeping** baby down gently. (나는 자고 있는 아기를 살며시 내려놓았다.: 앞에서 수식하는 현재분사 '진행')
- Do you have a client **named** Peters? (당신에게 Peters라는 이름을 가진 고객이 있습니까?: 뒤에서 수식하는 과거분사 '수동')
- She felt sure the letter had some **hidden** meaning. (그녀는 그 편지에 무슨 숨은 의미가 있다고 확신했다.: 앞에서 수식하는 과거분사 '수동')

■ 분사가 단독으로 명사를 수식할 때는 명사 앞에 붙지만 분사에 다른 어구(목적어, 수식어구 등)가 함께 있을 때는 뒤에서 명사를 수식한다.

- John is a student of **proven** ability. (John은 증명된 능력을 지닌 학생이다.)
- Look at the man **taking** pictures. (사진을 찍고 있는 남자를 보세요.)

■ 명사를 뒤에서 수식하는 경우에는 그 앞에 '주격 관계대명사+be동사'가 생략된 것으로 생각할 수 있다.

- I like the books (which were) **written** in plain English. (나는 평이한 영어로 쓰여진 책들을 좋아한다.)
- Look at the man (who is) **taking** pictures. (사진을 찍고 있는 남자를 보세요.)

■ 동명사와 현재분사는 둘 다 '동사원형+-ing'의 형태이지만, 동명사는 문장 내에서 명사의 역할을 하고, 현재분사는 문장 내에서 형용사의 역할을 한다.

- a **sleeping** baby (잠자는 아기: 현재분사)
- a **sleeping** bag (침낭: 동명사: 목적이나 용도를 나타냄.)

핵심 Check

1. 괄호 안에 주어진 어휘를 이용하여 빈칸을 알맞게 채우시오.

   (1) She showed me the letter _____ in English. (write)

   (2) There are eight men _____ on the stage. (sing)

   (3) A _____ stone gathers no moss. (roll)

② it(가목적어) ~ to부정사(진목적어)

> • I found **it** possible **to inspire** people by music.
> 나는 음악으로 사람들에게 영감을 주는 것이 가능하다는 것을 알았다.

- '주어+동사+목적어+목적격보어'로 이루어진 문장은 5형식 문장이라고 한다.
  - They made me repeat the whole story. (그들은 내게 그 이야기 전체를 반복하게 만들었다.)

- 길이가 긴 to부정사구가 목적어로 쓰일 때, 목적어 자리에 가목적어 it을 쓰고 to부정사는 문장의 맨 뒤에 쓴다. 이때 진목적어는 to 이하이다.
  - I think **it** important **to read** books. (나는 독서가 중요하다고 생각한다.)
  이 문장에서 it이 의미하는 것은 to read books이다. it 자리에 to부정사를 넣어 해석한다.

- 가목적어는 대개 목적격보어가 있는 5형식 문장에서 쓰인다.
  - Social media has made **it** possible for older people **to reconnect** with old friends. (소셜 미디어는 나이가 든 사람들이 옛 친구들과 다시 연결되는 것을 가능하게 해준다.)
  이 문장에서 possible은 목적어를 보충해 주는 목적격보어이다. 목적어 자리에 it이 쓰였지만, 가목적어 it은 아무 의미가 없는 단어이며, 목적격보어는 to부정사의 의미를 보충해 준다.(for older people to reconnect with old friends → possible) 특히 find, make, think 등은 to부정사(구)가 목적어로 나올 경우 가목적어 it을 쓴다.

- 의미상의 주어
  전체 문장과 to부정사구의 행위의 주체가 다른 경우 to부정사구의 주체를 의미상의 주어라고 하며, 주로 'for+목적격'의 형태로 to부정사 앞에 쓴다.
  - I thought **it** necessary for her **to do** so. (나는 그녀가 그렇게 하는 게 필요하다고 생각했다.)

- 가목적어 it은 to부정사를 문장의 맨 뒤로 보내고 그 목적어 자리에 it을 쓴 것이고, 가주어 it은 주어 역할을 하는 to부정사를 뒤로 보내고 가짜 주어인 it을 그 자리에 쓴 것이다.
  - They considered **it** impossible for us **to climb** the mountain. (그들은 우리가 그 산에 오르지 못할 것으로 생각했다.) 〈가목적어 it〉
  - **It** is quite reasonable for you **to act** that way. (네가 그렇게 행동해도 도리에 어긋나지 않는다.) 〈가주어 it〉

핵심 Check

2. 다음 빈칸에 알맞은 말을 쓰시오.
  (1) Do you find _____ easy to write poems?
  (2) My dad considers it important _____ stay healthy.

01 다음 빈칸에 들어갈 말로 알맞은 것은?

> I think _____ important to read books.

① this   ② that   ③ what
④ which   ⑤ it

02 다음 괄호 안에서 알맞은 말을 고르시오.

(1) The girl (smiling / smiled) over there is beautiful.
(2) There are no (hiding / hidden) costs.
(3) She is talking with a girl (wearing / wears) glasses.
(4) He watered the trees (planting / planted) in the garden.

03 다음 우리말을 바르게 영작한 것을 고르시오.

> 나는 해외로 여행하는 것이 신난다는 것을 알았다.

① I found that exciting to take a trip abroad.
② I found what exciting to take a trip abroad.
③ I found it exciting to take a trip abroad.
④ I found it exciting taking a trip abroad.
⑤ I found to take a trip abroad exciting.

04 다음 우리말에 맞게 주어진 어휘를 바르게 배열하시오.

(1) 음악회는 한 소녀가 자신의 반짝이는 첼로로 바흐의 <첼로 모음곡 1번>을 연주하는 것으로 시작되었다. (her, Bach's *Cello Suite No. 1*, the concert, a girl, cello, began, playing, shiny, on, with)

➡ _____

(2) 그는 한국에서 만들어진 차를 샀다. (he, Korea, car, bought, made, a, in)

➡ _____

(3) Anna는 피아노를 치는 것이 재미있다고 생각한다. (it, the piano, Anna, play, finds, fun, to)

➡ _____

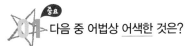

중요
01 다음 중 어법상 어색한 것은?

① Do you find it interesting to learn how to cook?

② The new law made for teenagers to drive possible.

③ I believe it helpful to listen to music while I study alone.

④ Some people think it impolite to ask someone's age.

⑤ It is advisable for you to go right now.

02 다음 중 어법상 어색한 것은?

① The woman attacked by a dog suffered severe injuries.

② Look at the crying baby.

③ Sam was surprised by the results posting on the Internet.

④ Graham saw a man lying on the bed.

⑤ The package containing the samples of accessories was received today.

중요
03 다음 빈칸에 알맞은 말이 바르게 짝지어진 것은?

> • Look at the children _____ on the stage.
> • Minsu found _____ exciting to dance in front of many people.

① singing – it
② singing – that
③ sung – what
④ sung – it
⑤ sing – that

서답형
04 다음 괄호 안에서 알맞은 말을 고르시오.

(1) He thought it logical (for / of) her to delay the plan.

(2) Do you find (it / that) fun to watch that kind of musical?

(3) The combined effort of everyone has made it possible (achieve / to achieve) this goal.

(4) I know the girl (talking / talked) to her teacher.

(5) The child (frightening / frightened) by the burning candle started to cry.

(6) He sent a personal letter to the (complaining / complained) customer.

중요
05 주어진 문장의 밑줄 친 부분의 쓰임이 나머지 넷과 다른 것은?

① *Yesterday* is a famous song sung by The Beatles.

② The army attacked by the enemy finally defeated them.

③ They made their desires known to the mayor.

④ His house is crowded with people invited to the party.

⑤ The boy has already taken a lot of pictures of the sea.

06 다음 문장의 밑줄 친 부분 중 어법상 어색한 것은?

> She ⓐ<u>made</u> ⓑ<u>it</u> ⓒ<u>possible</u> ⓓ<u>for us</u> ⓔ <u>singing</u> in the talent show.

① ⓐ   ② ⓑ   ③ ⓒ

④ ⓓ   ⑤ ⓔ

07 Which is suitable for the blank?

> The desert fox is famous for appearing in *The Little Prince* _____ by Antoine de Saint Exupery.

① write   ② wrote   ③ written

④ writing   ⑤ to write

08 다음 중 밑줄 친 it[It]의 용법이 나머지와 다른 하나는?

① <u>It</u> was 10 o'clock in the morning.

② Last Saturday, <u>it</u> rained on and off all day long.

③ <u>It</u> isn't that far from here to the museum.

④ Do you think <u>it</u> easy to play the guitar?

⑤ In the summer when <u>it</u> was really hot, she would send me over to the small house to get her a bottle of water.

09 다음 우리말을 바르게 영작한 것을 고르시오.

> 편지를 쓰고 있는 소년을 보아라.

① Look at the writing a letter boy.

② Look at the boy writing a letter.

③ Look at the boy written a letter.

④ Look at the writing boy a letter.

⑤ Look at the boy write a letter.

10 다음 두 문장을 한 문장으로 바꿔 쓸 때 가장 적절한 것은?

> • To play dodge ball is fun.
> • Some students think so.

① Some students think to play dodge ball fun.

② Some students think fun to play dodge ball.

③ Some students think fun to play dodge ball it.

④ Some students think it fun to play dodge ball.

⑤ Some students think fun it to play dodge ball.

11 다음 문장의 빈칸에 들어갈 수 <u>없는</u> 것은?

> *Fake Love* is a famous song _____ by many teenagers.

① singing   ② sung

③ which is sung   ④ loved

⑤ which is loved

12 다음 중 밑줄 친 it[It]이 가목적어로 쓰인 것을 고르시오.

① <u>It</u> gave me goose bumps just to think about it.

② <u>It</u> weighed between nine and ten kilos.

③ I consider <u>it</u> necessary to sleep at least six hours.

④ When <u>it</u> was really cold, we would sit on the floor and cover with a blanket.

⑤ He picked up a stone and then threw <u>it</u> at a crow.

13 다음 문장의 빈칸에 들어갈 수 없는 말은?

> The girl _____ is my daughter.

① taking a walk in the park
② invited to the party
③ playing in the garden
④ reads a book
⑤ wearing a pink dress

14 다음 빈칸에 it[It]이 들어갈 수 없는 것은?

① I know _____ many employees drive alone to work.
② _____ was she that became the first of three queens to rule the Silla Dynasty.
③ I make _____ a rule to go to bed at 11 o'clock.
④ _____ is not easy for Tom to climb the mountain.
⑤ Do you find _____ better to watch the performance on the left side?

15 다음 빈칸에 알맞은 말이 순서대로 바르게 짝지어진 것을 고르시오.

> • The results of the meeting _____ at the centre will be announced tomorrow.
> • They turned their attention to food _____ at the restaurant.

① held – serving
② held – served
③ hold – serves
④ holding – served
⑤ holding – serving

16 다음 우리말에 맞게 영작한 것을 모두 고르시오.

> 나는 대부분이 쓰레기로 가득 차 있는 마을에 살고 있는 어린이들을 보았습니다.

① I saw children lived in a town that was mostly filling with garbage.
② I saw children lived in a town that was mostly filled with garbage.
③ I saw children living in a town that was mostly filling with garbage.
④ I saw children living in a town that was mostly filled with garbage.
⑤ I saw children living in a town mostly filled with garbage.

서답형

17 다음 문장에서 생략되어 있는 것을 찾아 어법에 맞게 다시 쓰시오.

(1) An autograph is something written by a person, not a machine.

➡ _____

_____

(2) The image of a girl playing chess with the statue was taken on Jan. 7.

➡ _____

_____

18 다음 중 어법상 어색한 것을 고르시오. (2개)

① I found it easy to play the game.
② Nick thought that hard to sing a solo well.
③ The police officer helped a man lain on the street.
④ He wrote about his experience in a book titled 'Journey Man.'
⑤ Sarah opened the big box filled with a lot of books.

01 다음 빈칸에 알맞은 말을 쓰시오.

(1) I consider _____ important to keep a diary.
(2) He helped make it possible _____ children to play music with instruments made out of garbage.
(3) The situation made it hard for them _____ decide which direction they should go.

02 다음 우리말에 맞게 주어진 어구를 바르게 배열하시오.

(1) 나는 가치 없는 것도 영감을 주는 음악을 만들어 낼 수 있다는 것을 사람들이 알게 되기를 원합니다. (I, people, something, music, know, can, want, make, inspiring, that, even, worthless, to)

➡ _____
_____

(2) 선생님은 학생들이 숙제를 할 것을 분명히 했다. (the teacher, their homework, the students, it, do, made, clear, for, to)

➡ _____
_____

(3) Stravinsky는 매일 아침 15분 동안 물구나무 서는 것이 도움이 된다고 생각했다.
(Stravinsky, his head, morning, it, 15 minutes, helpful, considered, stand, every, to, on, for)

➡ _____
_____

03 다음 문장에서 생략된 것을 넣어 다시 쓰시오.

(1) There is an old family photo hanging on the wall.

➡ _____
_____

(2) Only the people invited to the meeting can attend the meeting.

➡ _____
_____

04 다음 문장의 it[It]이 대신하고 있는 것을 찾아 쓰시오.

(1) The gifted boy thinks it easy to draw pictures using his imagination.

➡ _____

(2) Some students find it more interesting to do experiments at a science lab.

➡ _____

(3) It is hard to memorize all the poems in the book.

➡ _____

05 괄호 안에 있는 단어를 어법에 맞게 고쳐 쓰시오.

(1) So here we have an artist (paint) her image.

➡ _____

(2) It has a chocolate flower (paint) in real gold dust.

➡ _____

(3) Who is that man (wear) a cowboy hat?

➡ _____

(4) My teacher got thank-you letters (write) by students.

➡ _____

06 그림을 보고, 주어진 어휘를 이용하여 빈칸을 알맞게 채우시오.

(1) The teacher is looking at the students _____ soccer. (play)

(2) Look at the teacher _____ with the letter _____ by the student. (satisfy)

(3) There is a girl _____ the guitar. (play)

07 두 문장의 의미가 같도록 빈칸에 알맞은 말을 쓰시오.

(1) Mary thought that it is fun to play the guitar.
   = Mary thought _____ fun _____ _____ the guitar.

(2) Do you find that it is helpful to listen to music before you swim?
   = Do you find _____ helpful _____ _____ to music before you swim?

08 다음 문장에서 어법상 <u>어색한</u> 것을 바르게 고치시오.

(1) We met a little girl walkcd with her sister in the park.
   ➡ _____

(2) He found a strange man lain motionless on the street.
   ➡ _____

(3) We're going to find out how a musical group calling "The Junk Orchestra" was formed.
   ➡ _____

(4) Do you find that interesting to watch old movies?
   ➡ _____

(5) The severe pain made it hard of her to work.
   ➡ _____

(6) Is it possible for us visiting Mars someday?
   ➡ _____

(7) I think to carry out our design at once necessary.
   ➡ _____
   _____

09 다음 문장을 같은 뜻의 문장으로 바꿔 쓸 때 빈칸에 알맞은 말을 쓰시오.

(1) I believe that it is difficult to support them.
   = I believe it difficult _____ them.

(2) I think that you should do it at once.
   = I think it necessary _____ at once.

Reading

The Junk Orchestra

– written by a music blogger, Lucy White

"The world sends us garbage, we send back music." This was written <u>on the back of</u> a concert ticket <u>I was given</u>. The musical group
~의 뒤에   I was given은 앞에 목적격 관계대명사 which[that]가 생략
was called "The Junk Orchestra." They played instruments <u>made</u>

entirely out of garbage. I could not imagine <u>what kind of sound these</u>
앞의 instruments를 후치 수식하는 과거 분사구   what kind ~ would make: 동사 imagine의 목적어 역할을 하는 간접의문문
<u>instruments would make</u>, so I was eager to find out.

Before the concert, I thought that the instruments <u>might</u> sound
may의 과거형
strange. After a few minutes, a group of young people began to walk

on the stage. The first thing <u>I noticed</u> was their instruments: a cello
I noticed 앞에 목적격 관계대명사 which[that]가 생략
<u>made out of a shiny oil tank</u>, a violin made with forks, and a flute made
a cello를 후치 수식하는 과거분사구
with a water pipe and buttons. The concert <u>began with</u> a girl <u>playing</u>
begin with+명사: ~로 시작하다
<u>Bach's *Cello Suite No. 1* on her shiny cello</u>. I was shocked by the deep
a girl을 후치 수식하는 현재분사구
sound. I was <u>so</u> <u>into</u> the music <u>that</u> I forgot that they were playing with
be into+명사: ~에 푹 빠지다, ~을 매우 좋아하다   so+형용사[부사]+that+주어+동사: 너무 ~해서 그 결과 …하다
instruments <u>made from recycled materials</u>.
instruments를 후치 수식하는 과거분사구. recycled는 뒤의 materials를 앞에서 수식하는 과거분사로 뒤에 다른 어구가 없으므로 명사를 앞에서 수식하고 있다.
After the concert, I was eager to write a story about the orchestra. I

met Favio Chávez, the conductor, and asked him about the orchestra.
Favios Chávez의 바로 뒤에 나오는 콤마(,)는 동격의 콤마. Favio Chávez의 직업이 the conductor임을 의미
Lucy White: Why did you start The Junk Orchestra?
Favio Chávez: When I went to a small town <u>called</u> Cateura in
called 이하: 과거분사구로 town을 후치 수식
Paraguay <u>to work</u> on a recycling program in 2005, I saw children
to부정사의 부사적 용법(목적)
<u>living in a town</u> <u>that</u> was mostly filled with garbage.
앞의 children을 수식하는 현재분사구. that: 주격 관계대명사

> garbage 쓰레기
> instrument 악기
> entirely 완전히, 전부
> imagine 상상하다
> send back ~을 돌려주다
> be eager to ~하고 싶어 하다
> notice ~을 알아차리다
> shiny 빛나는, 반짝거리는
> tank (물, 기름 등의) 저장 통
> shocked 충격을 받은
> recycle 재활용하다
> conductor 지휘자
> mostly 주로, 대부분

 확인문제

● 다음 문장이 본문의 내용과 일치하면 T, 일치하지 <u>않으면</u> F를 쓰시오.

1 The Junk Orchestra played instruments made entirely out of garbage. ☐

2 Lucy didn't long to find out what kind of sound these instruments would make. ☐

3 Before the concert, Lucy thought that the instruments might sound strange. ☐

4 The concert began with a girl playing Bach's *Cello Suite No. 1* on her shiny violin. ☐

I wanted to add something positive to their lives, so I decided to
share my love of music with them.
<small>positive가 앞에 있는 something을 꾸며 준다.</small>

Lucy White: Why did you use garbage to make instruments?
Favio Chávez: One person's garbage is another person's treasure.
<small>주격보어로, 주어 One person's garbage의 의미를 보충해 주는 내용. 즉 garbage = treasure임을 의미</small>
Nicolás Gómez, a local garbage picker, helped me a lot. He made
<small>Nicolás Gómez를 설명해 주는 동격어구, 동격의 콤마(,)를 사용</small>
it possible for children to play music by making instruments out of
<small>가목적어 / 의미상의 주어 / 진목적어 / ~을 이용해서, ~을 재료로 하여</small>
garbage. The wonderful thing about these instruments was that the
children didn't have to worry about spending a lot of money on them.
<small>~할 필요가 없었다 / = much</small>
Lucy White: What do you want people to learn through your music?
Favio Chávez: I want people to know that even something worthless
can make inspiring music.
<small>music을 앞에서 수식</small>
After interviewing Chávez, I realized that it really doesn't matter
<small>after+동명사 / 가주어 / 중요하다</small>
what instrument you play with as long as you put your heart into
<small>진주어, 간접의문문(의문사+주어+동사의 어순) / ~하는 한</small>
playing it. The children of Cateura showed me that an orchestra is
formed by people, not by instruments.
<small>be동사(is)+과거분사(formed)+by+목적격: 수동태</small>

Comments
Annie: (23 seconds ago) So moving to see how music can change
<small>원인을 나타내는 부사적 용법</small>
   lives. The power of music is endless!
Thomas: (1 minute ago) After the concert, I found it possible to
<small>가목적어</small>
   inspire people by music played with recycled instruments.
<small>music을 후치 수식하는 과거분사 / instruments를 독립적으로 앞에서 꾸며 주는 과거분사</small>
Kate: (5 days ago) Not only do these talented young people deliver
<small>Not only라는 부사가 문장 맨 앞에 쓰였기 때문에, 조동사 do가 주어보다 앞에 쓰여 도치를 이룸.</small>
   great music, but they also bring serious environmental problems
<small>not only A but also B: A뿐만 아니라 B도</small>
   to our attention.

<table><tr><td>positive 긍정적인
share 나누다
add ~ to ~을 …에 추가하다
treasure 보물, 보물 같은 것
local 현지의, 지역의
picker 줍는 사람, 채집자
worthless 쓸모없는, 가치 없는
as long as ~하는 한
put one's heart into ~에 정열을 쏟다, ~에 열중하다
endless 끝없는, 무한한
talented 재능이 있는
deliver 전하다, 배달하다
serious 심각한
environmental 환경의, 환경과 관련된
attention 관심, 주목
bring ~ to one's attention ~에 …가 주목하게 하다</td></tr></table>

확인문제

● 다음 문장이 본문의 내용과 일치하면 T, 일치하지 <u>않으면</u> F를 쓰시오.

1 Nicolás Gómez, a local garbage picker, helped Favio Chávez a lot. ☐

2 Favio Chávez wants people to know that even something priceless can make inspiring music. ☐

3 The children of Cateura showed the writer that an orchestra is formed by people, not by instruments. ☐

4 Thomas found it possible to inspire people by music played with musical instruments. ☐

● 우리말을 참고하여 빈칸에 알맞은 말을 쓰시오.

1 The _____ Orchestra

2 _____ _____ a music blogger, Lucy White

3 "The world sends us _____, we send back _____."

4 This was written _____ _____ _____ _____ a concert ticket I was given.

5 The musical group _____ _____ "The Junk Orchestra."

6 They played instruments _____ _____ _____ garbage.

7 I could not imagine what kind of sound these instruments would make, so I _____ _____ _____ _____ _____.

8 Before the concert, I thought that the instruments might _____ _____.

9 _____ _____ _____ _____, a group of young people began to walk on the stage.

10 _____ _____ _____ _____ _____ was their instruments: a cello made out of a shiny oil tank, a violin made with forks, and a flute made with a water pipe and buttons.

11 The concert began _____ _____ _____ _____ Bach's *Cello Suite No. 1* _____ her shiny cello.

12 I _____ _____ _____ the deep sound.

13 I _____ so _____ the music that I forgot that they were playing with instruments _____ _____ _____ _____.

14 After the concert, I _____ _____ _____ _____ a story about the orchestra.

15 I met Favio Chávez, _____ _____, and asked him about the orchestra.

16 Lucy White: _____ _____ _____ _____ **The Junk Orchestra?**

17 Favio Chávez: When I went to a small town called Cateura in Paraguay _____ _____ _____ a recycling program in 2005, I saw children living in a town that _____ _____ _____ _____ garbage.

---

1 정크 오케스트라

2 음악 블로거 Lucy White 씀

3 "세상이 우리에게 쓰레기를 보내면, 우리는 음악을 돌려준다."

4 이것은 내가 받은 음악회 입장권의 뒷면에 쓰여 있었다.

5 그 음악 그룹은 '정크 오케스트라'라고 불렸다.

6 그들은 완전히 쓰레기로만 만들어진 악기를 연주했다.

7 나는 그런 악기들이 어떤 종류의 소리를 낼지 상상할 수 없었고, 그래서 나는 알아보고 싶어졌다.

8 음악회가 시작되기 전에 나는 그 악기들이 이상한 소리를 낼지도 모른다고 생각했다.

9 몇 분 후에 한 무리의 젊은이들이 무대 위로 걸어 올라오기 시작했다.

10 내가 처음으로 알아차린 것은 그들의 악기였는데, 그것들은 반짝이는 기름통으로 만들어진 첼로, 포크로 만들어진 바이올린, 수도관과 단추로 만들어진 플루트였다.

11 음악회는 한 소녀가 자신의 반짝이는 첼로로 바흐의 〈첼로 모음곡 1번〉을 연주하는 것으로 시작되었다.

12 나는 그 깊은 소리에 충격을 받았다.

13 나는 음악에 너무 심취해서 그들이 재활용된 재료들로 만들어진 악기를 연주하고 있다는 것을 잊었다.

14 음악회가 끝나고, 나는 그 오케스트라에 대한 이야기를 몹시 쓰고 싶었다.

15 나는 지휘자인 Favio Chávez를 만나서 그에게 오케스트라에 대해 물었다.

16 Lucy White: 왜 당신은 정크 오케스트라를 시작하셨나요?

17 Favio Chávez: 2005년에 재활용 프로그램에서 일을 하기 위해서 내가 파라과이의 카테우라라고 불리는 작은 마을에 갔을 때, 나는 대부분이 쓰레기로 가득 차 있는 마을에 살고 있는 어린이들을 보았습니다.

18 I wanted to add _____ _____ to their lives, so I decided to _____ my love of music _____ them.

19 Lucy White: Why did you use garbage _____ _____ _____?

20 Favio Chávez: One person's _____ is another person's _____.

21 Nicolás Gómez, _____ _____ _____ _____, helped me a lot.

22 He made it possible for children to play music by making instruments _____ _____ _____.

23 _____ _____ _____ about these instruments was that the children _____ _____ _____ _____ _____ spending a lot of money on them.

24 Lucy White: What do you want people to learn _____ your music?

25 Favio Chávez: I want people to know that even something _____ can make _____ _____.

26 After interviewing Chávez, I realized that it really doesn't matter what instrument you play with _____ _____ _____ you put your heart _____ playing it.

27 The children of Cateura showed me that an orchestra is formed by people, _____ _____ _____.

28 Comments

29 Annie: (23 seconds ago) So moving to see _____ music can change lives.

30 The power of music is _____!

31 Thomas: (1 minute ago) After the concert, I found it possible to inspire people by music _____ _____ recycled instruments.

32 Kate: (5 days ago) _____ _____ these talented young people deliver great music, but they also _____ serious environmental problems _____ _____ _____.

18 나는 그들의 삶에 긍정적인 무엇인가를 더해 주고 싶어서, 음악에 대한 나의 사랑을 그들과 나누기로 결정했습니다.

19 Lucy White: 왜 당신은 악기를 만들기 위해 쓰레기를 이용했나요?

20 Favio Chávez: 한 사람의 쓰레기는 다른 사람의 보물입니다.

21 그 지역의 쓰레기 줍는 사람인 Nicolás Gámez가 나를 많이 도와주었습니다.

22 그는 쓰레기로 악기를 만들어 줌으로써 어린이들이 음악을 연주하는 것이 가능하도록 만들었습니다.

23 이 악기들의 멋진 점은 어린이들이 악기에 많은 돈을 쓸 것을 걱정하지 않아도 된다는 점이었죠.

24 Lucy White: 당신의 음악을 통해서 사람들이 무엇을 배우기를 원하십니까?

25 Favio Chávez: 나는 가치 없는 것도 영감을 주는 음악을 만들어 낼 수 있다는 것을 사람들이 알게 되기를 원합니다.

26 Chávez를 인터뷰한 후에 나는 사람들이 악기를 연주하는 데 마음을 쏟아붓는 한, 그 사람이 연주하는 악기가 무엇인지는 별로 중요하지 않다는 것을 깨달았다.

27 카테우라의 어린이들은 나에게 오케스트라는 악기에 의해서가 아니라 사람에 의해 이루어지는 것이라는 것을 보여 주었다.

28 감상평

29 Annie: (23초 전) 음악이 삶을 바꿀 수 있다는 것을 보아서 너무 가슴이 뭉클하다.

30 음악의 힘은 끝이 없다!

31 Thomas: (1분 전) 음악회가 끝난 후, 나는 재활용 악기로 연주되는 음악으로 사람들에게 영감을 주는 것이 가능하다는 것을 알았다.

32 Kate: (5일 전) 이 재능 있는 젊은이들은 훌륭한 음악을 전할 뿐만 아니라, 또한 심각한 환경 문제에 우리가 주목하게 한다.

● 우리말을 참고하여 본문을 영작하시오.

1 정크 오케스트라
➡ _____

2 음악 블로거 Lucy White 씀
➡ _____

3 "세상이 우리에게 쓰레기를 보내면, 우리는 음악을 돌려준다."
➡ _____

4 이것은 내가 받은 음악회 입장권의 뒷면에 쓰여 있었다.
➡ _____

5 그 음악 그룹은 '정크 오케스트라'라고 불렸다.
➡ _____

6 그들은 완전히 쓰레기로만 만들어진 악기를 연주했다.
➡ _____

7 나는 그런 악기들이 어떤 종류의 소리를 낼지 상상할 수 없었고, 그래서 나는 알아보고 싶어졌다.
➡ _____

8 음악회가 시작되기 전에 나는 그 악기들이 이상한 소리를 낼지도 모른다고 생각했다.
➡ _____

9 몇 분 후에 한 무리의 젊은이들이 무대 위로 걸어 올라오기 시작했다.
➡ _____

10 내가 처음으로 알아차린 것은 그들의 악기였는데, 그것들은 반짝이는 기름통으로 만들어진 첼로, 포크로 만들어진 바이올린, 수도관과 단추로 만들어진 플루트였다.
➡ _____
_____

11 음악회는 한 소녀가 자신의 반짝이는 첼로로 바흐의 〈첼로 모음곡 1번〉을 연주하는 것으로 시작되었다.
➡ _____

12 나는 그 깊은 소리에 충격을 받았다.
➡ _____

13 나는 음악에 너무 심취해서 그들이 재활용된 재료들로 만들어진 악기를 연주하고 있다는 것을 잊었다.
➡ _____

14 음악회가 끝나고, 나는 그 오케스트라에 대한 이야기를 몹시 쓰고 싶었다.
➡ _____

15 나는 지휘자인 Favio Chávez를 만나서 그에게 오케스트라에 대해 물었다.
➡ _____

16 Lucy White: 왜 당신은 정크 오케스트라를 시작하셨나요?
➡ _____

17 Favio Chávez: 2005년에 재활용 프로그램에서 일을 하기 위해서 내가 파라과이의 카테우라라고 불리는 작은 마을에 갔을 때, 나는 대부분이 쓰레기로 가득 차 있는 마을에 살고 있는 어린이들을 보았습니다.
➡ _____
_____

18 나는 그들의 삶에 긍정적인 무엇인가를 더해 주고 싶어서, 음악에 대한 나의 사랑을 그들과 나누기로 결정했습니다.

➡ _____

19 Lucy White: 왜 당신은 악기를 만들기 위해 쓰레기를 이용했나요?

➡ _____

20 Favio Chávez: 한 사람의 쓰레기는 다른 사람의 보물입니다.

➡ _____

21 그 지역의 쓰레기 줍는 사람인 Nicolás Gámez가 나를 많이 도와주었습니다.

➡ _____

22 그는 쓰레기로 악기를 만들어 줌으로써 어린이들이 음악을 연주하는 것이 가능하도록 만들었습니다.

➡ _____

23 이 악기들의 멋진 점은 어린이들이 악기에 많은 돈을 쓸 것을 걱정하지 않아도 된다는 점이었죠.

➡ _____
_____

24 Lucy White: 당신의 음악을 통해서 사람들이 무엇을 배우기를 원하십니까?

➡ _____

25 Favio Chávez: 나는 가치 없는 것도 영감을 주는 음악을 만들어 낼 수 있다는 것을 사람들이 알게 되기를 원합니다.

➡ _____

26 Chávez를 인터뷰한 후에 나는 사람들이 악기를 연주하는 데 마음을 쏟아붓는 한, 그 사람이 연주하는 악기가 무엇인지는 별로 중요하지 않다는 것을 깨달았다.

➡ _____
_____

27 카테우라의 어린이들은 나에게 오케스트라는 악기에 의해서가 아니라 사람에 의해 이루어지는 것이라는 것을 보여 주었다.

➡ _____

28 감상평

➡ _____

29 Annie: (23초 전) 음악이 삶을 바꿀 수 있다는 것을 보아서 너무 가슴이 뭉클하다.

➡ _____

30 음악의 힘은 끝이 없다!

➡ _____

31 Thomas: (1분 전) 음악회가 끝난 후, 나는 재활용 악기로 연주되는 음악으로 사람들에게 영감을 주는 것이 가능하다는 것을 알았다.

➡ _____
_____

32 Kate: (5일 전) 이 재능 있는 젊은이들은 훌륭한 음악을 전할 뿐만 아니라, 또한 심각한 환경 문제에 우리가 주목하게 한다.

➡ _____
_____

[01~03] 다음 글을 읽고 물음에 답하시오.

"The world sends us garbage, we send back music." This was written on the back of a concert ticket I was given. The musical group was called "The Junk Orchestra." ⓐ They played instruments made entirely into garbage. I could not imagine what kind of sound these instruments would make, so I ⓑ was eager to find out.

서답형

01 위 글의 밑줄 친 ⓐ에서 흐름상 어색한 부분을 찾아 고치시오.

➡ _____

02 위 글의 밑줄 친 ⓑwas eager to와 바꿔 쓸 수 있는 말을 모두 고르시오.

① was worried to
② was anxious to
③ was likely to
④ paid attention to
⑤ longed to

03 위 글의 뒤에 올 내용으로 가장 알맞은 것을 고르시오.

① the reason the world sends us garbage
② the way to send back music
③ to find out the sound of these instruments
④ the kinds of musical instruments
⑤ how to make a harmonious sound

[04~06] 다음 글을 읽고 물음에 답하시오.

Before the concert, I thought that the instruments might sound strange. After a few minutes, a group of young people began to walk on the stage. The first thing I noticed was their instruments: a cello made out of a shiny oil tank, a violin made with forks, and a flute made with a water pipe and buttons. The concert began ____ⓐ____ a girl playing Bach's *Cello Suite No. 1* ____ⓑ____ her shiny cello. I was shocked by the deep sound. I was so into the music that I forgot that they were playing with instruments made from recycled materials.

04 위 글의 빈칸 ⓐ와 ⓑ에 들어갈 전치사가 바르게 짝지어진 것은?

	ⓐ	ⓑ		ⓐ	ⓑ
①	for	on	②	with	in
③	on	by	④	for	by
⑤	with	on			

05 위 글의 제목으로 알맞은 것을 고르시오.

① A Strange Sound from Instruments Made out of Garbage
② How about Enjoying Bach's *Cello Suite No. 1*?
③ Unbelievable! Such a Deep Sound from Instruments Made out of Garbage?
④ The Difficulty of Making Instruments from Recycled Materials
⑤ Unbelievable! Such a Young Girl Plays Bach's *Cello Suite No. 1*!

06 위 글에서 알 수 있는 글쓴이의 심경 변화로 가장 알맞은 것을 고르시오.

① nervous → disappointed
② anxious → satisfied
③ excited → nervous
④ bored → pleased
⑤ surprised → bored

[07~09] 다음 글을 읽고 물음에 답하시오.

After the concert, I was eager to write a story about the orchestra. I met Favio Chávez, the conductor, and asked him about the orchestra.
Lucy White: ⓐ _____
Favio Chávez: When I went to a small town called Cateura in Paraguay ⓑto work on a recycling program in 2005, I saw children living in a town that was mostly filled with garbage. I wanted to add something positive to their lives, ⓒso I decided to share my love of music with them.

07 위 글의 빈칸 ⓐ에 들어갈 알맞은 질문을 고르시오.

① Why did you use garbage to make instruments?
② How did you start The Junk Orchestra?
③ Why did you start The Junk Orchestra?
④ How many children joined The Junk Orchestra?
⑤ What do you want people to learn through your music?

08 위 글의 밑줄 친 ⓑto work와 to부정사의 용법이 같은 것을 모두 고르시오.

① I was happy to work on a recycling program.
② Why did you want to work on a recycling program?
③ Who is the right man to work on a recycling program?
④ He was eager to work on a recycling program.
⑤ I think it worthwhile to work on a recycling program.

서답형
09 위 글의 밑줄 친 ⓒ를 다음과 같이 바꿔 쓸 때 빈칸에 들어갈 알맞은 단어를 쓰시오.

➡ so I decided to _____ my love of music in common with them

[10~12] 다음 글을 읽고 물음에 답하시오.

Before the concert, I thought that the instruments might sound strange. After a few minutes, a group of young people began to walk on the stage. The first thing I noticed was their instruments: a cello made out of a shiny oil tank, a violin made with forks, and a flute made with a water pipe and buttons. The concert began ⓐ한 소녀가 바흐의 <첼로 모음곡 1번>을 연주하는 것으로 on her shiny cello. I was shocked by the deep sound. I was so into the music that I forgot that they were playing with instruments made from recycled materials.

10 위 글에 나오는 악기의 재료에 속하지 않는 것을 고르시오.

① an oil tank   ② spoons
③ a water pipe   ④ forks
⑤ buttons

서답형

11 위 글의 밑줄 친 ⓐ의 우리말에 맞게 주어진 어휘를 이용하여 9 단어로 영작하시오.

> with, Bach's *Cello Suite No. 1*

➡ _____

12 According to the passage, which is NOT true?

① The writer thought that the instruments might sound strange before listening to their music.

② The first thing the writer noticed was their instruments.

③ The musicians of the concert were a group of young people.

④ The first music of the concert was a violin piece.

⑤ The musicians were playing with instruments made from recycled materials.

[13~15] 다음 글을 읽고 물음에 답하시오.

After the concert, I was eager to write a story about the orchestra. I met Favio Chávez, the conductor, and asked him about the orchestra.

Lucy White: Why did you start The Junk Orchestra?

Favio Chávez: When I went to a small town called Cateura in Paraguay to work on a recycling program in 2005, I saw children living in a town that was mostly filled with garbage. I wanted to add something ⓐ to their lives, so I decided to share my love of music with ⓑthem.

13 위 글의 빈칸 ⓐ에 들어갈 알맞은 말을 고르시오.

① passive   ② positive

③ temporary   ④ general

⑤ permanent

서답형

14 위 글의 밑줄 친 ⓑthem이 가리키는 것을 본문에서 찾아 쓰시오.

➡ _____

서답형

15 Why did the writer meet Favio Chávez, the conductor, after the concert? Fill in the blanks with suitable words.

> Because the writer wanted to write a story about _____ _____ very much.

[16~18] 다음 글을 읽고 물음에 답하시오.

Lucy White: Why did you use garbage to make instruments?

Favio Chávez: One person's garbage is another person's treasure. Nicolás Gómez, a local garbage picker helped me a lot. He made ⓐit possible ①of children to play music ②by making instruments out of garbage. The wonderful thing ③about these instruments was that the children didn't have to worry about spending a lot of money ④on them.

Lucy White: What do you want people to learn ⑤through your music?

Favio Chávez: I want people to know that even something worthless can make inspiring music.

서답형

16 위 글의 밑줄 친 ①~⑤에서 전치사의 쓰임이 적절하지 않은 것을 찾아 알맞게 고치시오.

➡ _____

17 위 글의 밑줄 친 ⓐit과 문법적 쓰임이 같은 것을 고르시오.

① It was raining this morning.

② He took a stone and threw it.

③ It is important for you to choose good friends.

④ It was she who told me the story.

⑤ I make it a rule to get up early.

18 위 글을 읽고 알 수 없는 것을 고르시오.

① Why did Favio Chávez use garbage to make instruments?

② Who was Nicolás Gómez?

③ Why did Nicolás Gómez help Favio Chávez a lot?

④ What was the wonderful thing about the instruments?

⑤ What does Favio Chávez want people to learn through his music?

[19~20] 다음 글을 읽고 물음에 답하시오.

After interviewing Chávez, I realized that ⓐ it really doesn't matter what instrument you play with ⓑas long as you put your heart into playing it. The children of Cateura showed me that an orchestra is formed by people, not by instruments.

서답형

19 위 글의 밑줄 친 ⓐ를 다음과 같이 바꿔 쓸 때 빈칸에 들어갈 알맞은 단어를 쓰시오.

➡ it isn't really _____

20 위 글의 밑줄 친 ⓑas long as와 바꿔 쓸 수 있는 말을 모두 고르시오.

① as far as　　② as well as

③ as much as　　④ as soon as

⑤ so long as

[21~23] 다음 글을 읽고 물음에 답하시오.

The Junk Orchestra
The world sends us garbage, we send back, music.
Comments
Annie: (23 seconds ago) So ⓐmoving to see how music can change lives. The power of music is endless!
Thomas: (1 minute ago) ⓑAfter the concert, I found it possible to inspire people by music played with recycling instruments.
Kate: (5 days ago) ⓒ이 재능 있는 젊은이들은 훌륭한 음악을 전할 뿐만 아니라, but they also bring serious environmental problems to our attention.

서답형

21 위 글의 밑줄 친 ⓐmoving과 바꿔 쓸 수 있는 말을 쓰시오.

➡ _____

서답형

22 위 글의 밑줄 친 ⓑ에서 어법상 틀린 부분을 찾아 고치시오.

➡ _____

서답형

23 위 글의 밑줄 친 ⓒ의 우리말에 맞게 한 단어를 보충하여, 주어진 어휘를 알맞게 배열하시오.

not only / great music / deliver / these talented young people

➡ _____

_____

Reading　**93**

[01~03] 다음 글을 읽고 물음에 답하시오.

"(A)The world sends us garbage, we send back music." This was written on the back of a concert ticket I ⓐ . The musical group was called "The Junk Orchestra." They played instruments made entirely out of garbage. (B)나는 그런 악기들이 어떤 종류의 소리를 낼지 상상할 수 없었고, so I was eager to find out.

01 위 글의 빈칸 ⓐ에 give를 알맞은 형태로 쓰시오.

➡ _____

02 다음 빈칸 (a)와 (b)에 알맞은 단어를 넣어 위 글의 밑줄 친 (A)의 의미를 완성하시오.

> We make musical instruments by recycling (a)_____, and perform (b)_____ playing the instruments.

03 위 글의 밑줄 친 (B)의 우리말에 맞게 주어진 어휘를 알맞게 배열하시오.

> instruments / would / what kind of sound / imagine / I / these / make / could not

➡ _____
_____

[04~06] 다음 글을 읽고 물음에 답하시오.

Before the concert, I thought that the instruments might sound (A)[strange / strangely]. After a few minutes, a group of young people began to walk on the stage. The first thing I noticed was their

instruments: a cello made out of a shiny oil tank, a violin made with forks, and a flute made with a water pipe and buttons. The concert began with a girl playing Bach's *Cello Suite No. 1* on her shiny cello. I was (B)[shocking / shocked] by the deep sound. I was so into the music that I forgot that they were playing with instruments made from (C)[recycling / recycled] materials.

04 위 글의 괄호 (A)~(C)에서 어법상 알맞은 낱말을 골라 쓰시오.

➡ (A) _____ (B) _____ (C) _____

05 What did the writer notice first when a group of young people began to walk on the stage? Fill in the blank with a suitable word.

➡ The writer first noticed their _____.

06 본문의 내용과 일치하도록 다음 빈칸에 알맞은 단어를 쓰시오.

> The concert began with a girl playing Bach's *Cello Suite No. 1* on her cello which was made out of _____ _____ _____ _____.

[07~08] 다음 글을 읽고 물음에 답하시오.

After interviewing Chávez, I realized that it really doesn't matter what instrument you play with as long as you put your heart into playing ⓐit. ⓑThe children of Cateura showed me that an orchestra is formed by people, not by instruments.

07 위 글의 밑줄 친 ⓐit이 가리키는 것을 두 단어로 쓰시오.

➡ _____

08 위 글의 밑줄 친 ⓑ를 다음과 같이 바꿔 쓸 때 빈칸에 들어갈 알맞은 말을 한 단어씩 쓰시오.

➡ The children of Cateura showed me that an orchestra is formed _____ by instruments _____ by people.

[09~11] 다음 글을 읽고 물음에 답하시오.

After the concert, I was eager to write a story about the orchestra. I met Favio Chávez, the conductor, and asked him about the orchestra.
Lucy White: Why did you start The Junk Orchestra?
Favio Chávez: When I went to a small town ⓐ Cateura in Paraguay to work on a recycling program in 2005, ⓑI saw children living in a town that was mostly filled with garbage. I wanted to add something positive to their lives, so I decided to share my love of music with them.

09 위 글의 빈칸 ⓐ에 call을 알맞은 형태로 쓰시오.

➡ _____

10 위 글의 밑줄 친 ⓑ에서 생략할 수 있는 부분을 생략하고 문장을 다시 쓰시오.

➡ _____
_____

11 본문의 내용과 일치하도록 다음 빈칸 (A)와 (B)에 알맞은 단어를 쓰시오.

When Favio Chávez went to Cateura in Paraguay to work on a recycling program in 2005, he decided to share (A)_____ _____ _____ _____ with the children living in a town that was mostly filled with garbage in order to add (B)_____ _____ to their lives.

[12~13] 다음 글을 읽고 물음에 답하시오.

Lucy White: Why did you use garbage to make instruments?
Favio Chávez: One person's garbage is another person's treasure. Nicolás Gómez, a local garbage picker helped me a lot. He made it possible for children to play music by making instruments out of garbage. ⓐThe wonderful thing about these instruments was that the children didn't have to worry about spending a lot of money on them.
Lucy White: What do you want people to learn through your music?
Favio Chávez: ⓑI want people to know that even something priceless can make inspiring music.

12 위 글의 밑줄 친 ⓐ를 다음과 같이 바꿔 쓸 때 빈칸에 들어갈 알맞은 말을 한 단어로 쓰시오.

➡ The wonderful thing about these instruments was that the children didn't _____ to worry about spending a lot of money on them.

13 위 글의 밑줄 친 ⓑ에서 흐름상 어색한 부분을 찾아 고치시오.

➡ _____

After You Read A

The Junk Orchestra
The world sends us garbage, we send back music.
_{garbage to us(3형식)}
About the concert
– The young people played instruments made out of garbage.
_{(which were) made}
– It started with a girl playing the cello made out of a shiny oil tank.
_{(which were) made}
– I was shocked by the deep sound.

The Interview with Mr. Chávez
– He went to Cateura in Paraguay to work on a recycling program.
_{to부정사의 부사적 용법(목적)}
– He decided to share his love of music with the children.
_{share A with B: A를 B와 공유하다}
– A local garbage picker helped him.

⇒ An orchestra is formed by people, not by instruments.
_{= not by instruments but by people}

구문해설 ·garbage: 쓰레기 ·send back: ~을 돌려주다 ·instrument: 악기 ·shiny: 빛나는, 반짝거리는 ·tank: (물, 기름 등의) 저장 통 ·shocked: 충격을 받은 ·recycle: 재활용하다 ·share: 나누다

Grammar in Real Life

I visited a broadcasting company. In the news room, I sat at the desk where
_{관계부사}
anchors give the news. There were two screens hanging on the wall. I could
_{two screens를 수식하는 현재분사}
read aloud sentences moving across the screen. After I came out of the room,
_{sentences를 수식하는 현재분사}
I could see myself recorded on the TV screen. I really liked the background
_{주어와 목적어가 같으므로 재귀대명사 myself를 수식하는 과거분사}
created with computer graphics.
_{background를 수식하는 과거분사}

구문해설 ·broadcasting company: 방송국 ·background: 배경

Wrap Up 2

M: Hi, Julie. Where are you going?
_{= Where are you off to?}
W: Hi, Chris. I'm going to my guitar lesson. Our band has a concert at the hospital this Sunday.
M: This Sunday? Are you planning to perform at the Happy Children's
Hospital? _{= Are you going to = Do you have a plan to}
W: Yes. How do you know about the concert?
M: Oh, my sister is going to play the piano there, so I'm going to the concert, too.
W: Great. Come and watch our performance!

구문해설 ·performance: 공연

해석

정크 오케스트라
세상이 우리에게 쓰레기를 보내면 우리는 음악을 돌려준다.
음악회에 관해
· 젊은이들은 쓰레기로 만들어진 악기를 연주했다.
· 음악회는 한 소녀의 반짝이는 기름통으로 만들어진 첼로 연주로 시작되었다.
· 나는 그 깊은 소리에 충격을 받았다.
Chávez 씨와의 인터뷰
· 그는 재활용 프로그램에서 일을 하기 위해 파라과이의 카테우라에 갔다.
· 그는 그의 음악에 대한 사랑을 아이들과 나누기로 결정했다.
· 그 지역의 쓰레기 줍는 사람이 그를 도와주었다.
⇒ 오케스트라는 악기에 의해서가 아니라 사람에 의해 이루어지는 것이다.

나는 방송국을 방문했다. 뉴스 룸에서 나는 앵커들이 뉴스를 전하는 책상에 앉았다. 벽에는 두 개의 스크린이 걸려 있었다. 나는 화면을 가로질러 움직이는 문장들을 소리 내어 읽을 수 있었다. 방에서 나온 후 TV 화면에 녹화된 내 모습을 볼 수 있었다. 나는 컴퓨터 그래픽으로 만들어진 배경이 정말 마음에 들었다.

M: 안녕, Julie. 어디 가는 길이니?
W: 안녕, Chris. 나는 기타 수업에 가는 길이야. 우리 밴드가 이번 주 일요일에 병원에서 공연을 하거든.
M: 이번 주 일요일? Happy 아동 병원에서 공연할 계획이니?
W: 응. 그 공연에 대해 어떻게 알고 있어?
M: 아, 내 여동생이 거기서 피아노를 연주할 거라서 나도 그 공연에 갈 거야.
W: 잘됐다. 와서 우리 공연을 봬!

Words & Expressions

01 다음 짝지어진 단어의 관계가 같도록 빈칸에 알맞은 말을 쓰시오.

> arrive : arrival = survive : _____

02 다음 영영풀이가 가리키는 것을 고르시오.

> to use something again for a different purpose

① recommend   ② share
③ recycle   ④ deliver
⑤ perform

03 다음 우리말에 맞게 빈칸에 알맞은 말을 쓰시오.

(1) 너는 물구나무를 설 수 있니?
⇒ Can you _____ _____ _____
_____?

(2) 나는 깨어 있기 위해 많은 커피를 마신다.
⇒ I drink much coffee to _____ me
_____.

(3) 재즈 댄스 수업에 어떻게 신청합니까?
⇒ How do I _____ _____ _____
the jazz dance class?

(4) 나는 거의 매일 체육관에서 운동한다.
⇒ I _____ _____ at the gym almost
every day.

04 다음 중 밑줄 친 부분의 뜻풀이가 바르지 않은 것은?

① I filled the gas tank before I left. (저장 통)
② She was shocked by his sudden death. (충격을 받은)
③ Why not recycle Christmas cards as gift tags? (재활용하다)
④ He has served as the conductor of the orchestra. (지휘자)
⑤ The people at the concert were mostly old people. (최대한)

05 다음 문장에 공통으로 들어갈 말을 고르시오.

> • Minsu showed up without any _____.
> • The first thing I _____ (e)d in the room was the smell.
> • Did you _____ how upset I was?

① compete   ② deliver
③ concentrate   ④ imagine
⑤ notice

06 다음 주어진 문장의 밑줄 친 touched와 같은 의미로 쓰인 것은?

> Her story touched us all deeply.

① I touched him lightly on the arm.
② You have never touched your food.
③ My mom touched my forehead.
④ He hardly touched the ball during the game.
⑤ I was so touched that I almost cried.

Conversation

07 다음 대화의 빈칸 (A)에 들어갈 말로 적절한 것은?

> Anna: Hey, Jake. I saw you won the swimming competition yesterday. Congratulations!
> Jake: Thanks, Anna.
> Anna: You always seem to listen to music before you compete. (A)_____
> Jake: Yes, it keeps me awake and it helps me focus.

① What do you think about listening to music before you swim?

② How do you feel when you listen to music before you swim?

③ Do you find it helpful to listen to music before you swim?

④ What's your opinion about listening to music before you swim?

⑤ What kind of music do you listen to music before you swim?

08 다음 대화의 (A)~(C)에 들어갈 말이 바르게 짝지어진 것은?

> Minho: Hi, Sally. Where are you (A)[on / off] to?
> Sally: I'm going to the music room. I have choir practice.
> Minho: Oh, yeah. I forgot (B)[that / which] you've joined the choir. Do you find it (C)[interested / interesting] to sing in the choir?
> Sally: Yeah, it's great to sing in harmony with others.

	(A)	(B)	(C)
①	on	that	interested
②	on	which	interesting
③	off	that	interesting
④	off	which	interested
⑤	off	that	interested

[09~11] 다음 대화를 읽고 물음에 답하시오.

> Sujin: Hi, Jason. Great to see you again. I've heard the new rap song, *Young and Wild*, that you recorded. It's really cool.
> Jason: (A) Oh, thanks.
> Sujin: (B) I really like your songs. Do you find it easy to write them?
> Jason: (C) I draw on my experiences and keep a journal.
> Sujin: (D) Wow! As they say, "No pain, no gain." Best of luck with your new song!
> Jason: (E) Thank you.

09 위 대화의 (A)~(E) 중 주어진 문장이 들어가기에 적절한 곳은?

> Well, it was hard in the beginning, but now it's getting easier.

① (A) ② (B) ③ (C) ④ (D) ⑤ (E)

10 위 대화에서 나타난 수진과 Jason의 관계로 적절한 것은?

① interviewer – rapper

② musician – dancer

③ guide – tourist

④ doctor – patient

⑤ teacher – student

11 위 대화를 읽고 대답할 수 <u>없는</u> 것은?

① What is the title of Jason's new song?

② What does Sujin think about Jason's new song?

③ What does Jason do to write the songs?

④ What proverb does Sujin use to describe Jason's effort?

⑤ How many times has Sujin heard Jason's new rap song?

[12~13] 다음 대화를 읽고 물음에 답하시오.

Emma: Hey, Anthony. Can you help me with something?

Anthony: Sure, what's up?

Emma: I'm going to a concert at the Arts Center, but I don't know which seat ⓐshould I choose.

Anthony: Are you planning ⓑto go to the orchestra concert?

Emma: Yes. I'm going to watch the orchestra concert.

Anthony: Then, you should get the seats ⓒon the second floor. You can hear the beautiful sounds of various musical instruments ⓓbetter.

Emma: Oh, do you find it better ⓔto hear the performance from the second floor?

Anthony: Yes. I find it better than from other seats.

12 위 대화의 밑줄 친 ⓐ~ⓔ 중 어법상 틀린 것을 찾아 바르게 고치시오.

➡ _____

13 위 대화의 내용과 일치하지 <u>않는</u> 것은?

① Emma는 예술 회관에서 하는 오케스트라 공연에 가려고 한다.

② Emma는 좌석을 고르는 데 있어 Anthony에게 도움을 요청했다.

③ Anthony는 2층 좌석을 얻는 것을 추천한다.

④ Anthony는 2층 좌석은 다양한 악기들의 아름다운 소리를 더 잘 들을 수 있기 때문에 추천한다.

⑤ Anthony는 2층에서 공연을 더 잘 볼 수 있었다.

14 다음 문장 중에서 어법상 어색한 문장을 <u>모두</u> 고르시오.

① Falling leaves are under the trees.

② They may feel discouraged to see the celebrities enjoying special treatments.

③ This is the newest smartphone make in Korea.

④ Mina sent me the photos taken last Saturday.

⑤ There were some girls swimming in the pool.

15 다음 빈칸에 들어갈 말로 알맞은 것은?

Does Amy think _____ to the top of the mountain?

① impossible to get
② to get impossible
③ it to get impossible
④ impossible it to get
⑤ it impossible to get

16 다음 그림을 참고하여, 괄호 안에 주어진 어휘를 이용하여 빈칸에 알맞게 쓰시오.

Becky thought _____ easy _____ _____ the clothes. (sew)

17 다음 두 문장의 의미가 같도록 빈칸에 알맞은 말을 쓰시오.

(1) I knew the students satisfied with the game result.

= I knew the students _____ satisfied with the game result.

(2) It started with a girl playing the cello made out of a shiny oil tank.

= It started with a girl _____ playing the cello _____ made out of a shiny oil tank.

18 밑줄 친 it의 쓰임이 나머지 넷과 다른 것은?

① Brian considered it exciting to play the main character.

② I found it was not easy to drive through the narrow streets.

③ The audience thought it fun to see their friends singing and dancing.

④ I found it helpful to listen to music when I was in the hospital.

⑤ Some students think it more relaxing to watch movies.

19 다음 ⓐ~ⓕ 중 어법상 옳은 것을 모두 고르시오.

ⓐ I consider it wonderful to have so many talented students in my school.

ⓑ The picture stealing from the museum was found.

ⓒ Be quiet not to awake the sleeping baby.

ⓓ There were many dogs run here and there in the field.

ⓔ Does John find it interesting to read books?

ⓕ My mom made to exercise every Sunday a rule.

➡ _____

Reading

[20~21] 다음 글을 읽고 물음에 답하시오.

Before the concert, I thought that the instruments might sound strange. After a few minutes, a group of young people began to walk on the stage. The first thing I noticed was their instruments: a cello made out of a shiny oil tank, a violin made with forks, and a flute made with a water pipe and buttons. The concert began with a girl playing Bach's *Cello Suite No. 1* on her shiny cello. ⓐI was shocked by the deep sound. I was so into the music that I forgot that ⓑthey were playing with instruments made from recycled materials.

20 위 글의 밑줄 친 ⓐ를 능동태로 고치시오.

➡ _____

21 위 글의 밑줄 친 ⓑthey가 가리키는 것을 본문에서 찾아 쓰시오.

➡ _____

[22~23] 다음 글을 읽고 물음에 답하시오.

After the concert, I was eager to write a story about the orchestra. I met Favio Chávez, the conductor, and asked him about the orchestra.

Lucy White: Why did you start The Junk Orchestra?

Favio Chávez: When I went to a small town called Cateura in Paraguay to work on a recycling program in ⓐ2005, I saw children living in a town that was mostly filled with garbage. I wanted to add something positive to their lives, so I decided to share my love of music with them.

22 위 글의 밑줄 친 @2005를 영어로 읽는 법을 쓰시오.

➡ _____

23 According to the passage, which is NOT true?

① After the concert, the writer was eager to write a story about the orchestra.
② After the concert, the writer met Favio Chávez, the conductor.
③ Favio Chávez was living in a town that was mostly filled with garbage.
④ Favio Chávez wanted to add something positive to the children's lives.
⑤ Favio Chávez made a decision to share his love of music with the children.

[24~26] 다음 글을 읽고 물음에 답하시오.

Lucy White: Why did you use garbage to make instruments?
Favio Chávez: One person's garbage is another person's treasure. Nicolás Gómez, a local garbage picker helped me a lot. He made it possible for children to play music by making instruments out of garbage. The wonderful thing about these instruments was that the children didn't have to worry about spending a lot of money on them.
Lucy White: What do you want people to learn through your music?
Favio Chávez: I want people to know that @가치 없는 것도 영감을 주는 음악을 만들어 낼 수 있다.

24 What was the wonderful thing about the instruments made out of garbage? Answer in English beginning with "It".

➡ _____
_____

25 위 글의 주제로 알맞은 것을 고르시오.

① the reason a local garbage picker helped Favio Chávez a lot.
② how to play music by making instruments out of garbage
③ the wonderful thing about the instruments made out of garbage
④ the worry about spending much money on the instruments
⑤ the reason and the goal to make instruments using garbage

26 위 글의 밑줄 친 @의 우리말에 맞게 주어진 어휘를 알맞게 배열하시오.

worthless / music / even / inspiring / make / something / can

➡ _____
_____

[27~28] 다음 글을 읽고 물음에 답하시오.

I want to recommend a song to those who need to ___@___ . The title of the song is "*Happy*," and the singer is Allan Hamilton. This song is about looking on the bright side of life and staying happy. I want to recommend this song because I found it helpful to listen to it when I was in the hospital. ⓑIt cheered up me and gave me hope.   <the writer: a girl>

27 위 글의 빈칸 @에 cheer up을 알맞은 형태로 쓰시오.

➡ _____

28 위 글의 밑줄 친 ⓑ에서 어법상 틀린 부분을 찾아 고치시오.

➡ _____

[01~03] 다음 대화를 읽고 물음에 답하시오.

Emma: Hey, Anthony. Can you help me with something?

Anthony: Sure, what's up?

Emma: I'm going to a concert at the Arts Center, but I don't know which seat I should choose.

Anthony: Are you planning to go to the orchestra concert?

Emma: Yes. I'm going to watch the orchestra concert.

Anthony: Then, you should get the seats on the second floor. You can hear the beautiful sounds of various musical instruments better.

Emma: Oh, (A)2층에서 공연을 듣는 것이 더 낫다는 거니?

Anthony: Yes. I find it better than from other seats.

출제율 90%

01 위 대화의 밑줄 친 (A)의 우리말을 〈보기〉에 주어진 어구를 배열하여 영작하시오.

┌─ 보기 ┐
from / it / to / you / do / find / the second / the performance / hear / floor / better
└───────┘

➡ _____

출제율 100%

02 위 대화를 읽고 대답할 수 <u>없는</u> 것은?

① Where is Emma planning to go?

② Where is the orchestra concert held?

③ Which seat does Anthony recommend?

④ Where does Anthony think Emma can hear the beautiful sounds better?

⑤ With whom is Emma going to watch the orchestra concert?

출제율 90%

03 위 대화의 내용과 일치하도록 Emma의 일기를 완성하시오.

I had a plan to watch the orchestra concert. But I was confused which (A)_____ I should choose. I asked Anthony to help me to select the seat. Anthony recommended (B)_____, because he found it better to (C)_____. He said I could hear (D)_____ better. It was very helpful information for me. I'm looking forward to watching the concert soon.

[04~06] 다음 대화를 읽고 물음에 답하시오.

Anna: Hey, Jake. I saw you won the swimming competition yesterday. Congratulations!

Jake: Thanks, Anna.

Anna: You always seem to listen to music before you compete. Do you find it helpful to listen to music before you swim?

Jake: Yes, it keeps me awake and it helps me focus.

출제율 90%

04 What competition did Jake win yesterday?

➡ _____

출제율 95%

05 What does Jake always do before he competes?

➡ _____

06 How is it helpful for Jake to listen to music before he competes?

➡ _____

[07~09] 다음 글을 읽고 물음에 답하시오.

W: (A)Are you planning to learn a musical instrument? (plan, do) I'd like to recommend the *kalimba*, a small African musical instrument. The sound it makes is similar to that of a music box. Playing the *kalimba* is very easy. You can learn to use your (B)_____ to play beautiful music in just one lesson!

07 위 글의 밑줄 친 (A)와 의도가 같도록 괄호 안에 주어진 단어를 사용하여 다시 쓰시오.

➡ _____

08 위 글의 빈칸 (B)에 '엄지손톱'을 나타내는 말을 두 단어로 쓰시오.

➡ _____

09 위 글의 내용과 일치하지 <u>않는</u> 것은?

① 여자는 칼림바를 배워 볼 것을 추천하고 있다.
② 칼림바는 아프리카의 작은 악기이다.
③ 악기가 내는 소리는 음악 상자의 소리와 비슷하다.
④ 엄지손톱을 사용해 아름다운 음악을 연주할 수 있다.
⑤ 칼림바를 배우는 데 약 한 달 정도 걸린다.

10 다음 대화가 자연스럽게 이어지도록 순서대로 배열하시오.

(A) You always seem to listen to music before you compete. Do you find it helpful to listen to music before you swim?
(B) Yes, it keeps me awake and it helps me focus.
(C) Hey, Jake. I saw you won the swimming competition yesterday. Congratulations!
(D) Thanks, Anna.

➡ _____

11 다음 중 어법상 적절한 문장은?

① The book borrowing from the library is heavy.
② These talenting young people deliver great music and bring serious environmental problems to our attention.
③ Do you like the cheese made from the milk from the farm?
④ She made it possible of us to sing in the talent show.
⑤ She thinks to sleep more relaxing.

12 괄호 안에 주어진 말을 이용해 밑줄 친 명사를 수식하는 문장으로 다시 쓰시오.

(1) Can you tell me <u>a name</u>? (begin with M)
➡ _____

(2) There was <u>a small boy</u>. (call "Mr. Big" in my school)
➡ _____
_____

(3) <u>The dog</u> is Mike's. (lie under the table)
➡ _____

13 다음 문장에서 밑줄 친 it이 가리키는 것을 찾아 쓰시오.

(1) Mr. Thompson considers it important to have breakfast every day.

➡ _____

(2) Molly found it difficult to write lyrics.

➡ _____

(3) Do you think it is important to exercise every day?

➡ _____

14 다음 우리말을 괄호 안에 주어진 어휘를 이용하여 영작하시오.

(1) 드럼을 치고 있는 그 남자는 유명한 음악가이다. (beat, drums, famous musician)

➡ _____

(2) 나는 Cateura라고 불리는 작은 마을에 갔다. (call)

➡ _____

(3) 우리 엄마는 내가 바이올린을 연주할 수 있도록 했다. (my mom, made, possible, to)

➡ _____

(4) 그 소녀는 외국어를 배우는 것이 어렵다고 생각한다. (think, hard, foreign languages, to)

➡ _____

[15~16] 다음 글을 읽고 물음에 답하시오.

"The world sends us garbage, we send back music." ⓐThis was written on the back of a concert ticket I was given. The musical group was called "The Junk Orchestra." They played instruments made entirely out of garbage. ⓑ I could not imagine what kind of sound these instruments would make, as I was eager to find out.

15 위 글의 밑줄 친 ⓐThis가 가리키는 것을 본문에서 찾아 쓰시오.

➡ _____

16 위 글의 밑줄 친 ⓑ에서 흐름상 어색한 부분을 찾아 고치시오.

➡ _____

[17~18] 다음 글을 읽고 물음에 답하시오.

After the concert, I was eager to write a story about the orchestra. I met Favio Chávez, the conductor, and asked him about the orchestra.

Lucy White: Why did you start The Junk Orchestra?

Favio Chávez: When I went to a small town called Cateura in Paraguay to work on a recycling program in 2005, I saw children living in a town that was mostly filled ⓐ_____ garbage. I wanted to add something positive to their lives, so I decided to share my love of music ⓑ_____ them.

17 위 글의 빈칸 ⓐ와 ⓑ에 공통으로 들어갈 알맞은 전치사를 쓰시오.

➡ _____

18 Why did Favio Chávez go to a small town called Cateura in Paraguay in 2005? Fill in the blanks with suitable words.

He went there in order that he might work on _____ _____ _____.

[19~21] 다음 글을 읽고 물음에 답하시오.

Lucy White: ⓐ_____

Favio Chávez: One person's garbage is another person's treasure. Nicolás Gómez, a local garbage picker helped me a lot. He made it possible for children to play music by making instruments out of garbage. The wonderful thing about these instruments was that the children didn't have to worry about spending a lot of money on them.

Lucy White: What do you want people to learn through your music?

Favio Chávez: I want people to know that even something ⓑworthless can make inspiring music.

출제율 100%

19 위 글의 빈칸 ⓐ에 들어갈 알맞은 질문을 고르시오.

① How do you make people play music?

② Why did Nicolás Gómez help you?

③ How did Nicolás Gómez make instruments out of garbage?

④ Why did you use garbage to make instruments?

⑤ Why did you start The Junk Orchestra?

출제율 90%

20 위 글의 밑줄 친 ⓑworthless와 바꿔 쓸 수 있는 말을 고르시오.

① invaluable　　　② valueless

③ worthwhile　　　④ valuable

⑤ priceless

출제율 95%

21 According to the passage, which is NOT true?

① Favio Chávez thinks that one person's garbage is another person's treasure.

② Nicolás Gómez was a local garbage picker.

③ Favio Chávez helped Nicolás Gómez a lot.

④ Nicolás Gómez made instruments out of garbage.

⑤ The children didn't have to worry about spending much money on the instruments made out of garbage.

[22~23] 다음 글을 읽고 물음에 답하시오.

After interviewing Chávez, I realized that it really doesn't matter what instrument you play with ⓐ<u>사람들이 악기를 연주하는 데 마음을 쏟아 붓는 한</u>. The children of Cateura showed me that an orchestra is formed by people, not by instruments.

출제율 90%

22 위 글의 밑줄 친 ⓐ의 우리말에 맞게 주어진 어휘를 이용하여 10 단어로 영작하시오.

> as long as, put, into, you

➡ _____

출제율 95%

23 다음 문장에서 위 글의 내용과 <u>다른</u> 부분을 찾아서 고치시오.

> What instrument you play with is really of importance.

➡ _____

[01~03] 다음 대화를 읽고 물음에 답하시오.

Sujin: Hi, Jason. Great to see you again. I've heard the new rap song, *Young and Wild*, that you recorded. It's really cool.

Jason: Oh, thanks.

Sujin: I really like your songs. Do you find it easy to write them?

Sujin: Well, it was hard in the beginning, but now it's getting easier. I draw on my experiences and keep a journal.

Sujin: Wow! As they say, "No pain, no gain." Best of luck with your new song!

Jason: Thank you.

01 What does Sujin think about the new rap song that Jason recorded?

➡ _____

02 What does Jason do to write songs?

➡ _____

_____

03 What proverb does Sujin use to describe Jason's effort?

➡ _____

04 다음 문장에서 어법상 어색한 것을 바르게 고쳐 다시 쓰시오.

(1) Einstein considered to solve math problems fun.

➡ _____

(2) We found enjoyable to sing the song writing by children.

➡ _____

_____

(3) The woman made a cake is my mother.

➡ _____

(4) We studied at desks making out of trees from the nearby mountain.

➡ _____

05 다음 문장에서 틀린 것을 고쳐 다시 쓰시오.

(1) The played the piano girl on the stage is my sister.

➡ _____

_____

(2) The box carrying into the building is very big.

➡ _____

(3) I found that possible to inspire people by music played with recycled instruments.

➡ _____

_____

(4) Rebecca thought to sing in front of others difficult even though she is a great singer.

➡ _____

_____

Before the concert, I thought that the instruments might sound strange. After a few minutes, a group of young people began to walk on the stage. The first thing I noticed was their instruments: a cello made out of a shiny oil tank, a violin made with forks, and a flute made with a water pipe and buttons. The concert began with a girl playing Bach's *Cello Suite No. 1* on her shiny cello. I was shocked by the deep sound. ⓐI was so into the music that I forgot that they were playing with instruments made from recycled materials.

06 위 글의 밑줄 친 ⓐ를 다음과 같이 바꿔 쓸 때 빈칸에 들어갈 알맞은 단어를 쓰시오.

➡ I was so _____ in the music

07 What was the violin made with? Answer in English in a full sentence. (5 words)

➡ _____

08 본문의 내용과 일치하도록 다음 빈칸 (A)와 (B)에 알맞은 단어를 쓰시오.

> Before the concert, the writer thought that the sound of the instruments might be (A)_____, but when the concert began with a girl playing Bach's *Cello Suite No. 1* on her shiny cello, the writer was shocked by the (B)_____ _____.

Lucy White: Why did you use garbage to make instruments?

Favio Chávez: ⓐ한 사람의 쓰레기는 다른 사람의 보물입니다. Nicolás Gómez, a local garbage picker helped me a lot. He made it possible for children to play music by making instruments out of garbage. The wonderful thing about these instruments was that the children didn't have to worry about spending a lot of money on ⓑthem.

Lucy White: What do you want people to learn through your music?

Favio Chávez: I want people to know that even something worthless can make inspiring music.

09 위 글의 밑줄 친 ⓐ의 우리말에 맞게 주어진 어휘를 이용하여 7 단어로 영작하시오.

> one person's, another, treasure

➡ _____

_____

10 위 글의 밑줄 친 ⓑthem이 가리키는 것을 본문에서 찾아 쓰시오.

➡ _____

11 본문의 내용과 일치하도록 다음 빈칸 (A)와 (B)에 알맞은 단어를 쓰시오.

> Through his music, Favio Chávez wants people to know that even something (A)_____ can make (B)_____ music.

01 다음 대화의 내용과 일치하도록 빈칸을 완성하시오.

> Sujin: Hi, Jason. Great to see you again. I've heard the new rap song, *Young and Wild*, that you recorded. It's really cool.
> Jason: Oh, thanks.
> Sujin: I really like your songs. Do you find it easy to write them?
> Jason: Well, it was hard in the beginning, but now it's getting easier. I draw on my experiences and keep a journal.
> Sujin: Wow! As they say, "No pain, no gain." Best of luck with your new song!
> Jason: Thank you.

> A rapper, Jason, released a new song, *Young and Wild*. His songs were cool. He said that writing songs was (A)_____ in the beginning, but it was getting (B)_____. To write songs, he draws on his (C)_____ and (D)_____. I wished him my best luck.

02 다음 내용을 바탕으로 상황에 어울리는 노래를 찾아 추천하는 글을 쓰시오.

> **Q1 To whom do you want to recommend a song?**
> **A1** I want to recommend a song to those who need to be cheered up.
> **Q2 What is the title of the song, and who is the singer?**
> **A2** The title of the song is "*Happy*," and the singer is Allan Hamilton.
> **Q3 What is the song about?**
> **A3** It is about looking on the bright side of life and staying happy.
> **Q4 Why do you want to recommend the song?**
> **A4** I found it helpful to listen to it when I was in the hospital. It cheered me up and gave me hope.

> I want to recommend a song to those who need to (A)_____. The title of the song is "*Happy*," and the singer is (B)_____. This song is about looking on the (C)_____ of life and staying happy. I want to recommend this song because I found it helpful to listen to it when I was (D)_____. It cheered me up and (E)_____.

단원별 모의고사

01 다음 영영풀이가 가리키는 고르시오.

> things that are no longer useful and that have been thrown out

① tank   ② thumb
③ treasure   ④ nail
⑤ garbage

02 다음 문장에 공통으로 들어갈 말을 고르시오.

> • Stop biting your _____ s.
> • I need to drive a _____ into a board.
> • The cat scratched me with its _____ s.

① nail   ② pain
③ title   ④ treasure
⑤ finger

03 다음 우리말에 맞게 빈칸에 알맞은 말을 쓰시오.

(1) 우리는 환경과 조화를 이루며 살아야 할 필요가 있다.
  ➡ We need to live _____
     _____ our environment.

(2) 엄마는 처음에는 요리를 잘 못하셨다.
  ➡ My mom wasn't good at cooking
     _____ _____ _____.

(3) 나는 왜 그녀가 나에게 나의 선물을 돌려보냈는지 모르겠다.
  ➡ I don't know why she _____
     _____ my present to me.

(4) 나는 영어로 일기를 쓰려고 노력한다.
  ➡ I try to _____ _____
     in English.

04 다음 우리말을 주어진 단어를 이용하여 영작하시오.

(1) 그의 방은 책들과 서류들로 가득하다. (filled) (8 words)
  ➡ _____

(2) 내 가방이 네 것과 비슷하지만 내 것이 더 크다. (similar) (10 words)
  ➡ _____

[05~06] 다음 대화를 읽고 물음에 답하시오.

Minho: Hi, Sally. Where are you off to?

Sally: I'm going to the music room. I have choir practice.

Minho: Oh, yeah. I forgot that you've joined the choir. Do you find it interesting to sing in the choir?

Sally: Yeah, it's great to sing in harmony with others.

05 Why is Sally going to the music room?
  ➡ _____

06 What does Sally think about singing in the choir?
  ➡ _____

[07~08] 다음 대화를 읽고 물음에 답하시오.

Megan: Hey, Tommy. When is the last day to sign up for the talent show?

Tommy: This Friday. (A)_____, Megan?

Megan: Yeah, I'm going to perform with a couple of people.

Tommy: How cool! What are you going to do?

Megan: We will play K-pop music with the violin and cello.

07 위 대화의 빈칸 (A)에 들어갈 말로 나머지와 의도가 <u>다른</u> 것은?

① Are you going to sign up for it
② Do you have a plan to sign up for it
③ Do you intend to sign up for it
④ Are you planning to sign up for it
⑤ Are you aware of signing up for it

08 위 대화의 내용과 일치하지 <u>않는</u> 것은?

① 장기 자랑 등록 마감은 이번 주 금요일이다.
② Megan은 장기 자랑에 등록할 계획이다.
③ Megan은 몇 사람과 함께 공연을 할 것이다.
④ Megan은 케이팝 음악을 연주할 계획이다.
⑤ Megan은 바이올린과 첼로로 연주되는 케이팝 공연을 관람할 것이다.

09 다음 주어진 문장이 자연스럽게 이어지도록 순서대로 배열하시오.

> Sujin: Hi, Jason. Great to see you again. I've heard the new rap song, *Young and Wild*, that you recorded. It's really cool.
> (A) Well, it was hard in the beginning, but now it's getting easier. I draw on my experiences and keep a journal.
> (B) I really like your songs. Do you find it easy to write them?
> (C) Wow! As they say, "No pain, no gain." Best of luck with your new song!
> (D) Oh, thanks.

➡ _____

[10~11] 다음 대화를 읽고 물음에 답하시오.

> Sue: Hello, I'd like to sign up for a drum class.
> Mike: Okay. Are you planning to take the class during the week or during the weekend?
> Sue: I'm planning to take a weekday class. When do you offer them?
> Mike: There is a class on Tuesday and another one on Thursday. Both classes start at 6 o'clock.
> Sue: Great. I'd like to sign up for the Tuesday class.

10 What kind of music class is Sue planning to sign up for?

➡ _____

11 What day and time is Sue going to take the class?

➡ _____

12 다음 짝지어진 대화가 <u>어색한</u> 것은?

① A: Are you planning to go to the K-pop concert Saturday afternoon?
　 B: No, I'm not. I'm thinking of watching the hip-hop dance competition.
② A: Are you going to enter the singing contest on Saturday morning?
　 B: Yes, I am.
③ A: Do you have a plan to hear an African dance Sunday afternoon?
　 B: I think you will enter the singing contest.
④ A: Are you planning to take the one-day cooking class?
　 B: Yes, I am. I'm looking forward to it.
⑤ A: What are you planning to do this Sunday?
　 B: I'm planning to have dinner with my grandmother.

13 다음 문장에서 밑줄 친 it이 가리키는 것을 찾아 쓰시오.

(1) Would you find it easy to play the guitar if you had the chance to play it?

➡ _____

(2) The weather made it impossible for everybody to come.

➡ _____

(3) It is helpful to clarify the objectives of the listening task.

➡ _____

14 다음 두 문장을 한 문장으로 바꿔 썼을 때 가장 적절한 것은?

> • I received a letter.
> • The letter was written by the student.

① I wrote a letter received by the student.
② I wrote a letter receiving by the student.
③ I received a letter writing by the student.
④ I received a letter write by the student.
⑤ I received a letter written by the student.

15 다음 주어진 단어의 형태를 알맞게 바꿔 문장을 완성하시오.

(1) My parents are drinking wine _____ from grapes we picked last year. (make)

(2) The farmer _____ cheese is my uncle. (make)

16 다음 문장에서 어법상 어색한 것을 바르게 고쳐 다시 쓰시오.

(1) Sally finds that bored to sing in the choir.

➡ _____

(2) She thinks to make good friends a key factor to success.

➡ _____

(3) He made possible for children playing music by making instruments out of garbage.

➡ _____
_____

(4) The singer wore a T-shirt which designed by an artist.

➡ _____
_____

(5) The man is taking pictures of people posed in front of the monuments.

➡ _____
_____

17 다음 빈칸에 들어갈 말이 적절하게 짝지어진 것을 고르시오.

> Look at the woman _____ on the stage that was _____ with flowers.

① stand – cover
② stood – covering
③ stood – covered
④ standing – covering
⑤ standing – covered

[18~19] 다음 글을 읽고 물음에 답하시오.

Before the concert, I thought that the instruments might sound strange. After a few minutes, a group of young people began to walk on the stage. The first thing I noticed was their instruments: a cello made out of a shiny oil tank, a violin made with forks, and a flute made with a water pipe and buttons. The concert began with a girl playing Bach's *Cello Suite No. 1* on her shiny cello. I was shocked by the deep sound. ⓐI was so into the music that I forgot that they were playing with instruments making from recycled materials.

18 What was the flute made with? Answer in English in a full sentence. (9 words)

➡ _____

19 위 글의 밑줄 친 ⓐ에서 어법상 **틀린** 부분을 찾아 고치시오.

➡ _____

[20~21] 다음 글을 읽고 물음에 답하시오.

The Junk Orchestra
The world sends us garbage, we send back music.

Comments
Annie: (23 seconds ago) So ⓐmoving to see how music can change lives. The power of music is endless!
Thomas: (1 minute ago) After the concert, I found it possible to inspire people by music played with recycled instruments.

Kate: (5 days ago) ⓑNot only do these talented young people deliver great music, but they also bring serious environmental problems to our attention.

20 위 글의 밑줄 친 ⓐmoving과 같은 의미로 쓰인 것을 고르시오.

① Ann is moving her chair to the corner.
② Look at the fast-moving water.
③ Shoot at the moving target.
④ He paid the moving expenses.
⑤ She cried to hear a moving story.

21 위 글의 밑줄 친 ⓑ를 as well as를 사용하여 고칠 때, 빈칸에 들어갈 알맞은 말을 쓰시오.

➡ These talented young people _____

_____ ,

as well as _____ .

[22~23] 다음 글을 읽고 물음에 답하시오.

After the concert, ⓐI was eager to write a story about the orchestra. I met Favio Chávez, the conductor, and asked him about the orchestra.
Lucy White: Why did you start The Junk Orchestra?
Favio Chávez: When I went to a small town called Cateura in Paraguay to work on a recycling program in 2005, ⓑ나는 대부분이 쓰레기로 가득 차 있는 마을에 살고 있는 어린이들을 보았습니다. I wanted to add something positive to their lives, so I decided to share my love of music with them.

22 위 글의 밑줄 친 ⓐ를 다음과 같이 바꿔 쓸 때 빈칸에 들어갈 알맞은 말을 쓰시오.

➡ I was eager for _____ a story about the orchestra.

23 위 글의 밑줄 친 ⓑ의 우리말에 맞게 주어진 어휘를 이용하여 13 단어로 영작하시오.

> a town, that, mostly, with, garbage

➡ _____

_____

[24~25] 다음 글을 읽고 물음에 답하시오.

Lucy White: Why did you use garbage ⓐto make instruments?

Favio Chávez: One person's garbage is another person's treasure. Nicolás Gómez, a local garbage picker helped me a lot. ⓑHe made it possible for children to play music by making instruments out of garbage. The wonderful thing about these instruments was that the children didn't have to worry about spending a lot of money on them.

24 아래 〈보기〉에서 위 글의 밑줄 친 ⓐto make와 to부정사의 용법이 다른 것의 개수를 고르시오.

┌─── 보기 ───┐
① It is difficult to make instruments.
② What did you use to make instruments?
③ He had no money to make instruments with.
④ He promised me to make instruments.
⑤ She had the talent to make instruments.
└────────────┘

① 1개   ② 2개   ③ 3개   ④ 4개   ⑤ 5개

25 위 글의 밑줄 친 ⓑ를 다음과 같이 바꿔 쓸 때 빈칸에 알맞은 말을 쓰시오.

➡ Thanks _____ his help, children _____ play music by making instruments out of garbage.

[26~27] 다음 글을 읽고 물음에 답하시오.

The Junk Orchestra
The world sends us garbage, we send back music.
About the concert
– The young people played instruments ①made out of garbage.
– It started with a girl ②played the cello ③made out of a shiny oil tank.
– I was ④shocked by the deep sound.
The Interview with Mr. Chávez
– He went to Cateura in Paraguay to work on a recycling program.
– He decided to share his love of music with the children.
– A local garbage picker helped him.
⇒ An orchestra is ⑤formed by people, not by instruments.

26 위 글의 밑줄 친 ①~⑤ 중 어법상 틀린 것을 찾아 고치시오.

➡ _____

27 Which question CANNOT be answered after reading the passage?

① What was the cello at the concert made of?
② How did the instrument sound?
③ Why did Mr. Chávez go to Cateura in Paraguay?
④ What did Mr. Chávez decide to do?
⑤ What was the name of the local garbage picker?

MEMO

Lesson 5

Critical Minds

의사소통 기능

- 자세한 설명 요청하기
  A: Did you know that bats aren't blind?
  B: No. **Can you tell me more about** it?
  A: Some bats can see three times better than humans.
- 의견에 대한 이유 묻기
  A: Books of riddles are really useful for adults.
  B: **Why do you say so?**
  A: They help us think more creatively.

언어 형식

- 분사구문
  Let's look into some articles **thinking about the hidden motives**.

- so that ~ can ...
  They made up this fake article **so that** they **could** draw the readers' attention.

Words & Expressions

Key Words

□ **admit**[ədmít] 동 인정하다, 자백하다

□ **adult**[ədʌ́lt] 명 성인, 어른

□ **argument**[á:rgjumənt] 명 논쟁, 언쟁

□ **awful**[ɔ́:fəl] 형 끔찍한, 지독한

□ **chemical**[kémikəl] 명 화학 물질

□ **chest**[tʃest] 명 가슴, 흉부

□ **citizen**[sítəzən] 명 시민

□ **competitor**[kəmpétətər] 명 경쟁자, 경쟁 상대

□ **condition**[kəndíʃən] 명 상태, 상황

□ **confess**[kənfés] 동 고백하다, 인정하다

□ **critical**[krítikəl] 형 위험한, 위독한

□ **critically**[krítikəli] 부 비판적으로

□ **criticize**[krítəsàiz] 동 비난하다

□ **current**[kə́:rənt] 형 현재의, 지금의

□ **describe**[diskráib] 동 기술하다

□ **disaster**[dizǽstər] 명 참사, 재난

□ **escape**[iskéip] 동 달아나다, 탈출하다, 벗어나다

□ **extremely**[ikstrí:mli] 부 극도로, 극히

□ **fake**[feik] 형 가짜의, 거짓의

□ **formation**[fɔːrméiʃən] 명 형성

□ **goldfish**[góuldfiʃ] 명 금붕어

□ **harmful**[há:rmfəl] 형 해로운, 유해한

□ **height**[hait] 명 키, 신장

□ **incident**[ínsədənt] 명 사건

□ **injure**[índʒər] 동 부상을 입히다

□ **judge**[dʒʌdʒ] 동 판단하다

□ **loose**[lu:s] 형 풀린, 헐거운

□ **measure**[méʒər] 동 측정하다, 재다

□ **mine**[main] 명 광산 동 채굴하다

□ **mislead**[mìslí:d] 동 잘못 이끌다, 오해하게 하다

□ **motive**[móutiv] 명 동기, 이유

□ **muscle**[mʌ́sl] 명 근육

□ **nevertheless**[nèvərðəlés] 부 그럼에도 불구하고

□ **panic**[pǽnik] 동 겁에 질려 어쩔 줄 모르다

□ **poem**[póuəm] 명 시, 운문

□ **prove**[pru:v] 동 입증하다, 증명하다

□ **public**[pʌ́blik] 명 대중, 일반 사람들

□ **publish**[pʌ́bliʃ] 동 발행하다, 출판하다, 게재하다

□ **recognize**[rékəgnàiz] 동 알아보다

□ **reliable**[riláiəbl] 형 믿을 만한, 신뢰할 만한

□ **riddle**[rídl] 부 수수께끼

□ **seriously**[síəriəsli] 부 진지하게, 심각하게

□ **shoot**[ʃu:t] 동 (총 등을) 쏘다

□ **Slav**[slɑːv] 명 슬라브인

□ **source**[sɔːrs] 명 출처, 자료

□ **spell**[spel] 동 철자를 말하다[쓰다]

□ **spot**[spɑt] 동 발견하다, 찾아내다

□ **strengthen**[stréŋkθən] 동 강하게 하다, 더 튼튼하게 하다

□ **support**[səpɔ́ːrt] 동 (사실임을) 입증하다, 뒷받침하다

□ **temperature**[témpərətʃər] 명 온도, 기온, 체온

□ **trust**[trʌst] 동 신뢰하다

□ **wound**[wuːnd] 동 상처를 입히다

Key Expressions

□ **according to** ~에 따르면

□ **be related to** ~와 연관되다

□ **be useful for** ~에게 유용하다

□ **break down** ~을 부수다, ~을 무너뜨리다

□ **catch a cold** 감기에 걸리다

□ **draw one's attention to** ~의 관심을 …로 끌다

□ **fall asleep** 잠들다

□ **get caught -ing** ~하다가 걸리다

□ **in that** ~라는 점에서, ~이기 때문에

□ **look into** 조사하다, 들여다보다

□ **lose weight** 몸무게를 줄이다

□ **make up** 지어내다, 만들어 내다

□ **on the loose** 잡히지 않은, 탈주 중인

□ **search for** ~을 찾다

□ **spend time -ing** ~하면서 시간을 보내다

□ **think outside the box** 고정관념에서 벗어나다

□ **What if** ~? 만약 ~라면 어떨까?

Word Power

※ 서로 비슷한 뜻을 가진 어휘

□ **adult** 성인, 어른 – **grownup** 성인
□ **awful** 끔찍한, 지독한 – **horrible** 끔찍한
□ **current** 현재의, 지금의 – **present** 현재의
□ **injure** 부상을 입히다 – **wound** 부상을 입히다

□ **argument** 논쟁, 언쟁 – **debate** 토론
□ **criticize** 비난하다 – **blame** 비난하다
□ **describe** 기술하다 – **illustrate** 설명하다
□ **spot** 발견하다, 찾아내다 – **detect** 찾아내다

※ 서로 반대의 뜻을 가진 어휘

□ **competitor** 경쟁자 ↔ **helper** 조력자
□ **fake** 가짜의, 거짓의 ↔ **true** 진실한
□ **reliable** 믿을 만한 ↔ **unreliable** 믿을 수 없는
□ **trust** 신뢰하다 ↔ **distrust** 불신하다

□ **criticize** 비난하다 ↔ **compliment** 칭찬하다
□ **harmful** 해로운, 유해한 ↔ **harmless** 무해한
□ **strengthen** 강하게 하다 ↔ **weaken** 약하게 하다

※ 접두사 mis- [mis+어근]: 잘못된, 나쁜, 나쁘게

□ **mis-+lead = mislead** (잘못 이끌다)
□ **mis-+fortune = misfortune** (불행, 불운)
□ **mis-+read = misread** (잘못 해석하다)
□ **mis-+use = misuse** (오용, 오용하다)

□ **mis-+take = mistake** (실수, 실수하다)
□ **mis-+behavior = misbehavior** (나쁜 행실)
□ **mis-+trust = mistrust** (불신하다)
□ **mis-+understand = misunderstand** (오해하다)

※ 접미사 –ize [명사/형용사+ize = 동사]: ~으로 되다, ~이 되게 만들다, ~와 같아지게 하다

□ **critic+-ize = criticize** (비판하다)
□ **regular+-ize = regularize** (합법화하다)
□ **fossil+-ize = fossilize** (화석화하다)
□ **harmony+-ize = harmonize** (조화를 이루다)
□ **moisture+-ize = moisturize** (촉촉하게 하다)

□ **real+-ize = realize** (실현하다)
□ **private+-ize = privatize** (민영화하다)
□ **theory+-ize = theorize** (이론을 세우다)
□ **memory+-ize = memorize** (암기하다)

English Dictionary

□ **disaster** 참사, 재난
→ an event causing great harm, damage, or suffering
해, 손상, 또는 고통을 초래하는 사건

□ **citizen** 시민
→ a person who lives in a particular city
특정 시에 살고 있는 사람

□ **describe** 기술하다
→ to say or write what someone or something is like
누군가 또는 무언가가 어떠한지 말하거나 쓰다

□ **panic** 겁에 질려 어쩔 줄 모르다
→ to suddenly feel so worried that you cannot be reasonable
너무 걱정이 되어서 이성적일 수 없다고 갑자기 느끼다

□ **shoot** (총 등을) 쏘다
→ to fire a weapon
무기를 발사하다

□ **chest** 가슴, 흉부
→ the upper front part of the body of humans
인간 신체의 상체 앞부분

□ **spell** 철자를 말하다, 쓰다
→ to form words with the letters in the correct order
글자를 가지고 알맞은 순서로 단어를 형성하다

□ **source** 출처, 자료
→ a place, person, or thing from which something comes
그것으로부터 무언가가 나오는 장소, 사람 또는 사물

서답형

01 다음 짝지어진 단어의 관계가 같도록 빈칸에 알맞은 말을 쓰시오.

> harmless : harmful = trust : _____

02 다음 영영풀이가 가리키는 것을 고르시오.

> an event causing great harm, damage, or suffering

① riddle   ② formation   ③ source
④ disaster   ⑤ temperature

중요
03 다음 문장의 빈칸에 공통으로 들어갈 말을 고르시오.

> • You can _____ me all the time.
> • Don't _____ what people are saying about me.
> • If you put your _____ in me, I'll do my best.
> • I have complete _____ in John.

① trust   ② judge   ③ spot
④ chest   ⑤ disaster

중요
04 다음 중 밑줄 친 부분의 뜻풀이가 바르지 않은 것은?

① They were caught at the airport because they had fake passports. (가짜의, 거짓의)
② Do you know geese fly in a V formation? (대형)
③ She wants to keep goldfish at home as pets. (금붕어)
④ He injured his back and legs on the mountain. (부상을 입히다)
⑤ My uncle found gold in a mine and became rich. (나의 것)

05 다음 주어진 문장의 밑줄 친 judge와 다른 의미로 쓰인 것은?

> Judging by her last letter, they are having a wonderful time.

① As far as I can judge, all of them are to blame.
② To judge from what he said, he was very disappointed.
③ Schools should not be judged only on exam results.
④ Their concert was judged to have been a great success.
⑤ Considering the results, I think the judge was too generous.

서답형
06 다음 우리말과 일치하도록 주어진 단어를 모두 배열하여 완성하시오.

(1) 그는 팔에 상처를 입었었다.
   (wounded / in / had / been / the / he / arm)
   ➡ _____

(2) 그녀가 또 거짓말을 했으므로 나는 그녀를 더 이상 신뢰할 수 없다.
   (trust / I / she / her / anymore / again / lied / can't / because)
   ➡ _____

(3) 기온이 오늘 40도까지 올랐다.
   (to / the / today / went / temperature / forty / up)
   ➡ _____

01 다음 짝지어진 단어의 관계가 같도록 빈칸에 알맞은 말을 쓰시오.

regular : regularize = real : _____

02 다음 우리말에 맞게 빈칸에 알맞은 말을 쓰시오.

(1) 나는 2,000명의 경쟁자들과 마라톤을 했다.
➡ I ran a marathon with 2,000 _____.

(2) 그 환자는 심각한 상태였다.
➡ The patient was in serious _____.

(3) 마침내, 그들은 경찰에게 모든 것을 고백했다.
➡ Finally, they _____ everything to the police.

(4) 그의 아버지는 위독한 상태이다.
➡ His father is in a _____ condition.

03 다음 문장의 빈칸에 들어갈 말을 〈보기〉에서 골라 쓰시오.

┌─ 보기 ─
catch a cold / got caught / on the loose /
search for / think outside the box
└─

(1) The prisoner escaped from jail, and he is still _____.

(2) We started to _____ to make something new.

(3) You can _____ a good hotel on this website.

(4) Be careful not to _____.

(5) One of my classmates _____ cheating.

04 다음 우리말에 맞게 주어진 단어를 사용하여 영작하시오.

(1) 너는 그 식당이 극도로 시끄럽다고 생각하지 않니? (loud, don't)
➡ _____

(2) 설탕을 너무 많이 먹는 것은 너의 치아에 해롭다. (too, for)
➡ _____

(3) 그는 내 여동생과 거의 같은 키이다. (as, the same)
➡ _____

05 다음 주어진 우리말과 일치하도록 주어진 단어를 모두 배열하여 완성하시오.

(1) 그녀는 그녀가 실수했다는 것을 인정했다.
(that / she / had / she / admitted / mistakes / made)
➡ _____

(2) 나는 어제 내 남자 친구와 논쟁을 했다.
(my boyfriend / I / with / yesterday / an argument / had)
➡ _____

(3) 어른들은 입장료를 내야 하지만, 아이들은 무료로 입장한다.
(should / adults / fee / but / an / in / children / get / pay / entrance / free)
➡ _____
_____

Conversation

① 자세한 설명 요청하기

> **A:** Did you know that bats aren't blind? 박쥐가 눈이 안 보이는 것이 아니라는 알고 있었니?
>
> **B:** No. Can you tell me more about it? 아니. 그걸 더 설명해 줄래?
>
> **A:** Some bats can see three times better than humans. 어떤 박쥐는 인간보다 3배 더 잘 볼 수 있어.

- 상대방이 말하는 내용을 잘 모르거나 상대방이 사용한 단어의 뜻을 몰라서 추가적인 설명을 요청할 때는 'Can you tell me more about it?(그걸 좀 더 설명해 줄래?)'이라고 하거나, 'What does that mean?(그것이 무슨 뜻입니까?)', 'What do you mean by that?(그것이 무슨 뜻이니?)'이라고 한다.

- 상대방에게 설명을 요청할 때는 '설명하다, 말하다'의 의미를 가지는 동사 explain, tell이나 give information, be specific 등의 표현을 사용하여 'Could you explain the meaning of it?', 'Could you tell me more about them?' 등의 표현을 사용하기도 한다. Could 대신 Would, Can, Will 등을 사용할 수 있고, 'Do you mind if I ask you to explain ~?'이라고 말할 수도 있다.

- 상대방의 말을 알아듣지 못했을 때는 'I'm not following you.(잘 못 알아듣겠습니다.)', 'I don't get it.(제대로 이해를 못하겠어요.)' 등의 표현을 사용하여 상대방이 다시 설명을 하도록 요청할 수도 있다.

자세한 설명 요청하기

- Can you tell me more about it? 그걸 좀 더 설명해 줄래?
- Could you give me more information? 좀 더 정보를 주시겠습니까?
- Can you explain more in detail? 좀 더 자세히 설명해 주시겠습니까?
- Could you be more specific? 좀 더 구체적으로 말해 주시겠습니까?
- What do you mean by that? 그게 무슨 말이야?
- Could you explain what it means? 그게 무엇을 의미하는지 설명해 주시겠습니까?

핵심 Check

1. 주어진 문장에 이어지도록 적절한 순서로 배열하시오.

> **W:** I think I caught a cold because I didn't dress warmly yesterday.
>
> (A) Really? Can you tell me more about it?
>
> (B) The article said that people catch colds because of viruses.
>
> (C) Well, I've read an article saying that you don't catch a cold because your body temperature is low.

➡

2 의견에 대한 이유 묻기

> A: Books of riddles are really useful for adults. 수수께끼 책이 어른들에게는 매우 유용해.
> B: Why do you say so? 왜 그렇게 말하니?
> A: They help us think more creatively. 그것들이 더 창의적으로 생각하게 도와주니까.

■ 상대방이 왜 그렇게 말하는지, 혹은 왜 그렇게 생각하는지 등에 대해 이유를 물을 때는 의문사 why를 써서 'Why do you say so?(왜 그렇게 말하니?)' 또는 'Why do you think so?(왜 그렇게 생각하니?)'처럼 물어본다.

■ why 대신 의문사 what을 사용해서 '무엇이 ~하도록 만들었느냐?'의 의미로 'What makes you+동사원형 ~?'의 형태를 사용할 수 있다. 'What makes you say that?(무엇 때문에 그렇게 말하니?)' 또는 'What makes you think so?(무엇 때문에 그렇게 생각하니?)'처럼 'What makes you ~?'로 이유를 물어볼 때 'what'은 '무엇'이라고 해석할 수도 있지만 '왜'라고 해석하기도 한다.

■ 의문사로 시작하는 이유를 묻는 말 앞에 'Can you tell me'나 'I'd like to know', 'I wonder' 등을 붙여, 간접의문문의 형식으로 좀 더 격식을 갖춰 물어볼 수도 있다. 이유를 말할 때에는 문장 앞에 'I think'나 'In my opinion' 등을 덧붙일 수도 있다.

이유 묻기

- Why do you say/think so? 왜 그렇게 말하니/생각하니?
- What makes you say so? 왜 그렇게 말하니?
- What makes you think so? 무어 때문에 그렇게 생각하니?
- Why is that? 왜 그렇지?
- Can you tell me (the reason) why ~? ~ 한 이유를 설명해 주겠니?

이유 말하기

- I did it because ~. ~ 때문에 그렇게 했어요.
- (Because) ~. 왜냐하면 ~ 때문이야.
- That's because ~. 그것은 ~ 때문입니다.
- Because of ~. ~ 때문이야.

핵심 Check

2. 다음 대화의 밑줄 친 문장과 같은 의미의 문장을 주어진 단어로 시작하여 쓰시오.

> W: I think children write better poems than adults.
> M: <u>Why do you say so?</u>
> W: They're really honest about their feelings and much more creative than adults.

➡ What _____?

Listen and Talk 1 B

W: I read an article ❶saying ❷that Napoleon was actually ❸fairly tall.

M: Oh, really? ❹Can you tell me more about it?

W: ❺According to the article, a French doctor wrote down Napoleon's height according to the French measuring system, not the English one.

M: What was the difference?

W: At that time, an inch in France was longer than an inch in England. So, Napoleon was actually about 168 cm tall, ❻which was not that short in those times.

W: 나폴레옹이 실제로 키가 꽤 컸다고 하는 기사를 읽었어.

M: 오, 정말? 그것에 대해 더 말해 줄 수 있니?

W: 기사에 따르면 한 프랑스 의사가 영국식이 아닌 프랑스식 측정법으로 나폴레옹의 키를 기록했다는 거야.

M: 차이가 뭐였니?

W: 그 당시에 프랑스에서의 1인치가 영국에서의 1인치보다 더 길었어. 그래서 나폴레옹은 사실 168cm 정도였는데, 그것이 그 시대에는 그렇게 작은 키가 아니었어.

❶ 현재분사로 an article을 수식한다. ❷ 접속사 that으로 명사절을 이끈다. ❸ fairly: 꽤
❹ 상대방이 말하는 내용을 잘 모르거나 상대방이 사용한 단어의 뜻을 몰라서 추가적인 설명을 요청할 때 사용하는 표현으로 'What does that mean?'이나 'What do you mean by that?'으로 바꾸어 표현할 수 있다.
❺ according to: ~에 따르면
❻ 관계대명사의 계속적인 용법으로 that으로 바꾸어 쓸 수 없다.

Check(√) True or False

(1) An inch in England was shorter than the one in France.　　　T ☐　F ☐

(2) Napoleon was actually not that short in those times.　　　T ☐　F ☐

 Listen and Talk 2 B

M: Hey, Sandy. Do you think I should buy this drink? It is said that it can help me ❶lose weight.

W: Let me read the label more closely. Hmm, it looks ❷a bit strange to me, David.

M: ❸Why do you say so?

W: There ❹isn't enough information about what's in the drink.

M: Oh, you're right.

W: Also, it doesn't tell you how much you have to drink to lose weight.

M: 안녕, Sandy. 너는 내가 이 음료를 사야 한다고 생각해? 내가 살을 빼는 것을 도와줄 수 있다고 적혀 있어.

W: 라벨을 더 자세히 읽어 볼게. 음, 내가 보기에 좀 이상해, David.

M: 왜 그렇게 생각해?

W: 음료 안에 무엇이 들었는지에 대한 충분한 정보가 없어.

M: 오, 네 말이 맞아.

W: 게다가, 체중을 감량하려면 얼마나 마셔야 하는지도 나와 있지 않아.

❶ lose weight: 살이 빠지다 ❷ a bit: 약간, 조금
❸ 상대방이 왜 그렇게 말하는지, 혹은 왜 그렇게 생각하는지 등에 대해 이유를 물을 때 쓰는 표현으로 'Why do you think so?' 등으로 바꾸어 표현할 수 있다.
❹ 'there is+단수 명사', 'there are+복수 명사': ~가 있다

Check(√) True or False

(3) David is wondering whether he should buy the drink or not.　　　T ☐　F ☐

(4) Sandy advised David to buy the drink to lose weight.　　　T ☐　F ☐

Listen and Talk 1 A-1

W: I think I ❶caught a cold ❷because I didn't dress warmly yesterday.

M: Well, I've read an article saying that you don't catch a cold because your body ❸ temperature is low.

W: Really? Can you tell me more about it?

M: The article said that people catch colds ❷ because of viruses.

❶ catch a cold: 감기에 걸리다 ❷ 'because+주어+동사', 'because of+명사(구)' ❸ temperature: 온도

 Listen and Talk 1 A-2

W: I usually drink ❶a glass of warm milk before I go to bed, but it doesn't ❷help me fall asleep.

M: I saw a show on TV, and a doctor said that a glass of warm milk doesn't actually help you fall asleep.

W: Oh, it doesn't? Can you tell me more about it?

M: Milk has special ❸chemicals ❹that make people sleepy. But the amount in a glass is ❺too small to have any effect.

❶ a glass of ~: 한 잔의 ~ ❷ help는 준사역동사로 목적격보어로 to부정사나 원형부정사(fall)가 이어진다. ❸ chemical: 화학물질 ❹ 관계대명사로 'which'로 바꾸어 쓸 수 있다. ❺ too ~ to ...: 너무 ~해서 …할 수 없다

 Listen and Talk 2 A-1

W: What are you reading, John?

M: I'm reading a book of ❶riddles.

W: Riddles? Aren't ❷they for children?

M: Actually, no. Books of riddles are really useful for adults.

W: Really? ❸Why do you say so?

M: ❷They help us think more creatively. We need to ❹think outside the box to find the answers.

❶ riddle: 수수께끼 ❷ they는 riddles를 가리킨다. ❸ 'What makes you think so?' 또는 'Why is that?' 등으로 바꾸어 표현할 수 있다. ❹ think outside the box: 고정관념에서 벗어나다

 Communication

W: There are so many pieces of information we call "facts" that are ❶completely wrong.

M: Why do you say so?

W: I read a book, and there were a lot of examples of these facts ❷that are wrong.

M: Like what?

W: Well, most people think ❸goldfish are not smart. But, goldfish are actually smart.

M: Really? Can you tell me more about ❹that?

W: They can ❺recognize their owners.

M: Oh, I didn't know that.

❶ completely: 완전히 ❷ 관계대명사로 which로 바꾸어 쓸 수 있다. ❸ goldfish: 금붕어 ❹ that은 금붕어가 실제로는 똑똑하다는 것을 가리킨다. ❺ recognize: 알아보다, 인식하다

 Wrap Up 1

M: Jane, do you usually get news online or from the newspaper?

W: Well, I usually watch TV news.

M: TV news? Is there any special reason?

W: I think ❶TV is the most useful way to get news.

M: Why do you say so?

W: I have to ❷spend too much time reading all the news online or in the newspaper. So, I just watch the main news on TV.

M: ❸I see your point.

❶ 접속사 that이 생략되어 있다. ❷ spend time ~ing: ~하는 데 시간을 보내다 ❸ I see your point.: 무슨 말인지 알겠다.

● 다음 우리말과 일치하도록 빈칸에 알맞은 말을 쓰시오.

Listen & Talk 1 A-1

W: I think I _____ _____ _____ because I didn't dress _____ yesterday.

M: Well, I've read an _____ saying that you don't catch a cold because your _____ _____ is low.

W: Really? Can you tell me _____ _____ _____?

M: The article said that people catch colds _____ _____.

Listen & Talk 1 A-2

W: I usually drink _____ _____ _____ _____ _____ before I go to bed, but it doesn't help me _____ _____.

M: I saw a show on TV, and a doctor said that a glass of warm milk doesn't actually _____ you _____ asleep.

W: Oh, it doesn't? Can you _____ _____ _____ _____ _____?

M: Milk has special _____ that make people sleepy. But the _____ in a glass is _____ small _____ have any _____.

Listen & Talk 2 A-1

W: _____ _____ _____ _____, John?

M: I'm reading a book of _____.

W: Riddles? Aren't they _____ children?

M: _____, no. Books of riddles are really _____ _____ _____.

W: Really? Why do you _____ _____?

M: They help us think more _____. We need to _____ _____ _____ _____ to find the answers.

Listen & Talk 2 A-2

M: Are these all _____ _____?

W: Yeah. These are all poems _____ by children.

M: By children?

W: Yeah. I think children _____ _____ poems than adults.

M: Why do you _____ _____?

W: They're really _____ about their _____ and much _____ _____ than adults.

해석

W: 어제 옷을 따뜻하게 입지 않아서 감기에 걸린 것 같아.
M: 글쎄, 체온이 낮다고 해서 감기에 걸리지는 않는다고 쓰여 있는 기사를 읽었어.
W: 정말? 그것에 대해 더 말해 줄 수 있니?
M: 기사에서는 사람들이 바이러스 때문에 감기에 걸린다고 했어.

W: 나는 보통 잠자리에 들기 전에 따뜻한 우유 한 잔을 마시는데, 그것이 잠드는 데 도움이 되지 않아.
M: 내가 텔레비전 프로그램에서 봤는데, 어떤 의사가 따뜻한 우유 한 잔이 실제로 잠드는 데 도움을 주는 건 아니라고 말했어.
W: 오, 그래? 그것에 대해 더 말해 줄 수 있니?
M: 우유에는 사람들을 졸리게 만드는 특별한 성분이 있어. 하지만 한 잔에 있는 양이 너무 적어서 효과가 없어.

W: 무엇을 읽고 있니, John?
M: 나는 수수께끼 책을 읽고 있어.
W: 수수께끼? 그거 아이들용 아니니?
M: 사실은, 그렇지 않아. 수수께끼 책은 어른들에게 굉장히 유용해.
W: 정말? 왜 그렇게 생각해?
M: 그 책들은 우리가 더 창의적으로 생각하도록 도와. 우리는 답을 찾기 위해 고정관념에서 벗어나야 하거든.

M: 이거 전부 시집이니?
W: 응. 이것들은 모두 아이들이 쓴 시야.
M: 아이들이?
W: 응. 내 생각에 아이들이 어른들보다 더 좋은 시를 쓰는 것 같아.
M: 왜 그렇게 생각해?
W: 아이들은 그들의 감정에 아주 솔직하고 어른들보다 훨씬 더 창의적이거든.

Listen & Talk 2 B

M: Hey, Sandy. Do you think _____ _____ _____ _____ _____? It is said that it can help me _____ _____.

W: Let me read the _____ more _____. Hmm, it looks a bit _____ to me, David.

M: Why do _____ _____ _____?

W: There isn't _____ _____ about _____ in the _____.

M: Oh, you're _____.

W: Also, it doesn't tell you _____ _____ _____ _____ _____ _____ to lose weight.

Communication

W: There are so many pieces of _____ we call "_____" that are _____ _____.

M: Why do you say so?

W: I read a book, and there were a lot of _____ of these _____ _____ _____ _____.

M: Like _____?

W: Well, most people think _____ are not smart. But, _____ are actually smart.

M: Really? Can you tell me more about that?

W: They can _____ _____ _____.

M: Oh, I didn't _____ _____.

Wrap Up 2

W: I read an _____ _____ about the Black Sea. Do you know _____ _____ _____ _____?

M: Yes. It's _____ Eastern Europe _____ Western Asia, right?

W: Right. _____ _____ do you think it is?

M: Well, black, I _____.

M: No, it isn't. It's blue.

M: Really? Then why is it _____ the Black Sea? Can you tell me more about it?

W: People call it the Black Sea because it is very _____.

M: 안녕, Sandy. 너는 내가 이 음료를 사야 한다고 생각해? 내가 살을 빼는 것을 도와줄 수 있다고 적혀 있어.

W: 라벨을 더 자세히 읽어 볼게. 음, 내가 보기에 좀 이상해, David.

M: 왜 그렇게 생각해?

W: 음료 안에 무엇이 들었는지에 대한 충분한 정보가 없어.

M: 오, 네 말이 맞아.

W: 게다가, 체중을 감량하려면 얼마나 마셔야 하는지도 나와 있지 않아.

W: 우리가 '사실'이라고 말하는 정보 중에 완전히 틀린 것들이 너무 많아.

M: 왜 그렇게 생각해?

W: 내가 책을 읽었는데, 거기에는 이러한 틀린 '사실'의 예시가 많이 있었어.

M: 예를 들면 어떤 것?

W: 음, 대부분의 사람들은 금붕어가 똑똑하지 않다고 생각해. 하지만 금붕어는 사실 똑똑해.

M: 정말? 그것에 대해 더 말해 줄 수 있니?

W: 그들은 그들의 주인을 알아 볼 수 있어.

M: 오, 그건 몰랐어.

W: 나는 흑해에 관한 흥미로운 기사를 읽었어. 너 그게 어디에 있는지 아니?

M: 응. 그것은 동유럽과 서아시아 사이에 있어, 그렇지?

W: 맞아. 그게 무슨 색일 거라고 생각해?

M: 글쎄, 검은색일 것 같아.

W: 아니야, 그렇지 않아. 그것은 파란색이야.

M: 정말? 그럼 왜 흑해라고 불리는 거야? 그것에 대해 더 말해 줄 수 있니?

W: 사람들이 흑해라고 부르는 이유는 그곳이 매우 위험하기 때문이야.

[01~02] 다음 대화를 읽고 물음에 답하시오.

> Suji: I usually drink a glass of warm milk ⓐbefore I go to bed, but it doesn't help me fall asleep.
>
> Minsu: I saw a show on TV, and a doctor said ⓑthat a glass of warm milk doesn't actually help you fall asleep.
>
> Suji: Oh, it doesn't? Can you tell me ⓒmore about it?
>
> Minsu: Milk has special chemicals that ⓓmakes people sleepy. But the amount in a glass is too ⓔsmall to have any effect.

01 위 대화의 밑줄 친 ⓐ~ⓔ 중 어법상 틀린 것을 찾아 바르게 고치시오.

➡ _____

02 위 대화의 내용과 일치하지 않는 것은?

① 수지는 자기 전에 따뜻한 우유 한 잔을 마신다.

② 자기 전에 따뜻한 우유 한 잔은 수지가 잠드는 데 도움이 되지 않았다.

③ 민수는 TV에서 어떤 의사가 따뜻한 우유 한 잔이 실제로 잠드는 데 도움을 주는 건 아니라고 말하는 것을 들었다.

④ 우유에는 사람들을 졸리게 만드는 특별한 성분이 있다.

⑤ 우유 한 잔에 있는 특별한 성분의 양으로 숙면을 취할 수 있다.

[03~04] 다음 대화를 읽고 물음에 답하시오.

> W: I think I caught a cold because I didn't dress ⓐwarmly yesterday.
>
> M: Well, I've read an article ⓑsaying that you don't catch a cold because your body temperature is low.
>
> W: Really? Can you tell me more ⓒabout it?
>
> M: The article said that people catch colds ⓓbecause viruses.

03 위 대화에서 밑줄 친 ⓐ~ⓓ 중 어법상 틀린 것을 찾아 바르게 고치시오

➡ _____

04 위 대화의 내용과 일치하도록 빈칸을 완성하시오.

> According to the article, people catch colds not because of (A)_____ but because of (B)_____.

[01~02] 다음 대화를 읽고 물음에 답하시오.

Jane: I read an article ⓐsaying that Napoleon was actually fairly tall.

Tom: Oh, really? Can you tell me more about it?

Jane: According to the article, a French doctor ⓑwrote down Napoleon's height according to the French measuring system, not the English ⓒone.

Tom: What was the difference?

Jane: At that time, an inch in France was ⓓlonger than an inch in England. So, Napoleon was actually about 168 cm tall, ⓔthat was not that short in those times.

서답형
01 위 대화의 밑줄 친 ⓐ~ⓔ 중 어법상 틀린 것을 찾아 바르게 고치시오.

➡ _____

중요
02 위 대화의 내용과 일치하지 않는 것은?

① Jane은 나폴레옹이 실제로 꽤 키가 컸었다는 기사를 읽었다.

② 기사에 따르면 프랑스 의사는 나폴레옹의 키를 프랑스 측정 체계에 따라 기록했다.

③ 나폴레옹 시대에 프랑스의 1인치는 영국의 1인치보다 더 길었다.

④ 나폴레옹은 실제로 약 168 cm로 그 당시에는 작은 편이 아니었다.

⑤ 프랑스 측정 체계와 영국의 측정 체계는 다르지 않았다.

[03~05] 다음 대화를 읽고 물음에 답하시오.

Suji: I usually drink a glass of warm milk before I go to bed, but it doesn't help me fall asleep.

Minsu: I saw a show on TV, and a doctor said that a glass of warm milk doesn't actually help you fall asleep.

Suji: Oh, it doesn't? Can you tell me more about it?

Minsu: Milk has special chemicals that make people sleepy. But the amount in a glass is too small to have any effect.

서답형
03 What does Suji do before going to bed?

➡ _____

서답형
04 What is the effect of special chemicals in milk?

➡ _____

서답형
05 Why are the chemicals in a glass of warm milk not holpful for falling acloop?

➡ _____
_____

서답형
06 다음 대화가 자연스럽게 이어지도록 순서대로 배열하시오.

M: Are these all poetry books?
(A) By children?
(B) Why do you say so?
(C) Yeah. These are all poems written by children.
(D) Yeah. I think children write better poems than adults.
(E) They're really honest about their feelings and much more creative than adults.

➡ _____

07 다음 짝지어진 대화가 <u>어색한</u> 것은?

① A: Did you know that bats aren't blind?

B: No. Can you tell me more about it?

② A: Books of riddles are really useful for adults.

B: Why do you say so?

③ A: Actually, frozen fruits are as good as fresh ones.

B: Really? Can you give me more information about it?

④ A: You know what? I'm planning to visit Canada this summer vacation.

B: I'm wondering if you could tell me more about your vacation plan.

⑤ A: Did you know that Bill's birthday is on May 4th?

B: I see your point.

[08~09] 다음 대화를 읽고 물음에 답하시오.

Susan: What are you reading, John?

John: I'm reading a book of riddles.

Susan: Riddles? Aren't they for children?

John: Actually, no. Books of riddles are really useful for adults.

Susan: Really? (A)_____

John: They help us think more creatively. (B)_____

08 위 대화의 빈칸 (A)에 들어갈 말로 나머지와 의도가 <u>다른</u> 것은?

① Why do you say so?

② What makes you say so?

③ What makes you think so?

④ Can you tell me the reason why?

⑤ What do you think about it?

서답형

09 위 대화의 빈칸 (B)에 들어갈 말을 보기에 주어진 단어들을 모두 배열하여 완성하시오.

┌─── 보기 ───┐

need / we / to / find / to / the answers / outside / think / the box

➡ _____

_____

[10~12] 다음 대화를 읽고 물음에 답하시오.

Mike: Are these all poetry books?

Sue: Yeah. These are all poems (A)_____ (write) by children.

Mike: By children?

Sue: Yeah. I think children write better poems than adults.

Mike: (B)Why do you say so?

Sue: (C)They're really honest about their feelings and much more creative than adults.

서답형

10 위 대화의 빈칸 (A)에 주어진 단어를 알맞은 형태로 쓰시오.

➡ _____

11 위 대화의 밑줄 친 (B)와 바꾸어 쓰기에 <u>어색한</u> 것은?

① Why do you think so?

② What makes you say so?

③ What makes you think so?

④ Can you tell me why?

⑤ How do you feel about that?

서답형

12 위 대화의 밑줄 친 (C)가 가리키는 것을 찾아 쓰시오.

➡ _____

[01~02] 다음 대화를 읽고 물음에 답하시오.

W: I think I caught a cold because I didn't dress warmly yesterday.

M: Well, I've read an article saying that you don't catch a cold because your body temperature is low.

W: Really? (A)_____?

M: The article said that people catch colds because of viruses.

Daily News, May 7th 2020

Was (A)_____Really Short?

　We have been wrong about Napoleon's (B)_____. The misunderstanding came from the difference between (C)_____ _____ and (D)_____ _____. He was actually about 168 cm tall!

01 위 대화의 빈칸 (A)에 들어갈 말을 〈보기〉에 주어진 단어들을 배열하여 완성하시오.

┌─ 보기 ─┐
you / more / it / can / about / tell / me

➡ _____?

02 Why does the woman think she caught a cold?

➡ _____
　 _____

03 다음 대화의 내용과 일치하도록 기사를 완성하시오.

Jane: I read an article saying that Napoleon was actually fairly tall.

Tom: Oh, really? Can you tell me more about it?

Jane: According to the article, a French doctor wrote down Napoleon's height according to the French measuring system, not the English one.

Tom: What was the difference?

Jane: At that time, an inch in France was longer than an inch in England. So, Napoleon was actually about 168 cm tall, which was not that short in those times.

[04~06] 다음 대화를 읽고 물음에 답하시오.

Mike: Are these all poetry books?

Sue: Yeah. These are all poems written by children.

Mike: By children?

Sue: Yeah. I think children write better poems than adults.

Mike: (A)왜 그렇게 생각해? (say)

Sue: They're really honest about their feelings and much more creative than adults.

04 위 대화의 밑줄 친 (A)의 우리말을 주어진 단어를 사용하여 5 단어로 영작하시오.

➡ _____

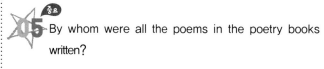
05 By whom were all the poems in the poetry books written?

➡ _____

06 Why does Sue think that children write better poems than adults?

➡ _____
　 _____

Grammar

1 분사구문

- • Let's look into some articles **thinking about the hidden motives.** 숨겨진 동기를 생각하면서 몇 가지 뉴스 기사를 살펴보자.

■ 분사가 이끄는 구를 분사구문이라고 하며, 이유, 조건, 시간, 동시동작, 양보 등의 뜻을 나타낸다. 분사구문은 '접속사+주어+동사'로 이루어진 부사절의 주어가 주절의 주어와 일치할 때 접속사와 주어를 생략하고 동사를 분사(동사원형+-ing)로 만든 구문이다. 이때 생략되는 접속사에 따라 뜻이 달라진다.

- • When I arrived at the party, it began to rain. → **Arriving at the party**, it began to rain. (시간) (파티에 도착했을 때 비가 내리기 시작했다.)

■ 부사절과 주절의 주어가 다를 때는 부사절의 주어를 생략하지 않고 사용하며 이것을 독립분사구문이라고 한다. 일반인이 주어일 경우에는 생략한다.(비인칭 독립분사구문)

- • As it was raining, we couldn't go out. → **It being raining**, we couldn't go out. (우리는 비가 오고 있었기 때문에 나갈 수가 없었다.)

■ 분사구문의 부정은 분사 앞에 'not'이나 'never'를 쓴다.

- • As he didn't feel well, he took the last Wednesday off. → **Not feeling well**, he took the last Wednesday off. (그는 지난 수요일 몸이 불편하여 쉬었다.)

■ 분사구문의 뜻을 명확히 하기 위해 접속사를 생략하지 않기도 한다. 이 경우는 부사절에서 '주어+be동사'를 생략한 것과 같은 형태가 된다.

- • I mailed a letter **while taking a walk**. (나는 산책을 하면서 편지를 부쳤다.)

■ 부사절의 시제가 주절보다 앞선 경우에는 완료분사구문(having+과거분사)으로 쓴다.

- • As he had done it before, he was going to do it.
  = **Having done it before**, he was going to do it.

■ 과거분사로 시작되는 분사구문은 being이 생략된 것으로 수동의 의미를 갖는다.

- **Written in English**, the book is not easy to read. (영어로 쓰여졌기 때문에, 그 책은 읽기에 쉽지 않다.)

핵심 Check

1. 다음 괄호 안에서 알맞은 말을 고르시오.
  ⑴ (Live / Living) next door, I often see Billy.
  ⑵ (Listening / Listened) to the music, she stayed up late.

2 so that ~ can ...

• They made up this fake article **so that** they **could** draw the readers' attention.
그들은 독자들의 주의를 끌기 위해 이 가짜 기사를 지어냈다.

■ so that은 '~하기 위해', '~하고자', '~하도록'의 의미로 '목적'이나 '의도'를 나타낸다. 일반적으로 '주절
+so that+주어+can/will+동사원형 ~'의 형태로 쓰인다.
   • He tried to make friends with him **so that** he **could** get help from the wolf. (그는 늑대로부터 도움을
   받을 수 있도록 그와 친구가 되려고 하였다.)
   • She worked hard **so that** everything **would** be ready in time. (그녀는 모든 것이 제시간에 준비될 수 있도
   록 열심히 일을 했다.)

■ 'so that ~ can ...'은 'in order that ~ can ...'으로 바꿔 쓸 수 있으며, 주절과 종속절의 주어가 같
   은 경우 '(in order[so as]) to부정사'로 바꿔 쓸 수 있다.
   • I borrowed a book **so that** I **could** read during weekends. (나는 주말 동안 읽으려고 책을 한 권 빌렸다.)
   = I borrowed a book **in order that** I **could** read during weekends.
   = I borrowed a book **to read** during weekends. 〈to부정사의 부사적 용법 – 목적〉
   = I borrowed a book **in order to read** during weekends.
   = I borrowed a book **so as to read** during weekends.

■ so that을 기준으로 앞과 뒤의 동사의 시제를 일치시킨다.
   • He takes a taxi **so that** he **won't** be late. (그는 지각하지 않기 위해 택시를 탄다.)
   • He took a taxi **so that** he **wouldn't** be late. (그는 지각하지 않기 위해 택시를 탔다.)

■ 'so that'은 '결과'의 부사절을 이끌어 '그래서, 그러므로'의 의미를 갖는 접속사로 쓰이기도 하는데,
   대개 앞에 쉼표(,)가 온다.
   • He always breaks his promises, **so that** he has no friends. (그는 항상 약속을 어긴다. 그래서 그는 친구가 없다.)

■ so와 that 사이에 수식어가 오면, '너무 ~해서 결국 …하다'라는 뜻이 되며, 'so+형용사[부사]+that+
   주어+can ...(매우 ~해서 …할 수 있는)'은 '형용사+enough to ...(…할 정도로 충분히 ~한)'로 바
   꿔 쓸 수 있으며, 'so+형용사[부사]+that+주어+can't ...(너무 ~해서 …할 수 없는)'은 'too+형용사
   [부사]+to부정사(…하기에 너무 ~한)'로 바꿔 쓸 수 있다.

   • I got **so** excited **that** I was at a loss for words. (나는 너무 흥분한 나머지 말문이 막혔다.)
   • He was **so** happy **that** he could dance. (그는 뛸 듯이 기뻐했다.)
   = He was happy **enough to** dance.

핵심 Check

2. 다음 괄호 안에서 알맞은 말을 고르시오.
   (1) She hurried up so (that / which) she could get there on time.
   (2) Use a hand signal (in that / so that) drivers can see you.

01 다음 우리말에 맞게 빈칸에 알맞은 것은?

> 당신이 그곳에 제시간에 도착할 수 있게 빨리 몰겠습니다.
> = I'll drive fast so _____ you can get there in time.

① this　　　② that　　　③ what
④ which　　⑤ it

02 다음 괄호 안에서 알맞은 말을 고르시오.

(1) (Have / Having) no money, I couldn't buy a new bike.

(2) (Knowing not / Not knowing) what to do, I was at my wits' end.

(3) I went to the zoo (though / so that) my sister could see wild animals.

(4) I was very excited, (because / so that) I couldn't get to sleep.

03 다음 빈칸에 들어갈 말로 알맞은 것은?

> _____ me, the man ran off.

① Seeing　　② Seen　　③ Sees
④ Saw　　　⑤ See

04 다음 우리말에 맞게 주어진 어휘를 바르게 배열하시오.

(1) 성적표를 보면서, 엄마의 얼굴이 어두워졌다.

(mom's face, the report card, looking, darkened, at)

➡ _____

(2) 우리는 책을 빌릴 수 있도록 도서관에 갈 것이다.

(we, we, can, are, borrow, going, so, books, the library, that, to)

➡ _____

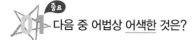

중요
01 다음 중 어법상 어색한 것은?

① Feeling happy, she sang a song.
② Working in the hospital, my aunt helped many pcoplc.
③ Aaron danced on the stage listened to the music.
④ He uses his cellphone while walking on the street.
⑤ Turning left, you can find the bus stop.

02 다음 중 어법상 바르지 않은 것은?

① Speak clearly so that we can understand you.
② I had to save much money to buy a new car.
③ The bird practiced flying hard so to fly up high.
④ I took a taxi in order that I could be there on time.
⑤ She arrived early in order to get a good seat.

중요
03 다음 빈칸에 알맞은 말이 바르게 짝지어진 것은?

• He is eating his favorite egg sandwich _____ a newspaper.
• Put on a helmet _____ that you can protect your head.

① reading – so
② reading – for
③ reads – so
④ reads – for
⑤ read – in

서답형
04 다음 괄호 안에서 알맞은 말을 고르시오.

(1) Save electricity so (that / as) we can save polar bears.
(2) IIe noted every detail so (as / that) to fix the scene in his mind.
(3) Come early in (order / condition) that you can see him.
(4) (Neglected / Neglecting) his duty, he was fired.
(5) When (process / processing) your request, an error occurred.
(6) (Knowing not / Not knowing) what to do, I asked for my mom's advice.

중요
05 주어진 두 문장을 한 문장으로 바꿀 때 옳지 않은 것은?

• I arrived home late at night.
• I saw some fruits and ate them.

① When I arrived home late at night, I saw some fruits and ate them.
② As I arrived home late at night, I saw some fruits and ate them.
③ Arriving home late at night, I saw some fruits and ate them.
④ When arriving home late at night, I saw some fruits and ate them.
⑤ When arrived home late at night, I saw some fruits and ate them.

06 빈칸 (A)와 (B)에 알맞은 것으로 바르게 짝지어진 것은?

• Get up early ___(A)___ as to be in time for the first train.
• He is ___(B)___ rich that he can buy the sports car.

	(A)	(B)
①	too	so
②	too	too
③	so	so
④	so	too
⑤	enough	as

07 다음 문장의 밑줄 친 부분 중 어법상 어색한 것은?

David, ⓐthought ⓑthat ⓒit ⓓwould soon pass, ⓔignored his headache.

① ⓐ   ② ⓑ   ③ ⓒ
④ ⓓ   ⑤ ⓔ

08 다음 밑줄 친 부분과 바꿔 쓸 수 있는 것은?

Jim sold his watch so that he could buy the coat.

① in that   ② so as to   ③ to
④ in order   ⑤ in order that

09 다음 두 문장을 한 문장으로 바꿔 쓸 때 빈칸에 들어갈 한 단어를 쓰시오.

• You cross the street.
• You should be careful.
= _____ the street, you should be careful.

10 다음 우리말을 바르게 영작한 것을 고르시오.

네가 건강해질 수 있도록 채소를 더 많이 먹어야 한다.

① You should eat more vegetables so what you can be healthy.
② You should eat more vegetables so that you can be healthy.
③ You should eat more vegetables in that you can be healthy.
④ You should eat more vegetables so as you can be healthy.
⑤ You should eat more vegetables so to you can be healthy.

11 분사구문의 의미가 밑줄 친 부분과 같은 것은?

Being small, the kitchen is well designed.

① Having nothing to do, I went for a walk to the park.
② The sun being shining, it wasn't very warm.
③ We need luck when taking tests.
④ He told me a shocking story while having lunch together.
⑤ Not paying the rent, you'll be thrown out.

12 다음 문장에서 생략할 수 있는 것을 찾아 쓰시오.

(1) Though he was young, he had much gray hair.
➡ _____

(2) She had her picture taken when she was in Italy.
➡ _____

13 다음 문장과 뜻이 같은 것을 고르시오.

> The girl is too shy to speak in front of others.

① The girl is shy so that she can't speak in front of others.
② The girl is so that shy she can't speak in front of others.
③ The girl is so shy that can't speak in front of others.
④ The girl is so shy that she can't speak in front of others.
⑤ The girl is too shy to she can't speak in front of others.

서답형

14 다음 문장에서 어법상 어색한 것을 바르게 고쳐 다시 쓰시오.

(1) Don't throw trash in the sea in order for animals can live safely.

➡ _____

_____

(2) Look for hidden ideas so as that you can see what the writer really means.

➡ _____

_____

(3) Swum in the pond, she was wearing her swimming cap.

➡ _____

_____

(4) Being fine, we went for a walk to the beach.

➡ _____

(5) Seeing from high above, the cars looked tiny.

➡ _____

15 다음 우리말을 바르게 영작한 것을 고르시오.

> Kathryn은 그들의 이름을 들었지만, 그들을 구별하지 못했다.

① Although she hearing their names, Kathryn couldn't recognize them.
② She having heard their names, Kathryn couldn't recognize them.
③ Having heard their names, Kathryn not recognizing them.
④ Kathryn having heard their names, she couldn't recognize them.
⑤ Having heard their names, Kathryn couldn't recognize them.

16 다음 중 어법상 어색한 것을 모두 고르시오. (2개)

① She became too weak to move her own body easily.
② I was enough stupid to believe him.
③ Come early so as that you can have plenty of time.
④ Don't use smartphones so that others can study in a quiet place.
⑤ They made up this fake article so that they could draw the readers' attention.

서답형

17 다음 두 문장을 'so that'을 이용하여 한 문장으로 바꿔 쓰시오.

> • They confessed that they made it up.
> • They could draw the readers' attention to the unsafe conditions at the zoo.

➡ _____

_____

_____

01 다음 문장을 분사구문으로 바꿔 쓰시오.

(1) Because my mom caught a bad cold, she couldn't get to work.

➡ _____

_____

(2) After I finished breakfast, I took a taxi to school.

➡ _____

(3) If you mix blue and yellow, you get green.

➡ _____

(4) Although she was nervous, she said it was a good experience.

➡ _____

_____

(5) Because I didn't know what happened, I called my friend, Sam.

➡ _____

_____

(6) If it is fine tomorrow, I will go hiking.

➡ _____

02 'so that'을 이용하여 다음 두 문장을 한 문장으로 바꿔 쓰시오.

(1) • Read the book carefully.
   • You can find hidden ideas.

➡ _____

_____

(2) • Sally bought a camera.
   • She could take great pictures.

➡ _____

_____

03 다음 우리말에 맞게 주어진 단어를 바르게 배열하시오.

(1) 그 뉴스가 거짓이라는 것을 알지 못했기 때문에 많은 사람이 겁에 질려 어쩔 줄 몰랐다. (people, the news, was, knowing, panicked, many, not, false)

➡ _____

_____

(2) 일찍 떠났지만, 그는 회의에 늦었다. (he, the, meeting, was, leaving, early, late, for)

➡ _____

(3) 그는 매우 열심히 공부해서 마침내 변호사가 되었다. (he, he, a lawyer, that, worked, became, hard, finally, so)

➡ _____

_____

(4) 그는 일찍 일어나서 첫 버스를 탈 수 있었다. (he, he, bus, catch, could, got, that, the, early, first, so, up)

➡ _____

_____

04 다음 문장에서 어법상 어색한 부분을 바르게 고치시오.

(1) Exhausting from the work, he lay down on the sofa.

➡ _____

(2) Failing twice, Jaden didn't want to try again.

➡ _____

136 Lesson 5. Critical Minds

05 그림을 보고 주어진 어휘를 이용하여 빈칸을 알맞게 채우시오.

(1) Mina reads newspapers every day _____ keep up with current affairs. (can, so)

(2) Mina reads newspapers every day _____ keep up with current affairs. (to, in)

(3) Mina reads newspapers every day _____ keep up with current affairs. (to, so)

06 그림을 보고 접속사 없이 주어진 어휘를 이용하여 빈칸을 알 맞게 채우시오.

(1) _____ rainy, they cannot go for a walk. (be)

(2) _____ the rain, they are talking about whether to go shopping. (watch)

07 다음 우리말을 괄호 안의 지시대로 영작하시오.

(1) 왼쪽으로 돌면, 그 집을 찾을 겁니다.
➡ _____
(분사구문을 써서)
➡ _____
(접속사를 써서)

(2) 그녀는 아파서 학교에 결석했다.
➡ _____
(분사구문을 써서)
➡ _____
(접속사를 써서)

(3) Lisa는 그녀의 엄마가 오렌지 주스를 만들 수 있도록 오렌지를 좀 샀다.
➡ _____
(that을 써서)

08 다음 문장에서 잘못된 것을 알맞게 고쳐 다시 쓰시오.

(1) Judy practices playing the piano in order to that she can win the top prize.
➡ _____

(2) I got up early so as to I could go jogging.
➡ _____

(3) Arrived late at the station, I saw the train leaving.
➡ _____

Reading

교과서

Can You Spot Fake News?

Every day we watch, hear, or read interesting news. However, have you ever seriously considered whether an article is really true?

현재완료(경험)   '~인지 아닌지'라는 뜻의 접속사

Everyone likes an interesting news story but what if it is completely made up?

~이라면 어떻게 될까?

Fake news can be very harmful in that it can make people less

~이므로, ~라는 점에서

informed or even misled. Nevertheless, there have been various fake

목적격보어로 수동의 의미를 지닌 과거분사를 사용   그럼에도 불구하고,   현재완료(계속)

news reports throughout history. Why have some people written such false information? Let's look into some articles thinking about the

동시동작을 나타내는 분사구문

hidden motives behind them.

AWFUL DISASTER

Last night, an angry group of rhinoceroses broke down the walls

a group of: '~의 무리'.   break down: ~을 부수다, 무너뜨리다

of the cage at the zoo and escaped. They also broke down the walls of the other wild animals' cages. These animals ran down the streets and injured hundreds of people. Twelve of the animals are still on the

수백의

loose. Citizens should stay indoors until further notice.

잡히지 않은, 탈주 중인   farther(×)

* Not a single act or incident described above has taken place.

과거분사로, 앞에 나온 명사 act와 incident를 수식   현재완료

spot 발견하다, 찾아내다
fake 가짜의, 거짓의
seriously 진지하게, 심각하게
harmful 해로운, 유해한
mislead 잘못 이끌다, 오해하게 하다
nevertheless 그럼에도 불구하고
motive 동기, 이유
make up 지어내다, 만들어 내다
awful 끔찍한, 지독한
disaster 참사, 재난
escape 달아나다, 탈출하다, 벗어나다
injure 부상을 입히다
citizen 시민
incident 사건
describe 기술하다
rhinoceros 코뿔소
break down ~을 부수다, ~을 무너뜨리다
on the loose 잡히지 않은, 탈주 중인
single 단 하나의
act 행동

 확인문제

● 다음 문장이 본문의 내용과 일치하면 T, 일치하지 않으면 F를 쓰시오.

1   Each day we watch, hear, or read interesting news. ☐

2   Fake news can make people well-informed. ☐

3   There have been various fake news reports throughout history. ☐

4   All the acts or incidents described in the article above actually took place. ☐

At that time, <u>those</u> who read the article carefully <u>laughed out loud</u>.
= the people 크게 웃었다

<u>Those who didn't read it to the end</u> got really worried. <u>Not knowing</u>
주격 관계대명사절 who didn't read it to the end가 선행사 Those를 수식   이유를 나타내는 분사구문의 부정

<u>the news was false</u>, many people panicked. Some tried to escape the
Because they didn't know the news was false.

city while <u>others</u> went into the parks with guns to hunt the animals.
= other people

So why did *The Herald* <u>make up</u> such news? Later, <u>they</u> confessed
(남을 속이거나 즐겁게 하기 위해 이야기 등을) 지어내다, 만들어 내다   = The Herald

that they made <u>it</u> up <u>so that they could draw</u> the readers' attention to
= such news   (in order) to draw

the unsafe conditions at the zoo.

SLAV SHOOTS A FRIEND IN ARGUMENT

<u>Mejk Swenekafew, a Slav worker at the Columbia Coal Mine</u>, was
Mejk Swenekafew와 a Slav worker at the Columbia Coal Mine은 동격

shot and seriously wounded by John Pecitello near the mining camp

Thursday evening.

The two men <u>had an argument</u> <u>during</u> a meeting. The argument led
언쟁을 벌었다, 말다툼을 했다   during+기간을 나타내는 명사

to a fight, and Pecitello shot Swenekafew twice, in the chest and leg.

He <u>is</u> now at the hospital in <u>critical condition</u>. Pecitello ran away after
be in critical condition: 위독한 상태에 있다

the shooting. <u>The police</u> <u>are searching for</u> him now and <u>are warning</u>
복수 취급   search for: ~을 찾다   are searching and are warning: 접속사 and에 의해 병렬 구조로 연결되어 있음.

citizens that he is extremely dangerous.

---

panic 겁에 질려 어쩔 줄 모르다
confess 고백하다, 인정하다
unsafe 안전하지 않은
condition 상태
Slav 슬라브인
shoot (총 등을) 쏘다
argument 논쟁, 언쟁
mine 광산, 채굴하다
lead to ~을 이끌다
twice 두 번
wound 상처를 입히다
chest 가슴, 흉부
critical 위험한, 위독한
extremely 극도로, 극히
run away 도망치다

확인문제

● 다음 문장이 본문의 내용과 일치하면 T, 일치하지 <u>않으면</u> F를 쓰시오.

1 At that time, those who read the article carefully laughed out loud. ☐

2 Those who read the article to the end got really worried. ☐

3 As they didn't know the news was false, many people panicked. ☐

4 John Pecitello was shot and seriously wounded by Mejk Swenekafew Thursday evening. ☐

5 Swenekafew is now at the hospital in critical condition. ☐

6 The police are warning citizens that Swenekafew is extremely dangerous. ☐

Is there anything strange about the article? Read the Slav's name backwards; it spells, "we-fake-news." Who wrote this and why?

<u>the Slav's name.</u> 즉 'Swenekafew'를 가리킨다. fake: '위조하다, 조작하다'

The Daily Telegram published this fake article <u>so that they could</u>
= in order to prove
<u>prove</u> if *The Daily News*, their competitor, was stealing their articles.

if(= whether): '~인지 아닌지'라는 의미의 명사절을 이끄는 접속사.

The Daily News published the same article about "Swenekafew" the next day and thus <u>got caught</u> stealing. The people at *The Daily News*

잡혔다, 포착되었다

had to admit <u>their act</u> and <u>were harshly criticized by the public.</u>

그동안 몰래 데일리 텔레그램 사의 기사를 훔쳤던 행위
The people at The Daily News를 주어로 하는 수동태 문장. "The public harshly criticized the people at The Daily News."(능동태)

The two articles were special cases, but <u>there are many</u> "fake" news

there+be동사: '~이 있다'는 의미, 주어는 many "fake" news articles

<u>articles published</u> every day. As readers, we need to read critically

과거분사로 앞에 나온 명사 articles를 수식

and judge <u>whether</u> the news is real or fake.

'~인지 아닌지'라는 의미의 접속사 = if

How to spot fake news!

how+to부정사: ~하는 방법

Consider the Source

기사의 출처인 원본 자료나 뉴스의 정보원 혹은 소식통을 의미

Is it from a reliable source?
Can we trust the writer?

Check the Date

Is it a new or an old story?
Is it related to current events?

be related to: ~와 관련이 있다

Read Beyond the Headlines

단순히 기사 제목만 읽고 뉴스의 내용을 짐작하여 판단하지 말고, 그 기사의 내용까지 모두 읽으라는 의미

Does the headline match the content?

Find Supporting Sources

Do other related stories provide similar content?

spell 철자를 말하다(쓰다)
publish 발행하다, 출판하다, 게재하다
competitor 경쟁자, 경쟁 상대
admit 인정하다, 자백하다
criticize 비난하다
public 대중, 일반 사람들
critically 비판적으로
judge 판단하다
source 출처, 자료
reliable 믿을 만한, 신뢰할 만한
current 현재의, 지금의
support 뒷받침하다

📎 **확인문제**

● 다음 문장이 본문의 내용과 일치하면 T, 일치하지 <u>않으면</u> F를 쓰시오.

1 *The Daily Telegram* published this fake article so that they could prove that *The Daily News* was stealing their articles. ☐

2 *The Daily News* published a little bit different article about "Swenekafew" the next day. ☐

3 The people at *The Daily News* were harshly criticized by the public. ☐

4 To spot fake news, we need not check many sources. ☐

5 To spot fake news, it is necessary to check the date. ☐

6 To spot fake news, we shouldn't read beyond the headlines. ☐

● 우리말을 참고하여 빈칸에 알맞은 말을 쓰시오.

1 Can You _____ _____ _____?

2 Every day we watch, hear, or read _____ _____.

3 However, have you ever seriously considered _____ an article is really true?

4 Everyone likes an interesting news story but _____ _____ it is completely _____ _____?

5 Fake news can be very harmful _____ _____ it can make people _____ _____ or even _____.

6 _____, there have been various fake news reports _____ _____.

7 Why have some people written _____ _____ _____?

8 Let's look into some articles _____ about _____ _____ _____ behind them.

9 _____ DISASTER

10 Last night, an angry group of rhinoceroses _____ _____ the walls of the cage at the zoo and escaped.

11 They also broke down the walls of _____ _____ wild animals' cages.

12 These animals ran down the streets and injured _____ people.

13 Twelve of the animals are still _____ _____ _____.

14 Citizens should stay indoors _____ _____ _____.

15 Not a single act or incident _____ _____ has taken place.

16 At that time, those who read the article carefully _____ _____ _____.

1	당신은 가짜 뉴스임을 알아챌 수 있는가?
2	매일 우리는 흥미로운 뉴스를 보고, 듣고, 읽는다.
3	그러나 당신은 뉴스 기사가 정말로 진실인지 심각하게 고려해 본 적이 있는가?
4	모든 사람이 흥미로운 뉴스 기사를 좋아하지만, 만약 그것이 완전히 지어낸 것이라면 어떻게 할 것인가?
5	가짜 뉴스는 사람들에게 정보를 부족하게 제공하거나 사람들을 잘못 이끌 수 있다는 점에서 매우 해로울 수 있다.
6	그럼에도 불구하고, 역사를 통틀어 다양한 가짜 뉴스 보도들이 존재해 왔다.
7	왜 어떤 사람들은 그러한 거짓 정보를 써 왔던 것일까?
8	그 뒤에 숨겨진 동기를 생각하면서 몇 가지 뉴스 기사를 살펴보자.
9	끔찍한 참사
10	어젯밤, 화가 난 코뿔소 떼가 동물원 우리의 벽을 부수고 도망쳤다.
11	그들은 또한 다른 야생 동물 우리의 벽도 부수었다.
12	이 동물들은 거리를 뛰어다니며 수백 명의 사람에게 부상을 입혔다.
13	그중 열두 마리의 동물들이 아직 잡히지 않았다.
14	시민들은 추후 안내가 있을 때까지 집 안에 머물러야 한다.
15	위에 기술된 어떤 행동이나 사건도 일어나지 않았다.
16	그 당시 이 기사를 주의 깊게 읽었던 사람들은 크게 웃었다.

17 Those who didn't read it to the end _____ _____ _____ .

18 _____ _____ the news was false, many people _____ .

19 _____ tried to escape the city while _____ went into the parks with guns to hunt the animals.

20 So why did *The Herald* _____ _____ _____ _____ ?

21 Later, they confessed that they _____ _____ _____ _____ _____ they _____ draw the readers' attention to the unsafe conditions at the zoo.

22 SLAV SHOOTS A FRIEND _____ _____

23 Mejk Swenekafew, a Slav worker at the Columbia Coal Mine, _____ _____ and seriously _____ by John Pecitello near the mining camp Thursday evening.

24 The two men _____ _____ _____ during a meeting.

25 The argument _____ _____ a fight, and Pecitello shot Swenekafew twice, _____ _____ _____ and leg.

26 He is now at the hospital _____ _____ _____ .

27 Pecitello ran away _____ _____ _____ .

28 The police _____ _____ _____ him now and _____ _____ citizens that he is extremely dangerous.

29 Is there _____ _____ about the article?

30 Read the Slav's name _____ ; it spells, "we-fake-news."

31 Who wrote this and _____ ?

17 그것을 끝까지 읽지 않은 사람들은 정말로 걱정하였다.

18 그 기사가 거짓이라는 것을 알지 못했기 때문에 많은 사람이 겁에 질려 어쩔 줄 몰랐다.

19 어떤 사람들은 도시를 빠져나가려고 했고 다른 사람들은 그 동물들을 사냥하기 위해 총을 들고 공원으로 나갔다.

20 그렇다면 왜 헤럴드 사는 이러한 뉴스를 만들어 냈을까?

21 나중에 그들은 동물원의 안전하지 않은 상태에 대해 독자들의 주의를 끌기 위해 그 기사를 지어냈다고 고백했다.

22 슬라브인이 언쟁 중에 친구에게 총을 쏘다

23 목요일 저녁 채굴 야영지 근처에서, 컬럼비아 광산 소속의 슬라브인 노동자 Mejk Swenekafew가 John Pecitello에 의해 총상을 입어 심각하게 다쳤다.

24 그 두 사람은 회의 중에 언쟁을 벌였다.

25 언쟁이 싸움으로 번졌고, Pecitello가 Swenekafew의 가슴과 다리에 두 번 총을 쏘았다.

26 현재 그는 위독한 상태로 입원 중이다.

27 Pecitello는 총격 이후 도주했다.

28 경찰이 지금 그를 찾고 있으며, 그가 극히 위험하다고 시민들에게 경고하고 있다.

29 이 기사에 뭔가 이상한 점이 있는가?

30 그 슬라브인의 이름을 거꾸로 읽어 보아라. 그것의 철자는 "우리는 뉴스를 조작한다."가 된다.

31 누가 이것을 썼고 왜 그랬을까?

32 *The Daily Telegram* published this fake article _____ _____ they _____ prove _____ *The Daily News*, their competitor, was stealing their articles.

33 *The Daily News* published the same article about "Swenekafew" the next day and thus _____ _____ _____.

34 The people at *The Daily News* had to _____ their act and _____ _____ _____ by the public.

35 The two articles were special cases, but there are many "fake" news articles _____ every day.

36 _____ readers, we need to read critically and judge _____ the news is real _____ fake.

37 _____ _____ _____ fake news!

38 Consider the _____

39 Is it from a _____ source?

40 Can we _____ the writer?

41 _____ the Date

42 Is it a _____ or an _____ story?

43 _____ it _____ _____ _____ events?

44 Read _____ _____ _____

45 Does the headline _____ _____ _____?

46 Find _____ Sources

47 Do other _____ stories provide _____ content?

32 데일리 텔레그램 사는 그들의 경쟁자인 데일리 뉴스 사가 그들의 기사를 훔치는지를 증명하기 위해서 이 거짓 기사를 발행했다.

33 데일리 뉴스 사는 그 다음 날 'Swenekafew'에 대한 동일한 기사를 발행했고 그래서 훔친 것이 발각되었다.

34 데일리 뉴스 사의 사람들은 그들의 행동을 인정해야만 했고 대중들로부터 혹독한 비난을 받았다.

35 이 두 기사는 특별한 경우였지만, 매일 발행되는 '가짜' 뉴스 기사는 많이 있다.

36 독자로서, 우리는 비판적으로 읽고 그 뉴스가 진짜인지 가짜인지 판단할 필요가 있다.

37 가짜 뉴스 판별 방법!

38 출처를 고려하라

39 그것은 믿을 만한 출처에서 온 것인가?

40 우리는 그 필자를 신뢰할 수 있는가?

41 날짜를 확인하라

42 그것은 새로운 이야기인가 혹은 오래된 이야기인가?

43 그것은 현재의 사건들과 관련된 것인가?

44 기사 제목 그 이상을 읽어라

45 기사 제목이 기사 내용과 일치하는가?

46 뒷받침하는 자료를 찾아라

47 다른 관련된 이야기도 비슷한 내용을 제공하는가?

• 우리말을 참고하여 본문을 영작하시오.

1 당신은 가짜 뉴스임을 알아챌 수 있는가?

➡ _____

2 매일 우리는 흥미로운 뉴스를 보고, 듣고, 읽는다.

➡ _____

3 그러나 당신은 뉴스 기사가 정말로 진실인지 심각하게 고려해 본 적이 있는가?

➡ _____

4 모든 사람이 흥미로운 뉴스 기사를 좋아하지만, 만약 그것이 완전히 지어낸 것이라면 어떻게 할 것인가?

➡ _____

5 가짜 뉴스는 사람들에게 정보를 부족하게 제공하거나 사람들을 잘못 이끌 수 있다는 점에서 매우 해로울 수 있다.

➡ _____

6 그럼에도 불구하고, 역사를 통틀어 다양한 가짜 뉴스 보도들이 존재해 왔다.

➡ _____

7 왜 어떤 사람들은 그러한 거짓 정보를 써 왔던 것일까?

➡ _____

8 그 뒤에 숨겨진 동기를 생각하면서 몇 가지 뉴스 기사를 살펴보자.

➡ _____

9 끔찍한 참사

➡ _____

10 어젯밤, 화가 난 코뿔소 떼가 동물원 우리의 벽을 부수고 도망쳤다.

➡ _____

11 그들은 또한 다른 야생 동물 우리의 벽도 부수었다.

➡ _____

12 이 동물들은 거리를 뛰어다니며 수백 명의 사람들에게 부상을 입혔다.

➡ _____

13 그중 열두 마리의 동물들이 아직 잡히지 않았다.

➡ _____

14 시민들은 추후 안내가 있을 때까지 집 안에 머물러야 한다.

➡ _____

15 위에 기술된 어떤 행동이나 사건도 일어나지 않았다.

➡ _____

16 그 당시 이 기사를 주의 깊게 읽었던 사람들은 크게 웃었다.

➡ _____

17 그것을 끝까지 읽지 않은 사람들은 정말로 걱정하였다.

➡ _____

18 그 기사가 거짓이라는 것을 알지 못했기 때문에 많은 사람이 겁에 질려 어쩔 줄 몰랐다.

➡ _____

19 어떤 사람들은 도시를 빠져나가려고 했고 다른 사람들은 그 동물들을 사냥하기 위해 총을 들고 공원으로 나갔다.

➡ _____

20 그렇다면 왜 헤럴드 사는 이러한 뉴스를 만들어 냈을까?

➡ _____

21 나중에 그들은 동물원의 안전하지 않은 상태에 대해 독자들의 주의를 끌기 위해 그 기사를 지어냈다고 고백했다.

➡ _____

_____

22 슬라브인이 언쟁 중에 친구에게 총을 쏘다

➡ _____

23 목요일 저녁 채굴 야영지 근처에서, 컬럼비아 광산 소속의 슬라브인 노동자 Mejk Swenekafew가 John Pecitello에 의해 총상을 입어 심각하게 다쳤다.

➡ _____

_____

24 그 두 사람은 회의 중에 언쟁을 벌였다.

➡ _____

25 언쟁이 싸움으로 번졌고, Pecitello가 Swenekafew의 가슴과 다리에 두 번 총을 쏘았다.

➡ _____

26 현재 그는 위독한 상태로 입원 중이다.

➡ _____

27 Pecitello는 총격 이후 도주했다.

➡ _____

28 경찰이 지금 그를 찾고 있으며, 그가 극히 위험하다고 시민들에게 경고하고 있다.

➡ _____

29 이 기사에 뭔가 이상한 점이 있는가?

➡ _____

30 그 슬라브인의 이름을 거꾸로 읽어 보아라. 그것의 철자는 "우리는 뉴스를 조작한다."가 된다.

➡ _____

31 누가 이것을 썼고 왜 그랬을까?

➡ _____

32 데일리 텔레그램 사는 그들의 경쟁자인 데일리 뉴스 사가 그들의 기사를 훔치는지를 증명하기 위해서 이 거짓 기사를 발행했다.

➡ _____

_____

33 데일리 뉴스 사는 그 다음 날 'Swenekafew'에 대한 동일한 기사를 발행했고 그래서 훔친 것이 발각되었다.

➡ _____

34 데일리 뉴스 사의 사람들은 그들의 행동을 인정해야만 했고 대중들로부터 혹독한 비난을 받았다.

➡ _____

34 이 두 기사는 특별한 경우였지만, 매일 발행되는 '가짜' 뉴스 기사는 많이 있다.

➡ _____

36 독자로서, 우리는 비판적으로 읽고 그 뉴스가 진짜인지 가짜인지 판단할 필요가 있다.

➡ _____

37 가짜 뉴스 판별 방법!

➡ _____

38 출처를 고려하라

➡ _____

39 그것은 믿을 만한 출처에서 온 것인가?

➡ _____

40 우리는 그 필자를 신뢰할 수 있는가?

➡ _____

41 날짜를 확인하라

➡ _____

42 그것은 새로운 이야기인가 혹은 오래된 이야기인가?

➡ _____

43 그것은 현재의 사건들과 관련된 것인가?

➡ _____

44 기사 제목 그 이상을 읽어라

➡ _____

45 기사 제목이 기사 내용과 일치하는가?

➡ _____

46 뒷받침하는 자료를 찾아라

➡ _____

47 다른 관련된 이야기도 비슷한 내용을 제공하는가?

➡ _____

[01~04] 다음 글을 읽고 물음에 답하시오.

Every day we watch, hear, or read interesting news. ___ⓐ___, have you ever seriously considered whether an article is really true? (①) Everyone likes an interesting news story but what if it is completely made up? (②)

ⓑ<u>Fake news can be very harmful in that they can make people less informed or even misled.</u> (③) Why have some people written such false information? (④) Let's look into some articles thinking about the hidden motives behind them. (⑤)

01 위 글의 빈칸 ⓐ에 들어갈 알맞은 말을 고르시오.

① In addition
② In other words
③ Therefore
④ However
⑤ For example

02 위 글의 흐름으로 보아, 주어진 문장이 들어가기에 가장 적절한 곳은?

Nevertheless, there have been various fake news reports throughout history.

①　　②　　③　　④　　⑤

03 According to the passage, which is NOT true?

① Day after day we watch, hear, or read interesting news.
② There is no one that doesn't like an interesting news story.
③ Fake news can be very damaging.
④ People may be well-informed because of fake news.
⑤ Fake news can mislead people.

서답형

04 위 글의 밑줄 친 ⓑ에서 어법상 틀린 부분을 찾아 고치시오.

➡ _____

[05~07] 다음 글을 읽고 물음에 답하시오.

AWFUL DISASTER

Last night, an angry group of rhinoceroses broke down the walls of the cage at the zoo and escaped. They also broke down the walls of the other wild animals' cages. These animals ran down the streets and injured hundreds of people. Twelve of the animals are still ___ⓐ___ the loose. Citizens should stay indoors ___ⓑ___ further notice.

*Not ⓒ<u>a single act or incident described above</u> has ⓓ<u>taken place</u>.

05 위 글의 빈칸 ⓐ와 ⓑ에 들어갈 전치사가 바르게 짝지어진 것은?

　　ⓐ　ⓑ　　　　　　ⓐ　ⓑ
① at – by　　　② on – until
③ in – until　　④ at – for
⑤ on – with

06 다음 중 위 글의 밑줄 친 ⓒ에 해당하지 않는 것을 고르시오.

① 어젯밤, 화가 난 코뿔소 떼가 동물원 우리의 벽을 부수고 도망쳤다.
② 코뿔소 떼가 다른 야생 동물 우리의 벽도 부수었다.
③ 이 동물들이 거리를 뛰어다녔다.
④ 수백 명의 사람들이 부상을 입었다.
⑤ 그 중 열두 마리의 동물들이 잡혔다.

⭐07 위 글의 밑줄 친 ⓓtaken place와 바꿔 쓸 수 있는 말을 모두 고르시오.

① been held   ② happened

③ occurred   ④ been hosted

⑤ arisen

[08~10] 다음 글을 읽고 물음에 답하시오.

At that time, those who read the article carefully laughed out loud. Those who didn't read it to the end got really worried. ⓐNot knowing the news was false, many people panicked. Some tried to escape the city while others went into the parks with guns to hunt the animals.

So why did *The Herald* ⓑmake up such news? Later, they confessed that they made it up so that they could draw the readers' attention to the unsafe conditions at the zoo.

08 아래 〈보기〉에서 위 글의 밑줄 친 ⓐ와 분사구문의 용법이 다른 것의 개수를 고르시오.

┌─ 보기 ─┐
① Not having much money, he acted like a rich man.
② Having nothing to do, I went to bed earlier than usual.
③ Finding my son in the mall, please let me know.
④ Not failing the test, she still looked miserable.
⑤ Being sick, she decided not to go to school.
└────────┘

① 1개   ② 2개   ③ 3개   ④ 4개   ⑤ 5개

09 위 글의 밑줄 친 ⓑmake up과 같은 의미로 쓰인 것을 고르시오.

① He likes to make up fun songs.
② Can I leave early this afternoon and make up the time tomorrow?
③ They fight and make up quite often.
④ Eleven players make up a team.
⑤ I make up my face to look like a clown.

⭐10 위 글의 주제로 알맞은 것을 고르시오.

① the laughter of the readers who read the article carefully
② the worry of the readers who didn't read the article to the end
③ the reason why many people panicked
④ the false news to draw the readers' attention
⑤ the unsafe conditions at the zoo

[11~13] 다음 글을 읽고 물음에 답하시오.

SLAV SHOOTS A FRIEND IN ARGUMENT
Mejk Swenekafew, a Slav worker at the Columbia Coal Mine, was (A)[shot / shut] and seriously wounded by John Pecitello near the mining camp Thursday evening.

The two men had an argument during a meeting. The argument led to a fight, and Pecitello shot Swenekafew twice, in the chest and leg. ⓐHe is now at the hospital in critical condition. Pecitello ran away after the shooting. The police (B)[is / are] searching for him now and (C)[is / are] warning citizens that he is extremely dangerous.

서답형

11 위 글의 괄호 (A)~(C)에서 문맥이나 어법상 알맞은 낱말을 골라 쓰시오.

➡ (A)_____ (B)_____ (C)_____

서답형

12 위 글의 밑줄 친 @He가 가리키는 것을 본문에서 찾아 쓰시오.

➡ _____

중요

13 위 글을 읽고 Mejk Swenekafew에 대해 알 수 <u>없는</u> 것을 고르시오.

① Where did he work?

② Why did he have an argument with John Pecitello?

③ When was he shot?

④ How many times was he shot?

⑤ Where is he now?

[14~16] 다음 글을 읽고 물음에 답하시오.

Every day we watch, hear, or read interesting news. However, @have you ever seriously considered whether an article is really true? Everyone likes an interesting news story but what if it is completely made up?

Fake news can be very harmful (A)[in that / in which] it can make people less informed or even (B)[misleading / misled]. Nevertheless, there have been various fake news reports throughout history. Why have some people written (C)[so / such] false information? Let's look into some articles thinking about the hidden motives behind them.

서답형

14 위 글의 괄호 (A)~(C)에서 어법상 알맞은 낱말을 골라 쓰시오.

➡ (A)_____ (B)_____ (C)_____

15 위 글의 밑줄 친 문장 @의 현재완료 <u>have considered</u>와 용법이 같은 것을 <u>모두</u> 고르시오.

① How many times <u>have</u> you <u>done</u> it?

② He has gone to New York.

③ He <u>has been</u> ill for two weeks.

④ She <u>has seen</u> my brother before.

⑤ I <u>have</u> just <u>finished</u> my homework.

중요

16 Which question CANNOT be answered after reading the passage?

① How many interesting news do we watch, hear, or read each day?

② What kind of news story does everyone like?

③ Can fake news make people less informed?

④ Can fake news mislead people?

⑤ Have there been various fake news reports throughout history?

[17~19] 다음 글을 읽고 물음에 답하시오.

The two articles were special cases, but there are many "fake" news articles ___@___ every day. As readers, we need to read critically and judge whether the news is real or fake.

How to spot fake news!

Consider the Source

Is it from a reliable source?

Can we trust the writer?

Check the Date

Is it a new or an old story?

Is it related to ⓑ<u>current</u> events?

Read Beyond the Headlines

Does the headline match the content?

Find Supporting Sources

Do other related stories provide similar content?

서답형

17 위 글의 빈칸 ⓐ에 publish를 알맞은 형태로 쓰시오.

➡ _____

18 위 글의 밑줄 친 ⓑcurrent와 같은 의미로 쓰인 것을 고르시오.

① These words are no longer current.
② He swam to the shore against a strong current.
③ The direct current flows in one direction.
④ Do you know the budget for the current year?
⑤ He doesn't want to swim against the current.

19 위 글을 읽고 가짜 뉴스 판별 방법에 해당하지 않는 것을 고르시오.

① to consider the source
② to guess the content by the headlines
③ to check the date
④ to read beyond the headlines
⑤ to find supporting sources

[20~23] 다음 글을 읽고 물음에 답하시오.

Is there anything strange about the article? ⓐ Read the Slav's name forward; it spells, "we-fake-news." Who wrote this and why?

The Daily Telegram published this fake article so that they could prove ⓑif *The Daily News*, their competitor, was stealing their articles. *The Daily News* published the same article about "Swenekafew" the next day and thus got caught stealing. The people at *The Daily News* had to admit their act and were harshly criticized by the public.

서답형

20 위 글의 밑줄 친 ⓐ에서 흐름상 어색한 부분을 찾아 고치시오.

➡ _____

21 위 글의 밑줄 친 ⓑif와 문법적 쓰임이 같은 것을 모두 고르시오.

① I can come at once if necessary.
② You can stay for the weekend if you like.
③ Do you know if he's married?
④ She will forgive you if you apologize to her.
⑤ I wonder if I should wear a coat.

22 According to the passage, which is NOT true?

① *The Daily Telegram* published this fake article.
② *The Daily News* was the competitor of *The Daily Telegram*.
③ *The Daily Telegram* published the same article about "Swenekafew" the next day.
④ *The Daily News* got caught stealing.
⑤ *The Daily News* were harshly criticized by the public.

서답형

23 다음 주어진 영영풀이에 해당하는 단어를 본문에서 찾아 쓰시오.

not genuine or real

➡ _____

[24~26] 다음 글을 읽고 물음에 답하시오.

Every day we watch, hear, or read interesting news. However, have you ever seriously considered whether an article is really true? Everyone likes an interesting news story but what if it is completely made up?

Fake news can be very harmful in that it can make people less informed or even misled. ⓐNevertheless, there have been various fake news reports throughout history. Why have some people written such false information? Let's look into some articles thinking about the hidden motives behind ⓑthem.

24 위 글의 밑줄 친 ⓐNevertheless와 바꿔 쓸 수 있는 말을 모두 고르시오.

① Despite
② Therefore
③ Still
④ Otherwise
⑤ Nonetheless

25 위 글의 밑줄 친 ⓑthem이 가리키는 것을 본문에서 찾아 쓰시오.

➡ _____

26 위 글의 제목으로 알맞은 것을 고르시오.

① Do You Want to Spot Fake News?
② Have You Considered If the News Is True?
③ Who Doesn't Like an Interesting News Story?
④ Harmful but Continuous Fake News Reports
⑤ Let's Write Faithful News Reports from Now on.

[27~29] 다음 글을 읽고 물음에 답하시오.

At that time, those who read the article carefully laughed out loud. (A)그것을 끝까지 읽지 않은 사람들은 정말로 걱정하였다. Not knowing the news was false, many people panicked. ⓐ tried to escape the city while ⓑ went into the parks with guns to hunt the animals.

So why did The Herald make up such news? (B)Later, they confessed that they made up it so that they could draw the readers' attention to the unsafe conditions at the zoo.

27 위 글의 빈칸 ⓐ와 ⓑ에 들어갈 알맞은 말을 고르시오.

① One – the other
② Some – the others
③ Another – the other
④ The first – the second
⑤ Some – others

28 위 글의 밑줄 친 (A)의 우리말에 맞게 주어진 어휘를 알맞게 배열하시오.

worried / end / who / to / didn't / got / it / those / really / the / read

➡ _____

29 위 글의 밑줄 친 (B)에서 어법상 틀린 부분을 찾아 고치시오.

➡ _____

Reading **151**

[01~03] 다음 글을 읽고 물음에 답하시오.

Every day we watch, hear, or read interesting news. However, have you ever seriously considered whether an article is really true? Everyone likes an interesting news story but what (A)[if / whether] it is completely made up?

Fake news can be very (B)[harmful / harmless] in that it can make people less (C)[informing / informed] or even misled. Nevertheless, there have been various fake news reports throughout history. ⓐ왜 어떤 사람들은 그러한 거짓 정보를 써 왔던 것일까? Let's look into some articles ⓑthinking about the hidden motives behind them.

01 위 글의 괄호 (A)~(C)에서 문맥이나 어법상 알맞은 낱말을 골라 쓰시오.

➡ (A) _____ (B) _____ (C) _____

02 위 글의 밑줄 친 ⓐ의 우리말에 맞게 주어진 어휘를 알맞게 배열하시오.

people / false / written / some / information / why / such / have / ?

➡ _____

_____

03 위 글의 밑줄 친 ⓑ를 부사절로 고치시오.

➡ _____

_____

[04~06] 다음 글을 읽고 물음에 답하시오.

AWFUL DISASTER
Last night, an angry group of rhinoceroses broke down the walls of the cage at the zoo and escaped. They also broke down the walls of the other wild animals' cages. These animals ran down the streets and injured hundreds of people. Twelve of the animals are still ⓐ_____ _____ _____. Citizens should stay indoors until further notice.
*ⓑNot a single act or incident described above has been taken place.

04 주어진 영영풀이를 참고하여 빈칸 ⓐ에 철자 o로 시작하는 어구를 쓰시오.

having escaped; not under control

➡ _____

05 위 글의 밑줄 친 ⓑ에서 어법상 틀린 부분을 찾아 고치시오.

➡ _____

06 Actually how many people were injured by the escaped animals from the zoo last night? Fill in the blanks (A) and (B) with suitable words.

(A)_____ one was injured by the escaped animals from the zoo because the animals didn't (B)_____ from the zoo last night in reality.

[07~08] 다음 글을 읽고 물음에 답하시오.

At that time, those who read the article carefully laughed out loud. Those who didn't read it to the end got really worried. Not knowing the news was false, many people panicked. Some tried to escape the city while ⓐothers went into the parks with guns to hunt the animals.

So why did *The Herald* make up such news? Later, they confessed that they made ⓑit up so that they could draw the readers' attention to the unsafe conditions at the zoo.

07 위 글의 밑줄 친 ⓐ를 다음과 같이 바꿔 쓸 때 빈칸에 들어갈 알맞은 말을 쓰시오.

➡ others went into the parks with guns _____ they _____ hunt the animals

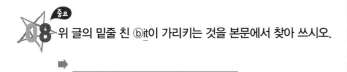

08 위 글의 밑줄 친 ⓑit이 가리키는 것을 본문에서 찾아 쓰시오.

➡ _____

[09~10] 다음 글을 읽고 물음에 답하시오.

SLAV SHOOTS A FRIEND IN ARGUMENT
Mejk Swenekafew, a Slav worker at the Columbia Coal Mine, was shot and seriously wounded ①by John Pecitello ②near from the mining camp Thursday evening.

The two men had an argument during a meeting. The argument led to a fight, and Pecitello shot Swenekafew twice, ③in the chest and leg. He is now at the hospital ④in critical condition. Pecitello ran away after the shooting. The police are searching ⑤for him now and are warning citizens that he is extremely dangerous.

09 위 글의 밑줄 친 ①~⑤에서 어법상 어색한 것을 찾아 알맞게 고치시오.

➡ _____

10 본문의 내용과 일치하도록 다음 빈칸 (A)와 (B)에 알맞은 단어를 쓰시오.

Mejk Swenekafew (A)_____ _____ _____ with John Pecitello during a meeting and Pecitello shot him. Swenekafew is now at the hospital and his condition is (B)_____.

[11~12] 다음 글을 읽고 물음에 답하시오.

Is there anything strange about the article? Read the Slav's name backwards; it spells, "we-fake-news." Who wrote this and why?
The Daily Telegram published this fake article so that they could prove ⓐif *The Daily News*, their competitor, was stealing their articles. *The Daily News* published the same article about "Swenekafew" the next day and thus got caught stealing. The people at *The Daily News* had to admit ⓑtheir act and were harshly criticized by the public.

11 위 글의 밑줄 친 ⓐif와 바꿔 쓸 수 있는 말을 쓰시오.

➡ _____

12 위 글의 밑줄 친 ⓑtheir act가 가리키는 것을 본문에서 찾아 쓰시오.

➡ _____
_____

Wrap Up 3

A: Wow! The news title says "Longer Vacation for Students." Hey, we're going to have a longer vacation!

B: Wait! We should check first if it is true.
　　　　　　　　　　　　　　　　= whether

A: Why do you say so?

B: Some news uses a shocking title but its content may tell a different story.
　　　　　　　　단수 동사　　　　　　　　　　　　　추측의 조동사

A: Oh, I see. I should read beyond the news title.

구문해설　• shocking: 충격적인 • content: 내용

해석

A: 와! 뉴스 제목이 "학생들을 위한 더 긴 방학"이야. 이봐, 우리 더 긴 방학을 갖나봐!
B: 기다려! 우리는 먼저 이게 사실인지를 확인해야 해.
A: 왜 그렇게 생각해?
B: 어떤 뉴스는 충격적인 제목을 사용하지만 그 내용은 다른 이야기를 할지도 몰라.
A: 오, 알았다. 뉴스 제목 너머를 읽어야 하는구나.

Read & Think After You Read B

Reporter: Why did *The Herald* write the "Awful Disaster" story, Mr. Right?

Mr. Right: They just wanted to draw the readers' attention to the unsafe
　　　　　　　　　　　　　　draw one's attention to ~: ~에 …의 주의를 끌다
　　　　　conditions at the zoo.

Reporter: Actually, readers were very upset to find that it was false. How
　　　　　= In fact/As a matter of fact: 사실.　　　　　　to부정사의 부사적 용법(원인)
　　　　　about "Slav Shoots a Friend in Argument?" What was the motive?
　　　　　= What about ~?: ~은 어떤가?

Mr. Right: *The Daily Telegram* wanted to prove that *The Daily News* was
　　　　　　　　　　　　　　　　　　명사절(목적어)을 이끄는 접속사(생략 가능)
　　　　　stealing their articles.
　　　　　= *The Daily Telegram's*

구문해설　• awful: 끔찍한 • disaster: 참사, 재난 • unsafe: 안전하지 않은 • upset: 속상한, 마음이 상한
　　　　　• motive: 동기 • article: 기사

기자: 왜 헤럴드 사는 〈끔찍한 참사〉 이야기를 썼을까요, Right 씨?
Mr. Right: 그들은 단지 동물원의 안전하지 않은 상태에 대해 독자들의 주의를 끌고 싶었답니다.
기자: 사실, 독자들은 그것이 거짓이라는 것을 알고 매우 화가 났어요. 〈슬라브인이 언쟁 중에 친구에게 총을 쏘다〉는 어떤가요? 동기가 무엇이었나요?
Mr. Right: 데일리 텔레그램 사는 데일리 뉴스 사가 그들의 기사를 훔치고 있다는 것을 증명하기를 원했어요.

Read & Think After You Read C

A: Among the four tips, which do you think is the most important, and why?
간접의문문(= Do you think? + Which is the most important?)이며 think 동사가 있어서 의문사 which가 문두로 이동 뒤에 do you think it is
　　　　　　　　　　　　　　　　　　　　　　　　　　　　the most important 생략

B: I think finding supporting sources is the most important because I can
　　　　동명사 주어　현재분사로 sources 수식　동명사 주어는 단수 취급　　간접의문문으로 명사절을 이끄는 접속사(~인지 아닌지)

　check if the information is correct.

구문해설　• tip: 조언 • support: (진술 따위를) 입증하다, 뒷받침하다 • source: 자료

A: 네 가지 조언 중에서 너는 어떤 것이 가장 중요하다고 생각하며, 그 이유는 무엇이니?
B: 나는 뒷받침하는 자료들을 찾는 것이 가장 중요하다고 생각하는데, 그 정보가 올바른지 확인할 수 있기 때문이야.

영역별 핵심문제

Words & Expressions

01 다음 짝지어진 단어의 관계가 같도록 빈칸에 알맞은 말을 쓰시오.

> lead : mislead = understand : _____

02 다음 중 밑줄 친 부분의 뜻풀이가 바르지 <u>않은</u> 것은?

① People <u>panicked</u> and screamed when the hotel caught on fire. (겁에 질렸다)
② <u>Nevertheless</u>, many people came to the festival. (더욱이, 게다가)
③ These exercises help keep your <u>muscles</u> strong. (근육)
④ The <u>motive</u> for the fight between them was unknown. (동기)
⑤ News often <u>misleads</u> us with wrong information. (잘못 이끌다)

03 다음 문장의 빈칸에 들어갈 말을 〈보기〉에서 골라 쓰시오.

> ┤ 보기 ├
> riddle / seriously / reliable / source / shoot

(1) We are looking for someone who is honest and _____.
(2) Solve this _____, or you can't open the door.
(3) He can't talk now because he is _____ hurt.
(4) They will _____ arrows at bottles.
(5) He couldn't find the _____ of the story.

04 다음 영영풀이가 가리키는 것을 고르시오.

> to suddenly feel so worried that you cannot be reasonable

① panic   ② reliable
③ current   ④ critical
⑤ private

05 다음 주어진 문장의 밑줄 친 current와 <u>다른</u> 의미로 쓰인 것은?

> Did you have any idea about the <u>current</u> issue?

① I'll interview the <u>current</u> Olympic title-holder soon.
② Corona 19 seems so serious that the <u>current</u> situation will continue.
③ We got together here to find the solution to the <u>current</u> crisis.
④ You can check the <u>current</u> price by visiting our website.
⑤ Mike swam to the shore against a strong <u>current</u>.

06 다음 우리말에 맞게 빈칸에 알맞은 말을 쓰시오.

(1) 소방관들은 집으로 들어가기 위해 문을 부숴야 했다.
➡ The firefighters had to _____ _____ the door to get into the house.
(2) 계획에 따르면, 그들은 목요일까지 그것을 끝내야 한다.
➡ _____ _____ the plan, they should finish it by Thursday.
(3) 그녀는 잠잘 때 보는 무서운 동화를 만들어 냈다.
➡ She _____ _____ a scary bedtime story.

07 다음 우리말을 주어진 단어를 이용하여 영작하시오.

(1) 그녀는 지난밤에 있었던 일을 기술했다. (happened) (6 words)

➡ _____

(2) 이것은 최악의 자연 재난 중의 하나이다. (worst) (8 words)

➡ _____

(3) 사자가 한 시간 전에 동물원에서 탈출했다. (ago, a lion) (9 words)

➡ _____

Conversation

08 다음 대화가 자연스럽게 이어지도록 순서대로 배열하시오.

Chris: Jane, do you usually get news online or from the newspaper?
Jane: Well, I usually watch TV news.
(A) I see your point.
(B) Why do you say so?
(C) TV news? Is there any special reason?
(D) I think TV is the most useful way to get news.
(E) I have to spend too much time reading all the news online or in the newspaper. So, I just watch the main news on TV.

➡ _____

[09~10] 다음 대화를 읽고 물음에 답하시오.

David: Hey, Sandy. Do you think I should buy this drink? It is said that it can help me lose weight.
Sandy: Let me read the label more closely. Hmm, it looks a bit strange to me, David.
David: Why do you say so?
Sandy: There isn't enough information about what's in the drink.

David: Oh, you're right.
Sandy: Also, it doesn't tell you how much you have to drink to lose weight.

09 위 대화에서 나타난 Sandy의 성격으로 적절한 것은?

① careful   ② diligent
③ creative   ④ adventurous
⑤ hardworking

10 위 대화의 내용과 일치하지 않는 것은?

① David is wondering if he should buy the drink.
② It is said that the drink can be helpful to lose weight.
③ Sandy finds out something strange about the drink.
④ There isn't enough information about how much David should drink to lose weight.
⑤ There's some information about what the drink is made of.

[11~12] 다음 대화를 읽고 물음에 답하시오.

Susan: What are you reading, John?
John: I'm reading a book of riddles.
Susan: Riddles? Aren't they for children?
John: Actually, no. Books of riddles are really useful for adults.
Susan: Really? Why do you say so?
John: They help us think more creatively. We need to think outside the box to find the answers.

11 Why does John think books of riddles are useful for adults?

➡ _____

12 What do we need to do to find the answers to riddles?

➡ _____

[13~14] 다음 대화를 읽고 물음에 답하시오.

> W: I think I caught a cold because I didn't dress warmly yesterday.
> M: Well, I've read an article saying that you don't catch a cold because your body temperature is low.
> W: Really? _____
> M: The article said that people catch colds because of viruses.

13 위 대화의 빈칸에 들어갈 말로 나머지와 의도가 <u>다른</u> 것은?

① Can you tell me more about it?
② Could you give me more information?
③ Can you explain more in detail?
④ Could you be more specific?
⑤ Can you give me your hand?

14 위 대화의 내용과 일치하지 <u>않는</u> 것은?

① The woman was not feeling well.
② The man read the article related to catching a cold.
③ The woman didn't dress warmly yesterday.
④ The article explained that people catch colds due to viruses.
⑤ The woman caught a cold because her body temperature was low.

Grammar

15 다음 두 문장을 괄호 안의 단어를 이용하여 한 문장으로 바꾸시오.

(1) • Linda was stupid.
    • She made a big mistake. (enough)
    ➡ _____

(2) • Bill is very poor.
    • So he can't buy the house. (too)
    ➡ _____

16 다음 밑줄 친 부분과 바꿔 쓸 수 있는 것은?

> Slow down <u>so that</u> children can cross the street safely.

① in order that   ② in order to
③ so as to   ④ such that
⑤ so which

17 다음 문장 중에서 어법상 어색한 문장을 고르시오.

① Not knowing the language, we had to use sign language.
② Working in a hospital, John is always busy.
③ Things getting more difficult, we should draw on our wisdom.
④ Arriving at the store, I found it closed.
⑤ Not handing out the report, she is responsible for the result.

18 다음 문장을 바꿔 썼을 때 빈칸에 알맞은 말을 쓰시오.

(1) The two articles having been special cases, there are many "fake" news articles published every day.
    ➡ _____,
    there are many "fake" news articles published every day.

(2) In the morning Harold greeted her smiling brightly.
    ➡ In the morning Harold greeted her _____.

(3) Being tired from the work, I fell asleep.
    ➡ _____,
    I fell asleep.

19 다음 문장의 빈칸에 공통으로 알맞은 것은?

> • He sat smiling, _____ his legs crossed.
> • Don't speak _____ your mouth full.

① in   ② with
③ of   ④ from
⑤ along

Reading

[20~23] 다음 글을 읽고 물음에 답하시오.

①Every day we watch, hear, or read interesting news. However, have you ever seriously considered ②whether an article is really true? Everyone likes an interesting news story but ③what if it is completely made up?

Fake news can be very harmful ④in that it can make people less informed or even misled. _____ⓐ_____, there have been various fake news reports throughout history. Why have some people written such false information? Let's look __ⓑ__ some articles thinking about the hidden ⑤motives behind them.

20 위 글의 빈칸 ⓐ에 알맞은 것을 고르시오.

① Furthermore   ② Nevertheless
③ Likewise   ④ That is
⑤ Thus

21 다음 중 위 글의 밑줄 친 ①~⑤와 바꿔 쓸 수 있는 말로 옳지 않은 것을 고르시오.

① Each day
② if
③ what would happen if
④ in the sense that
⑤ themes

22 위 글의 빈칸 ⓑ에 알맞은 것을 고르시오.

① for   ② at
③ on   ④ with
⑤ into

23 위 글의 뒤에 올 내용으로 가장 알맞은 것을 고르시오.

① the way we can spot fake news
② various kinds of interesting news we watch, hear, or read every day
③ some fake news articles through which we can think about the hidden motives behind them
④ people who are less informed or even misled by fake news
⑤ the harmful effects of fake news

[24~26] 다음 글을 읽고 물음에 답하시오.

AWFUL DISASTER
 Last night, an angry group of rhinoceroses ⓐ broke down the walls of the cage at the zoo and escaped. They also broke down the walls of (A)[another / the other] wild animals' cages. These animals ran down the streets and injured hundreds of people. ⓑ그중 열두 마리의 동물들이 아직 잡히지 않았다. Citizens should stay indoors until (B)[farther / further] notice.
*Not a single act or incident (C)[describing / described] above has taken place.

24 위 글의 밑줄 친 ⓐbroke down과 같은 의미로 쓰인 것을 고르시오.

① The peace talks between them broke down.
② Our car broke down on the freeway.
③ His health broke down under the pressure of work.
④ In the stomach, acids broke down food into bits.
⑤ The telephone system broke down.

25 위 글의 괄호 (A)~(C)에서 문맥이나 어법상 알맞은 낱말을 골라 쓰시오.

➡ (A)_____ (B)_____ (C)_____

26 위 글의 밑줄 친 ⓑ의 우리말에 맞게 주어진 어휘를 이용하여 9 단어로 영작하시오.

loose, of

➡ _____

[27~28] 다음 글을 읽고 물음에 답하시오.

SLAV SHOOTS A FRIEND IN ARGUMENT

Mejk Swenekafew, a Slav worker at the Columbia Coal Mine, was shot and seriously wounded by John Pecitello near the mining camp Thursday evening. (①)
The two men had an argument during a meeting. (②) He is now at the hospital in critical condition. (③) Pecitello ran away after the shooting. (④) The police are searching for him now and are warning citizens that ⓐhe is extremely dangerous. (⑤)

27 위 글의 밑줄 친 ⓐhe가 가리키는 것을 본문에서 찾아 쓰시오.

➡ _____

28 위 글의 흐름으로 보아, 주어진 문장이 들어가기에 가장 적절한 곳은?

> The argument led to a fight, and Pecitello shot Swenekafew twice, in the chest and leg.

① ② ③ ④ ⑤

[29~30] 다음 글을 읽고 물음에 답하시오.

Reporter: Why did *The Herald* write ⓐthe "Awful Disaster" story, Mr. Right?
Mr. Right: They just wanted to draw the readers' attention to the unsafe conditions at the zoo.
Reporter: Actually, readers were very upset to find that it was false. How about "ⓑSlav Shoots a Friend in Argument?" What was the motive?
Mr. Right: *The Daily Telegram* wanted to prove that *The Daily News* was stealing their articles.

29 위 글의 종류로 알맞은 것을 고르시오.

① article ② essay
③ review ④ interview
⑤ summary

30 위 글을 읽고 The Herald가 가짜 기사인 ⓐthe "Awful Disaster" story를 지어낸 동기와, The Daily Telegram이 가짜 기사인 ⓑSlav Shoots a Friend in Argument를 지어낸 동기를 각각 본문에서 찾아, to부정사로 시작하여 쓰시오.

➡ ⓐ _____
_____
ⓑ _____
_____

출제율 90%

01 다음 영영풀이가 가리키는 것을 고르시오.

> to form words with the letters in the correct order

① shoot   ② spot
③ support   ④ strengthen
⑤ spell

[02~03] 다음 대화를 읽고 물음에 답하시오.

Suji: I usually drink a glass of warm milk before I go to bed, but it doesn't help me fall asleep.

Minsu: I saw a show on TV, and a doctor said that a glass of warm milk doesn't actually help you fall asleep.

Suji: Oh, it doesn't? (A)Can you tell me more about it? (information)

Minsu: Milk has special chemicals that make people sleepy. But the amount in a glass is too small to have any effect.

출제율 90%

02 위 대화의 밑줄 친 (A)와 의도가 같도록 주어진 어휘를 사용하여 다시 쓰시오.

➡ _____

출제율 100%

03 위 대화를 읽고 대답할 수 없는 것은?

① What's the matter with Suji?
② What does Suji do before going to bed?
③ What is the effect of special chemicals in milk?
④ Why are the chemicals in a glass of warm milk not helpful for falling asleep?
⑤ How many glasses of milk should Suji drink to sleep better?

[04~05] 다음 대화를 읽고 물음에 답하시오.

Jane: I read an article saying that Napoleon was actually fairly tall. (A)

Tom: Oh, really? (B)

Jane: According to the article, a French doctor wrote down Napoleon's height according to the French measuring system, not the English one. (C)

Tom: What was the difference? (D)

Jane: At that time, an inch in France was longer than an inch in England. So, Napoleon was actually about 168 cm tall, which was not that short in those times. (E)

출제율 90%

04 위 대화의 (A)~(E) 중 주어진 문장이 들어가기에 적절한 곳은?

> Can you tell me more about it?

① (A)   ② (B)   ③ (C)   ④ (D)   ⑤ (E)

출제율 100%

05 위 대화를 읽고 대답할 수 없는 것은?

① What is the article about?
② Who wrote down Napoleon's height?
③ In what way was Napoleon's height written down?
④ Why was an inch in France different from an inch in England?
⑤ What was the difference between French and English measuring systems?

[06~07] 다음 대화를 읽고 물음에 답하시오.

Susan: What are you reading, John?

John: I'm reading a book of riddles.

Susan: Riddles? Aren't they for children?

John: Actually, no. Books of riddles are really useful for adults.

Susan: Really? Why do you say so?

John: They help us think more creatively. We need to think outside the box to find the answers.

06 위 대화에서 다음 영영풀이가 가리키는 말을 찾아 쓰시오.

> a question that is difficult to understand, and that has a surprising answer, that you ask somebody as a game

➡ _____

07 위 대화의 내용과 일치하지 <u>않는</u> 것은?

① John은 수수께끼 책을 읽고 있다.

② 수수께끼 책은 어른들에게 유용하다.

③ 수수께끼 책은 좀 더 창의적으로 생각하도록 돕는다.

④ 수수께끼 답을 찾기 위해 고정관념에서 벗어날 필요가 있다.

⑤ 수수께끼 답을 찾기 위해 상자를 밖으로 꺼내야 한다.

[08~09] 다음 대화를 읽고 물음에 답하시오.

W: I read an interesting article about the Black Sea. Do you know ⓐwhere is it?

M: Yes. It's ⓑbetween Eastern Europe and Western Asia, right?

W: Right. ⓒWhat color do you think it is?

M: Well, black, I guess.

W: No, it isn't. It's blue.

M: Really? Then why is it ⓓcalled the Black Sea? Can you tell me more about it?

W: People call it the Black Sea ⓔbecause it is very dangerous.

08 위 대화의 밑줄 친 ⓐ~ⓔ 중 어법상 틀린 것을 찾아 바르게 고치시오.

➡ _____

09 위 대화의 내용과 일치하지 <u>않는</u> 것은?

① 여자는 흑해에 관한 흥미로운 기사를 읽었다.

② 흑해는 동유럽과 서아시아 사이에 있다.

③ 흑해는 검은색이 아니라 파란색이다.

④ 사람들이 흑해라고 부르는 이유는 그곳이 매우 위험하기 때문이다.

⑤ 남자는 사람들이 흑해하고 부르는 이유에 대해 알고 있었다.

10 다음 중 어법상 <u>어색한</u> 문장을 고르시오.

① He didn't want to be late, so that he took a taxi.

② Put it down gently so that it doesn't break.

③ She was so tired to think straight.

④ Is she healthy enough to travel?

⑤ I studied Italian so that I would be able to read Dante in the original.

11 다음 분사구문을 접속사를 이용한 문장으로 바꿔 쓰시오.

(1) Driving my car, I couldn't reply to your text message.

➡ _____

_____

(2) Walking down the street, I met my friend.

➡ _____

_____

(3) There being no work to do, he remained at his office until late.

➡ _____

_____

12 다음 그림을 보고 주어진 어휘를 이용하여 빈칸을 알맞게 채우시오.

Mary was sitting on the sofa, _____

_____. (play, the guitar)

13 다음 중 의미가 다른 문장을 고르시오.

① Don't waste water so that we can prevent water shortages.

② Don't waste water in order that we can prevent water shortages.

③ Don't waste water so as to prevent water shortages.

④ Don't waste water in order can prevent water shortages.

⑤ Don't waste water to prevent water shortages.

[14~16] 다음 글을 읽고 물음에 답하시오.

Every day we watch, hear, or read interesting news. However, have you ever seriously considered whether an ⓐarticle is really true? Everyone likes an interesting news story but what if it is completely made up?

Fake news can be very harmful in that it can make people less informed or even misled. Nevertheless, there have been various fake news reports throughout history. Why have some people written such false information? Let's look into some articles ⓑthinking about the hidden motives behind them.

14 위 글의 밑줄 친 ⓐarticle과 같은 의미로 쓰인 것을 모두 고르시오.

① Bread is an article of food.

② He contributed an article to a journal.

③ That word has to have a definite article before it.

④ I read every last article in the newspaper.

⑤ I'm looking for an article of clothing.

15 위 글의 밑줄 친 ⓑthinking과 문법적 쓰임이 같은 것을 모두 고르시오.

① My hobby is reading books.

② Who is the girl playing the piano?

③ I saw the boy eating an apple.

④ Taking a walk every day is very good for you.

⑤ He is collecting stamps.

16 위 글의 주제로 알맞은 것을 고르시오.

① We are living in a flood of information.

② Everyone likes an interesting news story.

③ It is difficult to spot fake news.

④ There are many ways to write news reports faithfully.

⑤ Despite their harmful effects, there have been various fake news reports.

[17~19] 다음 글을 읽고 물음에 답하시오.

At that time, those who read the article carefully laughed out loud. Those who didn't read it to the end got really worried. (A)Not knowing the news was false, many people ⓐ_____. Some tried to escape the city while others went into the parks with guns to hunt the animals.

So why did *The Herald* make up such news? Later, they confessed that they made it up so that they could draw the readers' attention to the unsafe conditions at the zoo.

출제율 95%

17 위 글의 빈칸 ⓐ에 panic을 알맞은 형태로 쓰시오. (one word)

➡ _____

출제율 90%

18 위 글의 밑줄 친 (A)를 부사절로 고치시오.

➡ _____

출제율 95%

19 According to the passage, which is NOT true?

① The readers who read the article carefully laughed out loud.

② Some of the readers who didn't read the article to the end tried to escape the city.

③ Some of the readers who didn't read the article to the end went into the parks with guns to hunt the animals.

④ *The Herald* made up such false news to scare people.

⑤ The conditions of the zoo were unsafe.

[20~22] 다음 글을 읽고 물음에 답하시오.

Is there anything strange about the article? Read the Slav's name backwards; it spells, "we-fake-news." Who wrote this and why?

The Daily Telegram published this fake article so that they could prove if *The Daily News*, their competitor, was stealing (A)their articles. *The Daily News* published the same article about "Swenekafew" the next day and ⓐ____ got caught stealing. The people at *The Daily News* had to admit (B)their act and (C)were harshly criticized by the public.

출제율 90%

20 위 글의 빈칸 ⓐ에 들어갈 알맞은 말을 고르시오.

① additionally   ② alternatively

③ on the other hand   ④ moreover

⑤ thus

출제율 95%

21 위 글의 밑줄 친 (A)their와 (B)their가 가리키는 것을 각각 본문에서 찾아 쓰시오.

➡ (A) _____
   (B) _____

출제율 100%

22 위 글의 밑줄 친 (C)를 능동태로 고치시오.

➡ _____

_____

[01~03] 다음 대화를 읽고 물음에 답하시오.

Jane: I read an article saying that Napoleon was actually fairly tall.

Tom: Oh, really? Can you tell me more about it?

Jane: According to the article, a French doctor wrote down Napoleon's height according to the French measuring system, not the English one.

Tom: What was the difference?

Jane: At that time, an inch in France was longer than an inch in England. So, Napoleon was actually about 168 cm tall, which was not that short in those times.

01 What does the article say about Napoleon's height?

➡ _____

02 Who wrote down Napoleon's height and in what way was it written down?

➡ _____

_____

03 What was the difference between French and English measuring systems?

➡ _____

04 분사구문은 부사절로, 부사절은 분사구문으로 바꿔 쓰시오.

(1) Winning the first prize, Jenny was so happy.

➡ _____

_____

(2) Walking with Wing Walker, you burn more calories and get slimmer.

➡ _____

_____

(3) Because they use the hidden board technology, they strengthen leg muscles.

➡ _____

_____

(4) She studied very hard and passed the exam.

➡ _____

05 다음 문장을 같은 뜻을 갖는 문장으로 바꿔 쓰려고 한다. 빈칸을 알맞게 채우시오.

(1) I want to have Harry Potter's magic cloak so that I could become invisible.

= I want to have Harry Potter's magic cloak _____ _____ _____ I could become invisible.

(2) Take a rest every hour so that you can keep warm.

= Take a rest every hour _____ _____ _____ keep warm.

(3) Be so humble that you can learn from your mistakes.

= Be humble _____ _____ learn from your mistakes.

(4) It was so hot that we couldn't go out.

= It was _____ _____ for us _____ go out.

[06~08] 다음 글을 읽고 물음에 답하시오.

Every day we watch, hear, or read interesting news. @However, have you ever seriously considered that an article is really true? Everyone likes an interesting news story but ⓑ 만약 그것이 완전히 지어낸 것이라면 어떻게 할 것인가?

Fake news can be very harmful in that it can make people less informed or even misled. Nevertheless, there have been various fake news reports throughout history. Why have some people written such false information? Let's look into some articles thinking about the hidden motives behind them.

06 위 글의 밑줄 친 @에서 어법상 틀린 부분을 찾아 고치시오.

➡ _____

07 위 글의 밑줄 친 ⓑ의 우리말에 맞게 주어진 어휘를 이용하여 7 단어로 영작하시오.

what, made, completely

➡ _____

08 본문의 내용과 일치하도록 다음 빈칸 (A)와 (B)에 공통으로 들어갈 알맞은 단어를 쓰시오.

Though people can be less informed or even misled because of (A)_____ _____, there have been various (B)_____ _____ reports throughout history.

[09~11] 다음 글을 읽고 물음에 답하시오.

At that time, those who read the article carefully laughed out loud. Those who didn't read @it to the end got really worried. Not knowing the news was false, many people panicked. Some tried to escape the city while others went into the parks with guns to hunt the animals.

So why did *The Herald* make up such news? Later, they confessed that they made it up ⓑ so that they could draw the readers' attention to the unsafe conditions at the zoo.

09 위 글의 밑줄 친 @it이 가리키는 것을 본문에서 찾아 쓰시오.

➡ _____

10 위 글의 밑줄 친 ⓑ를 to부정사를 사용하여 고치시오.

➡ _____
_____

11 How did the readers who didn't know the news was false react? Fill in the blanks (A) and (B) with suitable words.

Some tried to (A)_____ _____ _____ while others (B)_____ _____ _____ _____ with guns to hunt the animals.

01 다음 대화를 읽고 Suji의 일기를 완성하시오.

> Suji: I usually drink a glass of warm milk before I go to bed, but it doesn't help me fall asleep.
> Minsu: I saw a show on TV, and a doctor said that a glass of warm milk doesn't actually help you fall asleep.
> Suji: Oh, it doesn't? Can you tell me more about it?
> Minsu: Milk has special chemicals that make people sleepy. But the amount in a glass is too small to have any effect.

> Recently, I couldn't sleep well, so (A)_____ before I went to bed. However, it didn't work at all. I talked about it to Minsu. He explained that (B)_____. According to the doctor, there are special chemicals in milk that (C)_____, but the (D)_____ in a glass is too small. I think I should find another way to get a sound sleep.

02 다음 내용을 바탕으로 제품의 광고 내용에 대해 문의하는 게시 글을 쓰시오.

> Q1 What product are they advertising?
> A1 They are advertising the walking shoes, Wing Walker.
> Q2 What are the strong points of the product?
> A2 Walking with Wing Walker, people burn more calories and get slimmer. They also strengthen leg muscles because they use the hidden board technology.
> Q3 What information is not shown in the ad?
> A3 First, is it scientifically proven that walking with Wing Walker, people burn more calories? Second, what materials are used for the hidden board?

> I saw the ad about (A)_____. It says that walking with Wing Walker, people (B)_____. They also strengthen leg muscles because they use (C)_____. But here are some questions. First, is it (D)_____ that walking with Wing Walker, people burn more calories? Second, (E)_____ are used for the hidden board? It would be great if you could answer my questions.

단원별 모의고사

01 다음 대화가 자연스럽게 이어지도록 순서대로 배열하시오.

> (A) Really? Can you tell me more about it?
>
> (B) The article said that people catch colds because of viruses.
>
> (C) Well, I've read an article saying that you don't catch a cold because your body temperature is low.
>
> (D) I think I caught a cold because I didn't dress warmly yesterday.

➡ _____

02 다음 우리말에 맞게 빈칸에 알맞은 말을 쓰시오.

(1) 저 치즈의 냄새는 지독하다.
➡ The smell of that cheese is _____.

(2) 너는 이 화학 물질을 다룰 때 장갑을 껴야만 한다.
➡ You must wear gloves when you handle these _____.

(3) 그는 가슴 위로 팔짱을 꼈다.
➡ He crossed his arms over his _____.

(4) 그는 한국인 여인과 결혼해서 한국 시민이 되었다.
➡ He married a Korean woman and became a Korean _____.

03 다음 문장의 빈칸에 들어갈 말을 〈보기〉에서 골라 알맞은 형태로 쓰시오.

> ┌─── 보기 ───┐
> public / recognize / publish / prove / poems

(1) He enjoys writing _____ in his free time.

(2) She should _____ they are wrong.

(3) The museum will be open to the _____ next month.

(4) He has _____ several novels, and I have read them all.

(5) I was able to _____ my old friend by her voice.

04 다음 문장에 공통으로 들어갈 말을 고르시오.

> • My grandfather used to work in the gold _____.
> • The _____ was closed because of the safety problem.
> • People _____ for coal in this area.
> • Half of the money was _____.

① panic   ② condition
③ mine   ④ strengthen
⑤ support

[05~06] 다음 대화를 읽고 물음에 답하시오.

Suji: There are so many pieces of information we call "facts" that are completely wrong.

Jack: (A) Why do you say so?

Suji: (B) I read a book, and there were a lot of examples of these facts that are wrong.

Jack: (C) Like what?

Suji: (D) But goldfish are actually smart.

Jack: (E) Really? Can you tell me more about that?

Suji: They can recognize their owners.

Jack: Oh, I didn't know that.

05 위 대화의 (A)~(E) 중 주어진 문장이 들어가기에 적절한 곳은?

> Well, most people think goldfish are not smart.

① (A)   ② (B)   ③ (C)   ④ (D)   ⑤ (E)

06 위 대화를 읽고 대답할 수 <u>없는</u> 것은?

① What did Suji read about?

② What do most people think about goldfish?

③ What can goldfish actually do?

④ Why does Suji think that goldfish are smart?

⑤ How can goldfish recognize their owners?

[07~09] 다음 대화를 읽고 물음에 답하시오.

David: Hey, Sandy. Do you think I should buy this drink? It is said that it can help me lose weight.

Sandy: Let me read the label more closely. Hmm, it looks a bit strange to me, David.

David: Why do you say so?

Sandy: There isn't enough information about what's in the drink.

David: Oh, you're right.

Sandy: Also, it doesn't tell you how much you have to drink to lose weight.

07 What does Sandy read closely?

➡ _____

08 Why does Sandy think that David shouldn't buy the drink?

➡ _____

_____

09 What are the two things that are not shown on the label?

➡ _____

_____

[10~11] 다음 대화를 읽고 물음에 답하시오.

Susan: What are you reading, John?

John: I'm reading a book of riddles.

Susan: Riddles? Aren't they for children?

John: Actually, no. Books of riddles are really (A)[useful / useless] for adults.

Susan: Really? Why do you say so?

John: They help us think more (B)[ordinarily / creatively]. We need to think (C)[inside / outside] the box to find the answers.

10 위 대화의 (A)~(C)에 들어갈 말로 바르게 짝지어진 것은?

	(A)	(B)	(C)
①	useful	ordinarily	inside
②	useful	creatively	outside
③	useful	creatively	inside
④	useless	creatively	outside
⑤	useless	ordinarily	inside

11 위 대화를 읽고 대답할 수 <u>없는</u> 것은?

① What is John reading now?

② Are the books of riddles for children?

③ Why are the books of riddles useful for adults?

④ What should people do to find the answers to the riddles?

⑤ What is there outside John's box?

12 다음 우리말을 주어진 단어를 이용하여 영작하시오.

(1) 비판적으로 생각하고 그들이 너에게 말하는 모든 것을 믿지는 마라. (critically)

➡ _____

(2) 너의 학급 친구들을 비난하거나 놀리지 마라. (of, fun)

➡ _____

(3) 이것이 너의 현재 주소니? (current)

➡ _____

(4) 그것이 맞는지 아닌지는 판단하기가 어렵다. (whether, difficult, judge)

➡ _____

13 다음 문장에서 어법상 어색한 것을 바르게 고쳐 다시 쓰시오.

(1) Sam saved some money so as to he could buy a new backpack.

➡ _____

(2) You must follow the rules in order to everyone enjoy the experience.

➡ _____

(3) She saw Thomas entered the classroom.

➡ _____

(4) Very embarrassing, she didn't tell us that news.

➡ _____

14 다음 우리말을 주어진 어휘를 이용하여 영작하시오.

(1) 할 일이 없을 때, 그는 낚시하러 간다. (have, work, do, 8 단어)

➡ _____

(2) Susan은 다른 사람들이 그녀의 목소리를 들을 수 없도록 조용히 얘기했다. (other people, voice, that, speak, hear, quietly, 11 단어)

➡ _____

15 Which is grammatically wrong?

① Getting up late, I brought some bread to school for breakfast.
② Never use your phone in order to look in front of you.
③ Wear a swimming cap in order to the pool be kept clean.
④ Wear bright-colored clothes in order that people can see you at night.
⑤ Let's plant many trees so that they can help provide fresh air.

16 다음 중 어법상 옳은 문장을 모두 고르시오.

① Starting a class, my teacher plays a pop song.
② Pass the exam, I felt really happy.
③ After taking a walk in the park, I went to bed.
④ He plays computer games with his friends having some snacks.
⑤ Feeling not hungry, I concentrated on reading.
⑥ Meeting her several times, he noticed her immediately.

17 다음 두 문장을 해석하고 그 차이를 설명하시오.

(1) Jinho studied English hard so that he could talk with foreigners in English.

➡ 해석 _____

_____

차이 _____

_____

(2) Jinho studied English so hard that he could talk with foreigners in English.

➡ 해석 _____

_____

차이 _____

_____

[18~19] 다음 글을 읽고 물음에 답하시오.

Every day we watch, hear, or read interesting news. However, have you ever seriously considered whether an article is really true? Everyone likes an interesting news story but what if ⓐit is completely made up?

Fake news can be very harmful in that it can make people less informed or even misled. Nevertheless, there ⓑhave been various fake news reports throughout history. Why have some people written such false information? Let's look into some articles thinking about the hidden motives behind them.

18 아래 〈보기〉에서 위 글의 밑줄 친 ⓑhave been과 현재완료의 용법이 같은 것의 개수를 고르시오.

┌─── 보기 ───┐
① I have lost my cellphone.
② Have you finished reading the book yet?
③ I have studied English since the third grade of elementary school.
④ He has now completed the project.
⑤ She has been to Japan twice.
└──────────┘

① 1개　② 2개　③ 3개　④ 4개　⑤ 5개

19 위 글의 밑줄 친 ⓐit이 가리키는 것을 본문에서 찾아 쓰시오.

➡ _____

[20~22] 다음 글을 읽고 물음에 답하시오.

At that time, those who read the article carefully laughed out loud. (①) Those who didn't read it ___ⓐ___ the end got really worried. (②) Not knowing the news was false, many people panicked. (③) Some tried to escape the city (A)while others went into the parks with guns to hunt the animals.

(④) Later, they confessed that they made it up so that they could draw the readers' attention ___ⓑ___ the unsafe conditions at the zoo. (⑤)

20 위 글의 빈칸 ⓐ와 ⓑ에 공통으로 들어갈 알맞은 전치사를 고르시오.

① of　　　　② from
③ to　　　　④ at
⑤ for

21 위 글의 밑줄 친 (A)while과 의미와 문법적 쓰임이 같지 않은 것을 고르시오.

① I've read fifty pages, while he's read only twenty.
② Some are rich, while others are poor.
③ They chatted for a while.
④ Tom's very good at science, while his brother is absolutely hopeless.
⑤ The walls are green, while the ceiling is white.

22 위 글의 흐름으로 보아, 주어진 문장이 들어가기에 가장 적절한 곳은?

So why did *The Herald* make up such news?

①   ②   ③   ④   ⑤

24 위 글의 밑줄 친 ⓑ의 우리말에 맞게 주어진 어휘를 알맞게 배열하시오.

during / men / a / argument / two / had / an / meeting / the

➡ _____

_____

[23~26] 다음 글을 읽고 물음에 답하시오.

ⓐ _____

Mejk Swenekafew, a Slav worker at the Columbia Coal Mine, was shot and seriously wounded by John Pecitello near the mining camp Thursday evening. ⓑ그 두 사람은 회의 중에 언쟁을 벌였다. The argument led to a fight, and Pecitello shot Swenekafew twice, in the chest and leg. He is now at the hospital in critical condition. Pecitello ran ⓒ ____ after the shooting. The police are searching for him now and are warning citizens that he is extremely dangerous.

23 위 글의 빈칸 ⓐ에 들어갈 제목으로 알맞은 것을 고르시오.

① A Slav Worker at the Columbia Coal Mine
② Argument Near the Mining Camp
③ Swenekafew Is in Critical Condition
④ Extremely Dangerous Criminal
⑤ Slav Shoots a Friend in Argument

25 위 글의 빈칸 ⓒ에 알맞은 것은?

① in   ② to
③ away   ④ from
⑤ along

26 According to the passage, which is NOT true?

① Mejk Swenekafew was a Slav worker at the Columbia Coal Mine.
② Mejk Swenekafew was seriously wounded by John Pecitello.
③ Swenekafew was shot in the chest and leg.
④ The police are searching for Swenekafew.
⑤ The police are warning citizens that Pecitello is extremely dangerous.

MEMO

INSIGHT
on the textbook
교과서 파헤치기

※ 다음 영어를 우리말로 쓰시오.

01 horrible

02 article

03 biography

04 ruin

05 husband

06 detective

07 fortress

08 gamble

09 disappointing

10 afterwards

11 fortune

12 general

13 include

14 locker

15 whenever

16 independence

17 movement

18 wooden

19 odd

20 officer

21 realistic

22 invention

23 embarrassing

24 strange

25 female

26 whisper

27 marriage

28 chest

29 since

30 merchant

31 clinic

32 solve

33 truth

34 scholar

35 instead of

36 yell at

37 be used to (동)명사

38 devote one's life to 명사

39 at that moment

40 make an arrangement

41 keep a secret

42 behind one's back

43 It is said that 주어+동사 ~

※ 다음 우리말을 영어로 쓰시오.

01	나중에, 그 뒤에		22	결혼, 혼인
02	상인		23	여자; 여자의, 여성의
03	자서전, 전기		24	궁금하다
04	서랍장, 큰 상자, 장롱		25	물건
05	(정치적 · 사회적) 운동		26	요새
06	망치다, 파산시키다		27	병원, 진료소
07	실망시키는		28	진짜 같은, 사실적인
08	부끄러운, 당황스러운		29	형사, 탐정
09	독립, 광복		30	구하다
10	이상한		31	남편
11	재산, 행운		32	나무로 된, 목재의
12	도박하다, ~을 도박으로 잃다		33	사물함
13	사회		34	낯선, 모르는
14	장군		35	비밀을 지키다
15	소곤소곤 이야기하다		36	~에게 고함치다
16	~을 포함하다		37	~을 보다
17	기계, 기구		38	청구하다, 청하다
18	학자		39	그 순간에
19	발명품, 발명		40	~ 대신에
20	끔찍한		41	입어 보다, 신어 보다
21	기사		42	~을 결정하다
			43	~하는 데 익숙하다

※ 다음 영영풀이에 알맞은 단어를 <보기>에서 골라 쓴 후, 우리말 뜻을 쓰시오.

1 _____ : relating to women or girls: _____

2 _____ : a very large amount of money: _____

3 _____ : the man that somebody is married to: _____

4 _____ : a large strong heavy box used for storing things: _____

5 _____ : to make someone lose all their money or power: _____

6 _____ : an officer of very high rank in the army or air force: _____

7 _____ : to contain someone or something as a part: _____

8 _____ : a book that someone writes about someone else's life: _____

9 _____ : someone who buys and sells goods in large quantities: _____

10 _____ : to make someone or something safe from danger, harm, or destruction:

_____

11 _____ : a large strong building used for defending an important place:

_____

12 _____ : freedom from control by another country or organization: _____

13 _____ : a piece of writing about a particular subject that is published in a
newspaper or magazine: _____

14 _____ : a gradual development or change of an attitude, opinion, or policy:

_____

15 _____ : a small cabinet that can be locked, where you can leave your clothes,
bags, etc. while you play a sport or go somewhered: _____

16 _____ : someone who studies a particular subject and knows a lot about it,
especially a subject that is not scientific: _____

보기			
article	husband	save	fortress
locker	ruin	include	chest
movement	female	merchant	fortune
scholar	independence	biography	general

※ 다음 우리말과 일치하도록 빈칸에 알맞은 말을 쓰시오.

Listen & Talk 1 Get Ready

A: Kim Deuksin _____ _____ _____.

B: No! I _____ a book and _____ _____ _____ that he was a

_____.

C: Don't _____. You are _____ _____.

A: 김득신은 화가였어.
B: 아니야! 내가 책을 읽었는데 그는 학자였다고 해.
C: 싸우지 마. 너희 둘 다 옳아.

Listen & Talk 1 A-1

M: Lisa, _____ are you _____?

W: I'm _____ a _____ of Gwon Giok.

M: I _____ _____ about her. Who is she?

W: She was _____ _____ _____ pilot in Korea. _____ _____

_____ _____ she had _____ 7,000 hours of _____ _____.

M: Wow, I didn't know that.

M: Lisa, 너 뭐 읽고 있니?
W: 권기옥의 전기를 읽고 있어.
M: 그녀에 대해 들어본 적이 없어. 그녀는 누구니?
W: 그녀는 한국의 첫 번째 여성 조종사야. 그녀는 비행시간이 7,000 시간이 넘는다고 해.
M: 와, 난 몰랐어.

Listen & Talk 1 A-2

M: I watched an _____ movie yesterday. Jeong Yakyong was a _____ in it.

W: Jeong Yakyong? Wasn't he a _____ in the Joseon Dynasty?

M: Yeah, _____ _____ _____ _____ _____ _____

_____ _____ a detective. He _____ about 90 _____.

W: Oh, I _____ _____ _____ he was also a _____.

M: 난 어제 흥미 있는 영화를 보았어. 그 영화에서 정약용이 탐정이었어.
W: 정약용? 그는 조선 왕조의 학자 아니었니?
M: 응, 하지만 그는 탐정이기도 했다고 해. 그는 약 90개의 사건을 해결했어.
W: 아, 그가 또한 탐정이었다는 건 몰랐어.

Listen & Talk 1 B

W: Hey, Mark, do you _____ _____ Father Lee Taeseok?

M: Yeah, I've _____ of him. Why?

W: _____ _____ _____ _____ this article. He is going

_____ _____ _____ in the _____ _____ textbook in

South Sudan.

M: Wow, that's great.

W: Yeah, he _____ the children _____ _____ _____ _____

and a school. It is said _____ _____ will _____

_____ _____ the textbook.

M: _____ is good _____ hear _____ students will learn about

_____ a great person.

W: 어이, Mark, 너 이태석 신부에 대해 아니?
M: 응, 그에 대해 들어본 적이 있어. 왜?
W: 이 기사를 봐. 그는 남수단의 사회 교과서에 실릴 거야.
M: 와, 그거 대단하구나.
W: 그래, 그는 병원과 학교를 지어 아이들을 도와주었어. 그런 이야기들이 교과서에 실릴 거라고 해.
M: 학생들이 그토록 훌륭한 사람에 대해 배울 거라는 말을 들으니 좋군.

Listen & Talk 2 A-1

W: Excuse me, you _____ _____ your backpack inside the _____.

M: Oh, I didn't know that. _____ _____ _____ if I bring in my _____ _____?

W: Yes, that's fine. You can _____ your bag _____ the locker.

M: Okay, thank you.

W: 죄송합니다만, 박물관에 가방을 가
지고 들어갈 수 없어요.

M: 아, 몰랐어요. 물병은 가지고 들어가
도 괜찮나요?

W: 네, 그건 괜찮아요. 가방은 라커에
두시면 돼요.

M: 알았어요. 감사합니다.

Listen & Talk 2 A-2

W: Hi, _____ _____ the National Museum. _____ can I help you?

M: Hi, _____ _____ _____ _____ _____ _____ _____ the museum?

W: Yes, but please _____ _____ a flash.

M: Oh, I see. Thank you.

W: 안녕하세요, 국립박물관에 오신 걸
환영합니다. 무엇을 도와드릴까요?

M: 안녕하세요, 박물관에서 사진을 찍
어도 괜찮나요?

W: 네, 하지만 플래시는 사용하지 마세
요.

M: 아, 알겠습니다. 감사합니다.

Listen & Talk 2 B

M: Hello, Ms. Jackson. _____ _____ your tour of the *Hanok Village*?

W: It was wonderful. The houses _____ really beautiful.

M: That's great.

W: Actually, I didn't _____ _____ _____ _____ have dinner. Is it _____ _____ _____ cook in the kitchen at this hour?

M: Yes, but please _____ _____ the kitchen _____ _____ 10 p.m.

W: Okay. The kitchen is _____ the _____ _____, right?

M: Yes, it is. _____ _____ _____ _____ you need anything.

M: 안녕하세요. Jackson 씨. 한옥 마을
관광은 어땠어요?

W: 굉장했어요. 집들이 정말 아름다웠
습니다.

M: 대단하네요.

W: 사실 전 저녁식사를 할 기회가 없었
어요. 이 시간에 부엌에서 요리해도
괜찮나요?

M: 네, 하지만 부엌이 오후 10시에 문을
닫는 걸 기억하세요.

W: 알겠습니다. 부엌은 5층에 있죠, 맞
나요?

M: 네, 그래요. 무언가 필요하시면 제게
말씀해 주세요.

Communication Step A

M: All right, everyone! This way, please. Now, we _____ _____ _____ the Joseon Dynasty. _____ _____ _____ _____, there were _____ interesting _____. This one _____ _____ the *Jagyeongnu*.

W: Is it a _____ _____?

M: Actually, this is a _____ _____. _____ _____ _____ _____ _____ _____ the _____ and _____ _____ water clock in Korea.

W: _____ amazing! _____ _____ _____ _____ I take a _____ _____ it?

M: Sure.

Wrap Up 1

W: James, _____ are you _____?

M: Oh, I'm _____ a video about Yi Sunsin.

W: _____ _____ the one that _____ Joseon from Japan?

M: Right. _____ _____ _____ _____ the war only with twelve _____ _____.

W: Wow, _____ can that be _____?

M: He was a _____ _____ _____ _____ _____ _____ plans.

Wrap Up 2

W: Excuse me, sir. _____ _____ _____ _____ _____ have curry or *bibimbap*?

M: _____ _____ _____ have *bibimbap*, please.

W: _____ you are.

M: Thank you. Oh, _____ _____ _____ _____ I use the _____ now?

W: Sure, but _____ the seat light is _____, you should _____ in _____ _____.

M: Okay, thank you.

M: 좋아요, 여러분! 이쪽으로 오세요. 이제, 우리는 조선 왕조로 옮겨갑니다. 보시다시피, 많은 흥미 있는 발명품들이 있습니다. 이것은 자격루라고 불립니다.

W: 그것은 악기인가요?

M: 사실은 이것은 물시계입니다. 그것은 한국에서 가장 오래되고, 가장 큰 물시계라고 합니다.

W: 정말 놀랍군요. 그것을 사진 찍어도 괜찮나요?

M: 물론입니다.

W: James, 뭘 보고 있니?

M: 아, 이순신에 관한 비디오를 보고 있어.

W: 그는 일본으로부터 조선을 구한 사람 아니니?

M: 맞아. 그는 겨우 12척의 목선으로 전쟁에 이겼다고 해.

W: 와, 그게 어떻게 가능할 수 있지?

M: 그는 창의적인 계획을 세운 현명한 장군이었어.

W: 실례합니다, 선생님. 카레를 드시겠어요 아니면 비빔밥을 드시겠어요?

M: 비빔밥을 먹고 싶습니다.

W: 여기 있습니다.

M: 고마워요. 아, 지금 화장실을 이용해도 괜찮나요?

W: 그럼요, 하지만 좌석 불이 켜져 있으면 선생님 좌석에 있으셔야 합니다.

M: 알았어요, 감사합니다.

※ 다음 우리말에 맞도록 대화를 영어로 쓰시오.

Listen & Talk 1 Get Ready

A: _____

B: _____

C: _____

 해석

A: 김득신은 화가였어.
B: 아니야! 내가 책을 읽었는데 그는 학자였다고 해.
C: 싸우지 마. 너희 둘 다 옳아.

Listen & Talk 1 A-1

M: _____

W: _____

M: _____

W: _____

_____

M: _____

M: Lisa, 너 뭐 읽고 있니?
W: 권기옥의 전기를 읽고 있어.
M: 그녀에 대해 들어본 적이 없어. 그녀는 누구니?
W: 그녀는 한국의 첫 번째 여성 조종사야. 그녀는 비행시간이 7,000 시간이 넘는다고 해.
M: 와, 난 몰랐어.

Listen & Talk 1 A-2

M: _____

W: _____

M: _____

W: _____

M: 난 어제 흥미 있는 영화를 보았어. 그 영화에서 정약용이 탐정이었어.
W: 정약용? 그는 조선 왕조의 학자 아니었니?
M: 응, 하지만 그는 탐정이기도 했다고 해. 그는 약 90개의 사건을 해결했어.
W: 아, 그가 또한 탐정이었다는 건 몰랐어.

Listen & Talk 1 B

W: _____

M: _____

W: _____

M: _____

W: _____

M: _____

W: 어이, Mark, 너 이태석 신부에 대해 아니?
M: 응, 그에 대해 들어본 적이 있어. 왜?
W: 이 기사를 봐. 그는 남수단의 사회 교과서에 실릴 거야.
M: 와, 그거 대단하구나.
W: 그래, 그는 병원과 학교를 지어 아이들을 도와주었어. 그런 이야기들이 교과서에 실릴 거라고 해.
M: 학생들이 그토록 훌륭한 사람에 대해 배울 거라는 말을 들으니 좋군.

※ 다음 우리말에 맞도록 대화를 영어로 쓰시오.

Listen & Talk 2 A-1

W: _____

M: _____

W: _____

M: _____

W: 죄송합니다만, 박물관에 가방을 가지고 들어갈 수 없어요.

M: 아, 몰랐어요. 물병은 가지고 들어가도 괜찮나요?

W: 네, 그건 괜찮아요. 가방은 라커에 두시면 돼요.

M: 알았어요. 감사합니다.

Listen & Talk 2 A-2

W: _____

M: _____

W: _____

M: _____

W: 안녕하세요, 국립박물관에 오신 걸 환영합니다. 무엇을 도와드릴까요?

M: 안녕하세요, 박물관에서 사진을 찍어도 괜찮나요?

W: 네, 하지만 플래시는 사용하지 마세요.

M: 아, 알겠습니다. 감사합니다.

Listen & Talk 2 B

M: _____

W: _____

M: _____

W: _____

M: _____

W: _____

M: _____

M: 안녕하세요. Jackson 씨. 한옥 마을 관광은 어땠어요?

W: 굉장했어요. 집들이 정말 아름다웠습니다.

M: 대단하네요.

W: 사실 전 저녁식사를 할 기회가 없었어요. 이 시간에 부엌에서 요리해도 괜찮나요?

M: 네, 하지만 부엌이 오후 10시에 문을 닫는 걸 기억하세요.

W: 알겠습니다. 부엌은 5층에 있죠, 맞나요?

M: 네, 그래요. 무언가 필요하시면 제게 말씀해 주세요.

Communication Step A

M: _____

_____

_____

W: _____

M: _____

_____

W: _____

M: _____

M: 좋아요, 여러분! 이쪽으로 오세요. 이제, 우리는 조선 왕조로 옮겨갑니다. 보시다시피, 많은 흥미 있는 발명품들이 있습니다. 이것은 자격루라고 불립니다.

W: 그것은 악기인가요?

M: 사실은 이것은 물시계입니다. 그것은 한국에서 가장 오래되고, 가장 큰 물시계라고 합니다.

W: 정말 놀랍군요. 그것을 사진 찍어도 괜찮나요?

M: 물론입니다.

Wrap Up 1

W: _____

M: _____

W: _____

M: _____

W: _____

M: _____

W: James, 뭘 보고 있니?

M: 아, 이순신에 관한 비디오를 보고 있어.

W: 그는 일본으로부터 조선을 구한 사람 아니니?

M: 맞아. 그는 겨우 12척의 목선으로 전쟁에 이겼다고 해.

W: 와, 그게 어떻게 가능할 수 있지?

M: 그는 창의적인 계획을 세운 현명한 장군이었어.

Wrap Up 2

W: _____

M: _____

W: _____

M: _____

W: _____

M: _____

W: 실례합니다, 선생님. 카레를 드시겠어요 아니면 비빔밥을 드시겠어요?

M: 비빔밥을 먹고 싶습니다.

W: 여기 있습니다.

M: 고마워요. 아, 지금 화장실을 이용해도 괜찮나요?

W: 그럼요, 하지만 좌석 불이 켜져 있으면 선생님 좌석에 있으셔야 합니다.

M: 알았어요, 감사합니다.

※ 다음 우리말과 일치하도록 빈칸에 알맞은 것을 골라 쓰시오.

1 The _____ of _____ _____
A. Father　　　B. Secret　　　C. My

2 In 1946, a _____ man _____ me and _____, "Are you Mr. Kim Yonghwan's _____?"
A. visited　　　B. daughter　　　C. asked　　　D. strange

3 For me, this was am _____ question because I was more _____ _____ _____ called the daughter of a *parakho*.
A. used　　　B. odd　　　C. to　　　D. being

4 "I'm _____ _____ _____.
A. father's　　　B. your　　　C. friend

5 You may _____ _____ it is _____, but your father...," the man said.
A. if　　　B. wonder　　　C. true

6 At that _____, I was _____ _____ news since I did not have good _____ of my father.
A. disappointing　　　B. memories　　　C. moment　　　D. expecting

7 _____ in the 1920's, _____ people saw me in the village, they would say, "_____ _____ the parakho's daughter."
A. goes　　　B. back　　　C. there　　　D. whenever

8 My father was a son _____ a very _____ _____.
A. rich　　　B. from　　　C. family

9 _____ of _____ the life of a *seonbi*, he was _____ at the _____ house.
A. gambling　　　B. living　　　C. instead　　　D. always

10 That is _____ he was called a *parakho*, _____ means someone who _____ his family's _____.
A. which　　　B. why　　　C. fortune　　　D. ruins

11 "Your father has _____ _____ all of the money, and now he's _____ _____ more.
A. away　　　B. asking　　　C. gambled　　　D. for

12 Go and tell him that we _____ no more money _____," my mother_____ tell me _____ she sent me to the gambling house.
A. left　　　B. whenever　　　C. would　　　D. have

13 Then, my father would _____ _____ me _____, "Why did you come _____?
A. angrily　　　B. empty-handed　　　C. at　　　D. yell

14 _____ me _____ money!"
A. more　　　B. bring

---

1 아버지의 비밀

2 1946년에, 낯선 남자가 나를 찾아와 물었다. "당신이 김용환 씨의 딸입니까?"

3 나는 파락호의 딸이라고 불리는 것이 더 익숙했으므로 나에게 이것은 이상한 질문이었다.

4 "나는 당신 아버지의 친구입니다.

5 당신은 이것이 사실인지 의아하겠지만, 당신의 아버지는…,"이라고 그 남자는 말했다.

6 나는 내 아버지에 대해 좋은 기억을 가지고 있지 않았으므로 그 순간에 실망스러운 소식을 예상하고 있었다.

7 1920년대에 마을에서 사람들이 나를 볼 때마다 그들은 "저기에 파락호의 딸이 가네."라고 말하곤 했다.

8 나의 아버지는 매우 부유한 집안의 아들이었다.

9 선비의 삶을 사는 대신, 아버지는 항상 도박장에 계셨다.

10 그것이 그가 집안의 재산을 탕진하는 사람이라는 뜻의 파락호로 불린 이유이다.

11 "네 아버지는 도박으로 모든 돈을 써 버리고 지금 더 요구하고 계신다.

12 가서 더 이상 남아 있는 돈이 없다고 말씀드려라."라고 나의 어머니는 나를 도박장으로 보낼 때마다 말씀하시곤 했다.

13 그러면, 아버지는 나에게 화를 내시며 소리치셨다. "왜 빈손으로 왔니?

14 돈을 더 가져와!"

15 When I was sixteen years old, my family _____ _____ _____ an _____ for me to marry Mr. Seo.

A. arrangement   B. already   C. made   D. had

16 As _____ of the wedding _____, Mr. Seo's family sent my family some money to buy a new _____ for _____.

A. part   B. chest   C. tradition   D. clothes

17 _____ _____ the wedding day, my mother came into my room and said, "Your father has _____ the _____ for the chest."

A. before   B. taken   C. right   D. money

18 I asked _____, "How could he do _____ a _____ _____?

A. thing   B. such   C. horrible   D. angrily

19 _____ _____ we _____ now?"

A. do   B. should   C. what

20 "We _____ _____ _____.

A. choice   B. no   C. have

21 You'll _____ _____ _____ your aunt's old _____," my mother said.

A. chest   B. to   C. have   D. take

22 "_____ _____ for the family," people would whisper _____ my _____.

A. embarrassing   B. back   C. how   D. behind

23 _____ the first day of _____, life at my husband's house had _____ _____ for me.

A. marriage   B. difficult   C. since   D. been

24 "Your father, my _____ friend...," my father's friend _____ his _____.

A. continued   B. dear   C. story

25 "He _____ _____ a _____.

A. not   B. was   C. gambler

26 Your father sent the _____ _____ to the _____ _____ in Manchuria.

A. money   B. fighters   C. family   D. independence

27 He _____ _____ look like a gambler to _____ this a _____ from the Japanese officers."

A. secret   B. himself   C. keep   D. made

28 At first, I was not _____ _____ he was _____ the _____.

A. telling   B. if   C. truth   D. sure

29 But _____, I found _____ the truth about my father and I _____ that I had been _____ about him.

A. wrong   B. afterwards   C. out   D. realized

30 Ever _____ that moment, I have been _____ to be the daughter of a *parakho* who had _____ his life to the independence _____.

A. proud   B. devoted   C. since   D. movement

---

15 내가 16살이 되었을 때, 나의 가족은 나를 서 씨와 결혼시키기로 이미 결정을 했었다.

16 결혼 풍습의 일부로, 서 씨네 가족은 새 장롱을 사라고 우리 가족에게 돈을 보냈다.

17 결혼식 바로 전날, 나의 어머니는 내 방에 들어오셔서 말씀하셨다. "네 아버지가 장롱을 살 돈을 가져가 버렸다."

18 나는 화가 나서 물었다 "어떻게 그리 끔찍한 일을 하실 수 있나요?

19 우린 이제 어떡해요?"

20 "우리에게 선택권은 없구나.

21 큰어머니의 옛 장롱을 가져가야겠구나."라고 어머니가 말씀하셨다.

22 "가문에 부끄러운 일이야."라고 사람들이 내 뒤에서 속삭이곤 했다.

23 결혼 첫날부터, 남편의 집에서의 생활은 나에게 힘겨웠다.

24 "당신의 아버지, 나의 친애하는 친구…," 나의 아버지의 친구분은 그의 이야기를 이어가셨다.

25 "그는 도박꾼이 아니었어요.

26 당신의 아버지는 가족의 돈을 만주에 있는 독립운동가들에게 보냈답니다.

27 그는 이것을 일본 순사들에게 비밀로 하기 위해 그 자신을 도박꾼처럼 보이게 했어요."

28 처음엔, 나는 그분이 사실을 얘기하시는 건지 확신할 수 없었다.

29 그러나 나중에, 나는 나의 아버지에 대한 진실을 알게 되었고 내가 아버지에 관해 오해하고 있었다는 것을 깨달았다.

30 그 순간부터, 나는 독립운동에 그의 인생을 헌신하신 파락호의 딸인 것이 자랑스러웠다.

※ 다음 우리말과 일치하도록 빈칸에 알맞은 말을 쓰시오.

1 The _____ of My _____

2 In 1946, _____ _____ _____ _____ me and _____, "Are you Mr. Kim Yonghwan's daughter?"

3 For me, this was _____ _____ _____ because I _____ _____ _____ _____ _____ the daughter of a *parakho*.

4 "I'm _____ _____ _____.

5 You may _____ _____ it is _____, but your father...," the man said.

6 At that moment, I was _____ _____ news _____ I did not have _____ _____ of my father.

7 _____ in the 1920's, _____ people saw me in the village, they would say, "_____ _____ the parakho's daughter."

8 My father was a son _____ a very _____ _____.

9 _____ _____ _____ the life of a *seonbi*, he was always at the _____ _____.

10 _____ _____ _____ he _____ _____ a *parakho*, _____ means someone who _____ his family's fortune.

11 "Your father _____ _____ _____ all of the money, and now he's _____ _____ more.

12 Go and tell him that we _____ _____ _____ _____ _____," my mother _____ tell me _____ she _____ me to the gambling house.

13 Then, my father _____ _____ _____ me _____, "Why did you come _____?

14 _____ _____ more _____!"

---

1 아버지의 비밀

2 1946년에, 낯선 남자가 나를 찾아와 물었다. "당신이 김용환 씨의 딸입니까?"

3 나는 파락호의 딸이라고 불리는 것이 더 익숙했으므로 나에게 이것은 이상한 질문이었다.

4 "나는 당신 아버지의 친구입니다.

5 당신은 이것이 사실인지 의아하겠지만, 당신의 아버지…,"이라고 그 남자는 말했다.

6 나는 내 아버지에 대해 좋은 기억을 가지고 있지 않았으므로 그 순간에 실망스러운 소식을 예상하고 있었다.

7 1920년대에 마을에서 사람들이 나를 볼 때마다 그들은 "저기에 파락호의 딸이 가네."라고 말하곤 했다.

8 나의 아버지는 매우 부유한 집안의 아들이었다.

9 선비의 삶을 사는 대신, 아버지는 항상 도박장에 계셨다.

10 그것이 그가 집안의 재산을 탕진하는 사람이라는 뜻의 파락호로 불린 이유이다.

11 "네 아버지는 도박으로 모든 돈을 써 버리고 지금 더 요구하고 계신다.

12 가서 더 이상 남아 있는 돈이 없다고 말씀드려라."라고 나의 어머니는 나를 도박장으로 보낼 때마다 말씀하시곤 했다.

13 그러면, 아버지는 나에게 화를 내시며 소리치셨다. "왜 빈손으로 왔니?

14 돈을 더 가져와!"

15 When I was sixteen years old, my family _____ _____
_____ _____ _____ for me to _____ Mr. Seo.

16 _____ _____ _____ the wedding tradition, Mr. Seo's
family sent my family some money to buy _____ _____
_____ _____ _____ .

17 _____ _____ the wedding day, my mother _____
_____ my room and said, "Your father _____ _____
_____ _____ for the chest."

18 I asked _____, "How could he do _____ _____ _____
_____?

19 _____ should we do now?"

20 "We have _____ _____ .

21 _____ _____ _____ _____ _____ your aunt's old chest," my
mother said.

22 "_____ _____ for the family," people would _____
_____ _____ _____ .

23 Since the first day of _____, life at my husband's house
_____ _____ _____ _____ _____ _____ .

24 "Your father, my dear friend...," my father's friend _____
_____ _____ .

25 "He was not _____ _____ .

26 Your father sent the family money to the _____ _____ in
Manchuria.

27 He _____ _____ look like a gambler to _____ _____
_____ _____ _____ the _____ _____ ."

28 At first, I was not sure _____ he was _____ the _____ .

29 But _____, I found out the truth about my father and I
realized that I _____ _____ _____ about him.

30 Ever since that moment, I have been proud to be the daughter of
a *parakho* who _____ _____ _____ _____ _____
the _____ _____ .

---

15 내가 16살이 되었을 때, 나의 가족은 나를 서 씨와 결혼시키기로 이미 결정을 했었다.

16 결혼 풍습의 일부로, 서 씨네 가족은 새 장롱을 사라고 우리 가족에게 돈을 보냈다.

17 결혼식 바로 전날, 나의 어머니는 내 방에 들어오셔서 말씀하셨다. "네 아버지가 장롱을 살 돈을 가져가 버렸다."

18 나는 화가 나서 물었다 "어떻게 그리 끔찍한 일을 하실 수 있나요?

19 우린 이제 어떡해요?"

20 "우리에게 선택권은 없구나.

21 큰어머니의 옛 장롱을 가져가야겠구나."라고 어머니가 말씀하셨다.

22 "가문에 부끄러운 일이야."라고 사람들이 내 뒤에서 속삭이곤 했다.

23 결혼 첫날부터, 남편의 집에서의 생활은 나에게 힘겨웠다.

24 "당신의 아버지, 나의 친애하는 친구…," 나의 아버지의 친구분은 그의 이야기를 이어가셨다.

25 "그는 도박꾼이 아니었어요.

26 당신의 아버지는 가족의 돈을 만주에 있는 독립운동가들에게 보냈답니다.

27 그는 이것을 일본 순사들에게 비밀로 하기 위해 그 자신을 도박꾼처럼 보이게 했어요."

28 처음엔, 나는 그분이 사실을 얘기하시는 건지 확신할 수 없었다.

29 그러나 나중에, 나는 나의 아버지에 대한 진실을 알게 되었고 내가 아버지에 관해 오해하고 있었다는 것을 깨달았다.

30 그 순간부터, 나는 독립운동에 그의 인생을 헌신하신 파락호의 딸인 것이 자랑스러웠다.

※ 다음 문장을 우리말로 쓰시오.

1 ▶ The Secret of My Father

➡ _____

2 ▶ In 1946, a strange man visited me and asked, "Are you Mr. Kim Yonghwan's daughter?

➡ _____

3 ▶ For me, this was an odd question because I was more used to being called the daughter of a *parakho*.

➡ _____

4 ▶ "I'm your father's friend.

➡ _____

5 ▶ You may wonder if it is true, but your father...," the man said.

➡ _____

6 ▶ At that moment, I was expecting disappointing news since I did not have good memories of my father.

➡ _____

7 ▶ Back in the 1920's, whenever people saw me in the village, they would say, "There goes the *parakho's* daughter."

➡ _____

8 ▶ My father was a son from a very rich family.

➡ _____

9 ▶ Instead of living the life of a seonbi, he was always at the gambling house.

➡ _____

10 ▶ That is why he was called a parakho, which means someone who ruins his family's fortune.

➡ _____

11 ▶ "Your father has gambled away all of the money, and now he's asking for more.

➡ _____

12 ▶ Go and tell him that we have no more money left," my mother would tell me whenever she sent me to the gambling house.

➡ _____

13 ▶ Then, my father would yell at me angrily, "Why did you come empty-handed?

➡ _____

14 ▶ Bring me more money!"

➡ _____

15 When I was sixteen years old, my family had already made an arrangement for me to marry Mr. Seo.

➡ _____

16 As part of the wedding tradition, Mr. Seo's family sent my family some money to buy a new chest for clothes.

➡ _____

17 Right before the wedding day, my mother came into my room and said, "Your father has taken the money for the chest."

➡ _____

18 I asked angrily, "How could he do such a horrible thing?

➡ _____

19 What should we do now?"

➡ _____

20 "We have no choice.

➡ _____

21 You'll have to take your aunt's old chest," my mother said.

➡ _____

22 "How embarrassing for the family," people would whisper behind my back.

➡ _____

23 Since the first day of marriage, life at my husband's house had been difficult for me.

➡ _____

24 "Your father, my dear friend...," my father's friend continued his story.

➡ _____

25 "He was not a gambler.

➡ _____

26 Your father sent the family money to the independence fighters in Manchuria.

➡ _____

27 He made himself look like a gambler to keep this a secret from the Japanese officers."

➡ _____

28 At first, I was not sure if he was telling the truth.

➡ _____

29 But afterwards, I found out the truth about my father and I realized that I had been wrong about him.

➡ _____

30 Ever since that moment, I have been proud to be the daughter of a parakho who had devoted his life to the independence movemen

➡ _____

※ 다음 괄호 안의 단어들을 우리말에 맞도록 바르게 배열하시오.

1 (Secret / The / My / of / Father)
➡ _____

2 (1946, / in / strange / a / visited / man / me / asked, / and / "are / Mr. / you / Kim / daughter?" / Yonghwan's)
➡ _____

3 (me, / for / was / this / odd / an / question / I / because / was / used / more / to / called / being / daughter / the / a / of / *parakho*.)
➡ _____

4 (your / "I'm / friend. / father's)
➡ _____

5 (may / you / wonder / it / if / true, / is / but / father...," / your / man / the / said.)
➡ _____

6 (that / at / moment, / was / I / expecting / news / disappointing / since / did / I / have / not / good / of / memories / father. / my)
➡ _____

7 (in / back / 1920's, / the / whenever / saw / people / me / the / in / village, / would / they / say, / goes / "there / *parakho*'s / the / daughter.")
➡ _____

8 (father / my / a / was / son / a / from / rich / very / family.)
➡ _____

9 (of / instead / living / life / the / a / of / *seonbi*, / was / he / at / always / the / house. / gambling)
➡ _____

10 (is / that / why / was / he / called / *parakho*, / a / means / which / who / someone / ruins / family's / his / fortune.)
➡ _____

11 (father / your / has / away / gambled / all / the / of / money, / now / and / he's / for / asking / more.)
➡ _____

12 (tell / and / go / him / we / that / no / have / money / more / left," / mother / my / tell / would / whenever / me / she / me / sent / to / gambling / the / house.)
➡ _____

13 (my / then, / father / yell / would / me / at / angrily, / did / "why / come / you / empty-handed?)
➡ _____

14 (me / bring / money!" / more)
➡ _____

---

1 아버지의 비밀

2 1946년에, 낯선 남자가 나를 찾아와 물었다. "당신이 김용환 씨의 딸입니까?"

3 나는 파락호의 딸이라고 불리는 것이 더 익숙했으므로 나에게 이것은 이상한 질문이었다.

4 "나는 당신 아버지의 친구입니다.

5 당신은 이것이 사실인지 의아하겠지만, 당신의 아버지는…,"이라고 그 남자는 말했다.

6 나는 내 아버지에 대해 좋은 기억을 가지고 있지 않았으므로 그 순간에 실망스러운 소식을 예상하고 있었다.

7 1920년대에 마을에서 사람들이 나를 볼 때마다 그들은 "저기에 파락호의 딸이 가네."라고 말하곤 했다.

8 나의 아버지는 매우 부유한 집안의 아들이었다.

9 선비의 삶을 사는 대신, 아버지는 항상 도박장에 계셨다.

10 그것이 그가 집안의 재산을 탕진하는 사람이라는 뜻의 파락호로 불린 이유이다.

11 "네 아버지는 도박으로 모든 돈을 써 버리고 지금 더 요구하고 계신다.

12 가서 더 이상 남아 있는 돈이 없다고 말씀드려라."라고 나의 어머니는 나를 도박장으로 보낼 때마다 말씀하시곤 했다.

13 그러면, 아버지는 나에게 화를 내시며 소리치셨다. "왜 빈손으로 왔니?

14 돈을 더 가져와!"

15 (I / when / was / years / sixteen / old, / family / my / already / had / an / made / arrangement / me / for / marry / to / Seo. / Mr.)
➡ _____

16 (part / as / the / of / tradition, / wedding / Seo's / Mr. / sent / family / my / some / family / money / buy / to / a / chest / new / clothes. / for)
➡ _____

17 (before / right / the / day, / wedding / mother / my / into / came / room / my / and / said, / father / "your / taken / has / the / for / money / chest." / the)
➡ _____

18 (asked / I / angrily, / could / "how / do / he / a / such / thing? / horrible)
➡ _____

19 (should / what / do / we / now?")
➡ _____

20 (have / "we / choice. / no)
➡ _____

21 (have / you'll / take / to / aunt's / your / chest," / old / mother / my / said.)
➡ _____

22 (embarrassing / "how / the / for / family," / would / people / whisper / my / behind / back.)
➡ _____

23 (the / since / day / first / marriage, / of / life / my / at / husband's / had / house / been / for / difficult / me.)
➡ _____

24 (father / "your / dear / my / friend...," / father's / my / continued / friend / story. / his)
➡ _____

25 (was / "he / a / not / gambler.)
➡ _____

26 (father / your / sent / family / the / to / money / the / fighters / independence / Manchuria. / in)
➡ _____

27 (made / he / look / himself / like / gambler / a / keep / to / this / secret / a / from / Japanese / the / officers.")
➡ _____

28 (first, / at / was / I / sure / not / he / if / telling / was / truth. / the)
➡ _____

29 (afterwards, / but / found / I / the / out / truth / about / father / my / and / realized / I / that / been / had / about / him. / wrong)
➡ _____

30 (since / ever / moment, / that / have / I / been / to / proud / be / daughter / the / a / of / *parakho* / who / devoted / had / life / his / the / to / movement. / independence)
➡ _____

15 내가 16살이 되었을 때, 나의 가족은 나를 서 씨와 결혼시키기로 이미 결정을 했었다.

16 결혼 풍습의 일부로, 서 씨네 가족은 새 장롱을 사라고 우리 가족에게 돈을 보냈다.

17 결혼식 바로 전날, 나의 어머니는 내 방에 들어오셔서 말씀하셨다. "네 아버지가 장롱을 살 돈을 가져가 버렸다."

18 나는 화가 나서 물었다 "어떻게 그리 끔찍한 일을 하실 수 있나요?

19 우린 이제 어떡해요?"

20 "우리에게 선택권은 없구나.

21 큰어머니의 옛 장롱을 가져가야겠구나."라고 어머니가 말씀하셨다.

22 "가문에 부끄러운 일이야."라고 사람들이 내 뒤에서 속삭이곤 했다.

23 결혼 첫날부터, 남편의 집에서의 생활은 나에게 힘겨웠다.

24 "당신의 아버지, 나의 친애하는 친구…," 나의 아버지의 친구분은 그의 이야기를 이어가셨다.

25 "그는 도박꾼이 아니었어요.

26 당신의 아버지는 가족의 돈을 만주에 있는 독립운동가들에게 보냈답니다.

27 그는 이것을 일본 순사들에게 비밀로 하기 위해 그 자신을 도박꾼처럼 보이게 했어요."

28 처음엔, 나는 그분이 사실을 얘기하시는 건지 확신할 수 없었다.

29 그러나 나중에, 나는 나의 아버지에 대한 진실을 알게 되었고 내가 아버지에 관해 오해하고 있었다는 것을 깨달았다.

30 그 순간부터, 나는 독립운동에 그의 인생을 헌신하신 파락호의 딸인 것이 자랑스러웠다.

※ 다음 우리말을 영어로 쓰시오.

1 아버지의 비밀
➡ _____

2 1946년에, 낯선 남자가 나를 찾아와 물었다. "당신이 김용환 씨의 딸입니까?"
➡ _____

3 나는 파락호의 딸이라고 불리는 것이 더 익숙했으므로 나에게 이것은 이상한 질문이었다.
➡ _____

4 "나는 당신 아버지의 친구입니다.
➡ _____

5 당신은 이것이 사실인지 의아하겠지만, 당신의 아버지는…,"이라고 그 남자는 말했다.
➡ _____

6 나는 내 아버지에 대해 좋은 기억을 가지고 있지 않았으므로 그 순간에 실망스러운 소식을 예상하고 있었다.
➡ _____

7 1920년대에 마을에서 사람들이 나를 볼 때마다 그들은 "저기에 파락호의 딸이 가네."라고 말하곤 했다.
➡ _____
_____

8 나의 아버지는 매우 부유한 집안의 아들이었다
➡ _____

9 선비의 삶을 사는 대신, 아버지는 항상 도박장에 계셨다.
➡ _____

10 그것이 그가 집안의 재산을 탕진하는 사람이라는 뜻의 파락호로 불린 이유이다.
➡ _____

11 "네 아버지는 도박으로 모든 돈을 써 버리고 지금 더 요구하고 계신다.
➡ _____

12 가서 더 이상 남아 있는 돈이 없다고 말씀드려라."라고 나의 어머니는 나를 도박장으로 보낼 때마다 말씀하시곤 했다.
➡ _____
_____

13 그러면, 아버지는 나에게 화를 내시며 소리치셨다. "왜 빈손으로 왔니?
➡ _____

14 돈을 더 가져와!"
➡ _____

15 내가 16살이 되었을 때, 나의 가족은 나를 서 씨와 결혼시키기로 이미 결정을 했었다.
➡ _____

16 결혼 풍습의 일부로, 서 씨네 가족은 새 장롱을 사라고 우리 가족에게 돈을 보냈다.
➡ _____
_____

17 결혼식 바로 전날, 나의 어머니는 내 방에 들어오셔서 말씀하셨다. "네 아버지가 장롱을 살 돈을 가져가 버렸다."
➡ _____
_____

18 나는 화가 나서 물었다 "어떻게 그리 끔찍한 일을 하실 수 있나요?
➡ _____

19 우린 이제 어떡해요?"
➡ _____

20 "우리에게 선택권은 없구나.
➡ _____

21 큰어머니의 옛 장롱을 가져가야겠구나."라고 어머니가 말씀하셨다.
➡ _____

22 "가문에 부끄러운 일이야."라고 사람들이 내 뒤에서 속삭이곤 했다.
➡ _____

23 결혼 첫날부터, 남편의 집에서의 생활은 나에게 힘겨웠다.
➡ _____

24 "당신의 아버지, 나의 친애하는 친구…," 나의 아버지의 친구분은 그의 이야기를 이어가셨다.
➡ _____

25 "그는 도박꾼이 아니었어요.
➡ _____

26 당신의 아버지는 가족의 돈을 만주에 있는 독립운동가들에게 보냈답니다.
➡ _____

27 그는 이것을 일본 순사들에게 비밀로 하기 위해 그 자신을 도박꾼처럼 보이게 했어요."
➡ _____

28 처음엔, 나는 그분이 사실을 얘기하시는 건지 확신할 수 없었다.
➡ _____

29 그러나 나중에, 나는 나의 아버지에 대한 진실을 알게 되었고 내가 아버지에 관해 오해하고 있었다는 것을 깨달았다.
➡ _____
_____

30 그 순간부터, 나는 독립운동에 그의 인생을 헌신하신 파락호의 딸인 것이 자랑스러웠다.
➡ _____
_____

※ 다음 우리말과 일치하도록 빈칸에 알맞은 말을 쓰시오.

Grammar in Real Life A

1. Mary Jane, your fans _____ _____ _____ about _____ _____.
2. 1. _____ you _____ _____ _____ a new song this month?
3. 2. Are you _____ _____ _____ music _____?
4. 3. Do you have any _____ _____ _____ _____ _____?
5. 4. Are you _____ _____ _____ a _____ this year?

1. Mary Jane, 너의 팬들은 너의 계획에 대해 많은 질문들을 가지고 있어.
2. 1. 넌 이 달에 새 노래를 발표할 거니?
3. 2. 넌 다양한 음악 장르에 관심이 있니?
4. 3. 넌 다른 아티스트들과 일할 계획을 가지고 있니?
5. 4. 넌 금년에 월드 투어를 떠날 거니?

Grammar in Real Life B

1. When I _____ _____ _____, my parents _____ _____ _____ out for a walk.
2. The house was dark and quiet, but it _____ _____ _____ _____ _____.
3. I _____ that I _____ _____ the door in my room open.
4. I _____ that someone _____ _____ the lamp.
5. I _____ _____ that someone _____ _____ my cookies on the table.
6. _____ _____ I knew _____ _____ _____!
7. I _____ _____ _____ of my dog, Lucy, and the cat next door

1. 내가 집에 돌아왔을 때 나의 부모님은 산보를 나가셨다.
2. 집은 어둡고 조용했지만, 조금 이상해 보였다.
3. 나는 내 방문을 열어둔 것이 기억났다.
4. 나는 누군가가 램프를 깨뜨린 것을 알았다.
5. 나는 누군가가 식탁 위에 있던 내 쿠키를 먹은 것을 알아냈다.
6. 마침내 나는 누가 그런 일을 했는지 알았다!
7. 나는 내 개 Lucy와 옆집 고양이의 작은 발자국들을 발견했다.

After You Read: Read and Write A

1. The _____ of My Father
2. I _____ my father was ...
3. My father _____ _____ _____ a *parakho*.
4. He _____ _____ _____ a rich family but he _____ _____ all of the money.
5. He _____ _____ the money for _____ _____ _____ _____ _____.
6. _____ my father was ...
7. My father was not a gambler.
8. He _____ the family money to the _____ _____ in Manchuria.
9. He _____ _____ _____ _____ a gambler to _____ _____ _____ _____ from the Japanese officers.

1. 나의 아버지의 비밀
2. 나는 아버지가 …라고 생각했다.
3. 나의 아버지는 '파락호'라고 알려져 있었다.
4. 그는 부잣집에 태어났지만, 모든 돈을 노름으로 날렸다.
5. 그는 심지어 새 장롱을 살 돈도 가져갔다.
6. 사실 나의 아버지는 …이었다.
7. 나의 아버지는 노름꾼이 아니었다.
8. 그는 가족의 돈을 만주에 있는 독립 운동가들에게 보냈다.
9. 그는 일본 경찰들로부터 이것을 비밀로 지키려고 스스로를 노름꾼처럼 보이게 했다.

※ 다음 우리말을 영어로 쓰시오.

Grammar in Real Life A

1. Mary Jane, 너의 팬들은 너의 계획에 대해 많은 질문들을 가지고 있어.
➡ _____

2. 1. 넌 이 달에 새 노래를 발표할 거니?
➡ _____

3. 2. 넌 다양한 음악 장르에 관심이 있니?
➡ _____

4. 3. 넌 다른 아티스트들과 일할 계획을 가지고 있니?
➡ _____

5. 4. 넌 금년에 월드 투어를 떠날 거니?
➡ _____

Grammar in Real Life B

1. 내가 집에 돌아왔을 때 나의 부모님은 산보를 나가셨다.
➡ _____

2. 집은 어둡고 조용했지만, 조금 이상해 보였다.
➡ _____

3. 나는 내 방문을 열어둔 것이 기억났다.
➡ _____

4. 나는 누군가가 램프를 깨뜨린 것을 알았다.
➡ _____

5. 나는 누군가가 식탁 위에 있던 내 쿠키를 먹은 것을 알아냈다.
➡ _____

6. 마침내 나는 누가 그런 일을 했는지 알았다!
➡ _____

7. 나는 내 개 Lucy와 옆집 고양이의 작은 발자국들을 발견했다.
➡ _____

After You Read: Read and Write A

1. 나의 아버지의 비밀
➡ _____

2. 나는 아버지가 …라고 생각했다.
➡ _____

3. 나의 아버지는 '파락호'라고 알려져 있었다.
➡ _____

4. 그는 부잣집에 태어났지만, 모든 돈을 노름으로 날렸다.
➡ _____

5. 그는 심지어 새 장롱을 살 돈도 가져갔다.
➡ _____

6. 사실 나의 아버지는 …이었다.
➡ _____

7. 나의 아버지는 노름꾼이 아니었다.
➡ _____

8. 그는 가족의 돈을 만주에 있는 독립 운동가들에게 보냈다.
➡ _____

9. 그는 일본 경찰들로부터 이것을 비밀로 지키려고 스스로를 노름꾼처럼 보이게 했다.
➡ _____

※ 다음 영어를 우리말로 쓰시오.

01	background	22	compete
02	anchor	23	positive
03	conductor	24	entirely
04	deliver	25	worthless
05	thumb	26	garbage
06	imagine	27	review
07	beat	28	environmental
08	recommend	29	recycle
09	talented	30	orchestra
10	instrument	31	notice
11	broadcast	32	shiny
12	choir	33	perform
13	local	34	pure
14	pain	35	in the beginning
15	mostly	36	calm down
16	endless	37	in harmony with
17	touch	38	be similar to
18	attention	39	send back
19	concentrate	40	sign up for
20	treasure	41	be filled with
21	consider	42	as long as
		43	be eager to

※ 다음 우리말을 영어로 쓰시오.

01 방송하다 _____

02 합창단 _____

03 완전히, 전부 _____

04 (뉴스 등의) 진행자 _____

05 감동시키다 _____

06 관심, 주목 _____

07 주로, 대부분 _____

08 긍정적인 _____

09 배경 _____

10 상상하다 _____

11 집게손가락 _____

12 악기 _____

13 현지의, 지역의 _____

14 (경기 등에) 출전하다 _____

15 재능이 있는 _____

16 쓰레기 _____

17 집중하다 _____

18 울림, 맥박; 때리다, 두드리다 _____

19 ~이라고 여기다, 생각하다 _____

20 쓸모없는, 가치 없는 _____

21 재검토하다, 복습하다 _____

22 끝없는, 무한한 _____

23 공연하다, 수행하다 _____

24 재활용하다 _____

25 고통, 아픔 _____

26 엄지손가락 _____

27 지휘자 _____

28 전하다 _____

29 추천하다 _____

30 보물, 보물 같은 것 _____

31 ~을 알아차리다 _____

32 깨끗한, 순수한 _____

33 심각한 _____

34 환경의, 환경과 관련된 _____

35 ~하는 한 _____

36 진정하다 _____

37 ~을 돌려주다 _____

38 ~로 가득 차다 _____

39 ~을 신청하다, ~에 가입하다 _____

40 ~을 하고 싶어 하다 _____

41 처음에, 초반에 _____

42 ~와 비슷하다 _____

43 ~와 조화를 이루어 _____

※ 다음 영영풀이에 알맞은 단어를 <보기>에서 골라 쓴 후, 우리말 뜻을 쓰시오.

1 _____ : having no end: _____

2 _____ : a device that is used to make music: _____

3 _____ : giving cause for hope and confidence: _____

4 _____ : a very valuable object: _____

5 _____ : a person who writes, sings, or plays music: _____

6 _____ : having no real value or use: _____

7 _____ : having a special ability to do something well: _____

8 _____ : a person or machine that gathers something: _____

9 _____ : to use something again for a different purpose: _____

10 _____ : having a smooth, shining, bright appearance: _____

11 _____ : a container for holding a liquid or gas: _____

12 _____ : to entertain an audience by singing, acting, etc.: _____

13 _____ : to give your attention to the thing you are doing, reading, etc.: _____

14 _____ : a person who directs the performance of an orchestra or choir: _____

15 _____ : things that are no longer useful and that have been thrown out: _____

16 _____ : to tell someone that something is good or useful, or that someone would be suitable for a particular job, etc.: _____

보기			
tank	worthless	recycle	picker
recommend	talented	conductor	endless
shiny	instrument	perform	musician
garbage	treasure	concentrate	positive

※ 다음 우리말과 일치하도록 빈칸에 알맞은 말을 쓰시오.

Listen & Talk 1 A-1

W: Hey, Jake. I saw you _____ the _____ _____ yesterday. _____!

M: Thanks, Anna.

W: You always seem to listen to music before you _____. Do you _____ _____ _____ to listen to music before you swim?

M: Yes, it _____ me _____ and it _____ me _____.

Listen & Talk 1 A-2

M: Hi, Sally. Where are you _____ _____?

W: I'm _____ to the music room. I have _____ _____.

M: Oh, yeah. I _____ that you've joined the _____. Do you _____ it _____ _____ _____ in the choir?

W: Yeah, it's great to sing _____ _____ _____ _____.

Listen & Talk 1-B

W: Hi, Jason. Great to see you again. I've _____ the new rap song, *Young and Wild*, that _____ _____. It's really cool.

M: Oh, thanks.

W: I really like your songs. Do you _____ _____ _____ _____ _____ _____?

M: Well, it was hard in the _____, but now it's getting easier. I _____ _____ my experiences and _____ _____ _____.

W: Wow! As they say, "_____ _____, _____ _____." Best of luck _____ your new song!

M: Thank you.

Listen & Talk 2 A-1

W: Hey, Tommy. When is the last day to _____ _____ _____ the talent show?

M: This Friday. _____ _____ _____ _____ _____ it, Megan?

W: Yeah, I'm going _____ _____ _____ a couple of people.

M: How cool! What _____ you _____ _____ do?

W: We will play K-pop music _____ the _____ and _____.

W: 안녕, Jake. 어제 수영 대회에서 네가 이긴 것을 봤어. 축하해!
M: 고마워, Anna.
W: 너는 경기하기 전에 항상 음악을 듣는 것 같더라. 수영하기 전에 음악을 듣는 게 도움이 되니?
M: 응, 그것은 나를 깨어 있게 하고 집중하는 데 도움을 줘.

M: 안녕, Sally. 어디 가는 길이야?
W: 음악실에 가는 중이야. 합창단 연습이 있거든.
M: 오, 그래. 네가 합창단에 들어간 걸 잊고 있었어. 합창단에서 노래하는 것은 재미있니?
W: 응, 다른 사람들과 조화를 이루어 노래하는 게 좋아.

W: 안녕하세요, Jason. 다시 만나서 반갑습니다. 녹음하신 새로운 랩 노래, '젊고 무모한(Young and Wild)'을 들었어요. 정말 멋지던데요.
M: 오, 고마워요.
W: 당신 노래들은 정말 좋아요. 곡을 쓰는 일이 쉬우세요?
M: 글쎄요, 처음에는 어려웠어요. 하지만 지금은 쉬워지고 있어요. 저는 제 경험을 활용해서 일기를 쓰고 있거든요.
W: 와! '고통 없이는 얻는 것도 없다.'라는 말이 있잖아요. 새 노래가 잘 되길 바랍니다!
M: 고마워요.

W: 안녕, Tommy. 장기 자랑 등록 마감이 언제야?
M: 이번 주 금요일이야. 너 그거 등록할 계획이니, Megan?
W: 응, 나는 몇 사람과 함께 공연할 거야.
M: 정말 멋지다! 무엇을 할 거야?
W: 우리는 케이팝 음악을 바이올린과 첼로로 연주할 거야.

Listen & Talk 2 A-2

W: Hello, I'd like to _____ _____ _____ a drum class.

M: Okay. Are you _____ _____ _____ _____ _____ during the week or _____ the weekend?

W: I'm _____ to take a _____ _____ . When do you _____ them?

M: There is a class on Tuesday and _____ _____ on Thursday. _____ classes start at 6 o'clock.

W: Great. I'd like to _____ _____ for the Tuesday class.

Listen & Talk 2-B

W: Are you planning to learn a _____ _____ ? I'd like to _____ the *kalimba*, a small African musical instrument. The sound it makes _____ _____ _____ that of a music box. _____ the *kalimba* is very easy. You can learn _____ _____ your _____ _____ _____ _____ beautiful music in just one lesson!

Communication

W: Hey, Anthony. Can you _____ me _____ _____ ?

M: Sure, what's _____ ?

W: I'm going to a concert at the Arts Center, but I don't know _____ _____ _____ _____ _____ .

M: Are you _____ _____ go to the _____ concert?

W: Yes. I'm going to watch the _____ concert.

M: Then, you should _____ _____ _____ on the _____ _____ . You can hear the beautiful sounds of _____ _____ better.

W: Oh, do you find it _____ _____ _____ the performance _____ _____ _____ _____ ?

M: Yes. I _____ _____ _____ than from _____ _____ .

Wrap Up

M: Hey, Alice.

W: Hi, Sam. How _____ you _____ ?

M: Great. Actually, _____ _____ a lot of pop news from your blog.

W: Oh, _____ ? Thanks _____ _____ my blog!

M: Do you _____ it interesting to _____ the _____ pop news?

W: Yes, I love to _____ _____ to people.

W: 안녕하세요, 드럼 수업에 등록하고 싶은데요.

M: 알겠습니다. 수업을 주중에 들으실 건가요, 주말에 들으실 건가요?

W: 주중 수업을 들을 계획이에요. 수업이 언제 있나요?

M: 화요일 수업이 하나 있고 또 하나는 목요일에 있어요. 두 수업 모두 6시 정각에 시작합니다.

W: 좋아요. 화요일 수업에 등록할게요.

W: 악기를 배울 계획인가요? 아프리카의 작은 악기인 '칼림바'를 추천하고 싶습니다. 그 악기가 내는 소리는 음악 상자의 소리와 비슷합니다. '칼림바'를 연주하는 것은 아주 쉬워요. 단 한 번의 수업으로 엄지손톱을 사용해 아름다운 음악을 연주하는 걸 배울 수 있어요!

W: 저기, Anthony. 나 뭐 좀 도와줄래?

M: 물론, 무슨 일이야?

W: 예술 회관에서 하는 공연에 가려고 하는데, 어떤 좌석을 골라야 할지 모르겠어.

M: 오케스트라 공연에 갈 계획이니?

W: 응. 나는 오케스트라 공연을 보려고 해.

M: 그럼, 너는 2층 좌석을 얻는 게 좋아. 다양한 악기들의 아름다운 소리를 더 잘 들을 수 있거든.

W: 오, 2층에서 공연을 듣는 것이 더 낫다는 거니?

M: 응. 다른 좌석들보다 더 낫다고 생각해.

M: 안녕, Alice.

W: 안녕, Sam. 어떻게 지내?

M: 좋아. 사실, 네 블로그에서 팝 소식을 많이 읽었어.

W: 오, 그랬어? 내 블로그를 방문해 줘서 고마워!

M: 최신 팝 소식을 올리는 게 재미있니?

W: 응, 사람들에게 소식을 전하는 게 좋아.

※ 다음 우리말에 맞도록 대화를 영어로 쓰시오.

 해석

Listen & Talk 1 A-1

W: _____

M: _____

W: _____

_____

M: _____

W: 안녕, Jake. 어제 수영 대회에서 네가 이긴 것을 봤어. 축하해!
M: 고마워, Anna.
W: 너는 경기하기 전에 항상 음악을 듣는 것 같더라. 수영하기 전에 음악을 듣는 게 도움이 되니?
M: 응, 그것은 나를 깨어 있게 하고 집중하는 데 도움을 줘.

Listen & Talk 1 A-2

M: _____

W: _____

M: _____

_____

W: _____

M: 안녕, Sally. 어디 가는 길이야?
W: 음악실에 가는 중이야. 합창단 연습이 있거든.
M: 오, 그래. 네가 합창단에 들어간 걸 잊고 있었어. 합창단에서 노래하는 것은 재미있니?
W: 응, 다른 사람들과 조화를 이루어 노래하는 게 좋아.

Listen & Talk 1-B

W: _____

_____

M: _____

W: _____

M: _____

_____

W: _____

M: _____

W: 안녕하세요, Jason. 다시 만나서 반갑습니다. 녹음하신 새로운 랩 노래, '젊고 무모한(Young and Wild)'을 들었어요. 정말 멋지던데요.
M: 오, 고마워요.
W: 당신 노래들은 정말 좋아요. 곡을 쓰는 일이 쉬우세요?
M: 글쎄요, 처음에는 어려웠어요, 하지만 지금은 쉬워지고 있어요. 저는 제 경험을 활용해서 일기를 쓰고 있거든요.
W: 와! '고통 없이는 얻는 것도 없다.'라는 말이 있잖아요. 새 노래가 잘 되길 바랍니다!
M: 고마워요.

Listen & Talk 2 A-1

W: _____

M: _____

W: _____

M: _____

W: _____

W: 안녕, Tommy. 장기 자랑 등록 마감이 언제야?
M: 이번 주 금요일이야. 너 그거 등록할 계획이니, Megan?
W: 응, 나는 몇 사람과 함께 공연할 거야.
M: 정말 멋지다! 무엇을 할 거야?
W: 우리는 케이팝 음악을 바이올린과 첼로로 연주할 거야.

Listen & Talk 2 A-2

W: _____

M: _____

W: _____

M: _____

_____

W: _____

Listen & Talk 2-B

W: _____

_____

_____

_____

Communication

W: _____

M: _____

W: _____

_____

M: _____

W: _____

M: _____

_____

W: _____

M: _____

Wrap Up

M: _____

W: _____

M: _____

W: _____

M: _____

W: _____

W: 안녕하세요, 드럼 수업에 등록하고 싶은데요.
M: 알겠습니다. 수업을 주중에 들으실 건가요, 주말에 들으실 건가요?
W: 주중 수업을 들을 계획이에요. 수업이 언제 있나요?
M: 화요일 수업이 하나 있고 또 하나는 목요일에 있어요. 두 수업 모두 6시 정각에 시작합니다.
W: 좋아요. 화요일 수업에 등록할게요.

W: 악기를 배울 계획인가요? 아프리카의 작은 악기인 '칼림바'를 추천하고 싶습니다. 그 악기가 내는 소리는 음악 상자의 소리와 비슷합니다. '칼림바'를 연주하는 것은 아주 쉬워요. 단 한 번의 수업으로 엄지손톱을 사용해 아름다운 음악을 연주하는 걸 배울 수 있어요!

W: 저기, Anthony. 나 뭐 좀 도와줄래?
M: 물론, 무슨 일이야?
W: 예술 회관에서 하는 공연에 가려고 하는데, 어떤 좌석을 골라야 할지 모르겠어.
M: 오케스트라 공연에 갈 계획이니?
W: 응. 나는 오케스트라 공연을 보려고 해.
M: 그럼, 너는 2층 좌석을 얻는 게 좋아. 다양한 악기들의 아름다운 소리를 더 잘 들을 수 있거든.
W: 오, 2층에서 공연을 듣는 것이 더 낫다는 거니?
M: 응. 다른 좌석들보다 더 낫다고 생각해.

M: 안녕, Alice.
W: 안녕, Sam. 어떻게 지내?
M: 좋아. 사실, 네 블로그에서 팝 소식을 많이 읽었어.
W: 오, 그랬어? 내 블로그를 방문해 줘서 고마워!
M: 최신 팝 소식을 올리는 게 재미있니?
W: 응, 사람들에게 소식을 전하는 게 좋아.

※ 다음 우리말과 일치하도록 빈칸에 알맞은 것을 골라 쓰시오.

1 **The** _____ _____
A. Orchestra   B. Junk

2 _____ _____ a music _____, Lucy White
A. by   B. blogger   C. written

3 "The world _____ us _____, we send _____."
A. back   B. garbage   C. sends   D. music

4 This was _____ _____ the _____ of a concert ticket I was _____.
A. back   B. given   C. written   D. on

5 The _____ group _____ _____ "The Junk Orchestra."
A. called   B. musical   C. was

6 They played instruments _____ _____ _____ _____ garbage.
A. out   B. made   C. of   D. entirely

7 I could not _____ what _____ of sound these instruments would make, so I was _____ to find _____.
A. eager   B. out   C. kind   D. imagine

8 Before the concert, I _____ that the instruments _____ _____ _____.
A. strange   B. might   C. sound   D. thought

9 After a _____ _____, a group of young people began to _____ on the _____.
A. minutes   B. stage   C. few   D. walk

10 The first _____ I _____ was their instruments: a cello made out of a shiny oil tank, a violin _____ with forks, and a flute made _____ a water pipe and buttons.
A. made   B. noticed   C. with   D. thing

11 The concert began _____ a girl _____ Bach's *Cello Suite No. 1* _____ her _____ cello.
A. on   B. with   C. playing   D. shiny

12 I _____ _____ _____ the _____ sound.
A. deep   B. shocked   C. was   D. by

13 I was so _____ the music that I forgot that they were playing _____ instruments _____ from _____ materials.
A. recycled   B. into   C. with   D. made

14 _____ the concert, I was _____ to _____ a story _____ the orchestra.
A. eager   B. after   C. write   D. about

15 I _____ Favio Chávez, the _____, and _____ him about the _____.
A. asked   B. conductor   C. met   D. orchestra

16 **Lucy White**: _____ _____ _____ _____ **The Junk Orchestra?**
A. did   B. why   C. start   D. you

17 **Favio Chávez**: When I went to a small town called Cateura in Paraguay to _____ _____ a recycling program in 2005, I saw children living in a town that was mostly _____ _____ garbage.
A. on   B. filled   C. work   D. with

1 정크 오케스트라

2 음악 블로거 Lucy White 씀

3 "세상이 우리에게 쓰레기를 보내면, 우리는 음악을 돌려준다."

4 이것은 내가 받은 음악회 입장권의 뒷면에 쓰여 있었다.

5 그 음악 그룹은 '정크 오케스트라'라고 불렸다.

6 그들은 완전히 쓰레기로만 만들어진 악기를 연주했다.

7 나는 그런 악기들이 어떤 종류의 소리를 낼지 상상할 수 없었고, 그래서 나는 알아보고 싶어졌다.

8 음악회가 시작되기 전에 나는 그 악기들이 이상한 소리를 낼지도 모른다고 생각했다.

9 몇 분 후에 한 무리의 젊은이들이 무대 위로 걸어 올라오기 시작했다.

10 내가 처음으로 알아차린 것은 그들의 악기였는데, 그것들은 반짝이는 기름통으로 만들어진 첼로, 포크로 만들어진 바이올린, 수도관과 단추로 만들어진 플루트였다.

11 음악회는 한 소녀가 자신의 반짝이는 첼로로 바흐의 〈첼로 모음곡 1번〉을 연주하는 것으로 시작되었다.

12 나는 그 깊은 소리에 충격을 받았다.

13 나는 음악에 너무 심취해서 그들이 재활용된 재료들로 만들어진 악기를 연주하고 있다는 것을 잊었다.

14 음악회가 끝나고, 나는 그 오케스트라에 대한 이야기를 몹시 쓰고 싶었다.

15 나는 지휘자인 Favio Chávez를 만나서 그에게 오케스트라에 대해 물었다.

16 Lucy White: 왜 당신은 정크 오케스트라를 시작하셨나요?

17 Favio Chávez: 2005년에 재활용 프로그램에서 일을 하기 위해서 내가 파라과이의 카테우라라고 불리는 작은 마을에 갔을 때, 나는 대부분이 쓰레기로 가득 차 있는 마을에 살고 있는 어린이들을 보았습니다.

18 I wanted to add _____ _____ to their lives, so I decided to _____ my love of music _____ them.

    A. share   B. positive   C. with   D. something

19 Lucy White: Why did you _____ garbage _____ _____ _____?

    A. make   B. to   C. instruments   D. use

20 Favio Chávez: One person's _____ is _____ person's _____.

    A. another   B. garbage   C. treasure

21 Nicolás Gómez, a _____ _____ _____, helped me a _____.

    A. lot   B. local   C. picker   D. garbage

22 He made it _____ for children to play music by _____ instruments _____ of _____.

    A. out   B. possible   C. making   D. garbage

23 The wonderful _____ about these _____ was that the children didn't have to _____ about _____ a lot of money on them.

    A. thing   B. spending   C. instruments   D. worry

24 Lucy White: What do you _____ people _____ _____ your music?

    A. to   B. through   C. want   D. learn

25 Favio Chávez: I want people to know that _____ something _____ can make _____ _____.

    A. worthless   B. music   C. even   D. inspiring

26 After interviewing Chávez, I realized that it really doesn't _____ what instrument you play with _____ _____ as you put your heart _____ playing it.

    A. into   B. matter   C. long   D. as

27 The children of Cateura showed me that an orchestra is _____ by people, _____ _____ _____.

    A. formed   B. by   C. not   D. instruments

28 Comments

29 Annie: (23 _____ ago) So _____ to see _____ music can change _____.

    A. moving   B. lives   C. how   D. seconds

30 The _____ of _____ is _____!

    A. endless   B. power   C. music

31 Thomas: (1 minute ago) After the concert, I _____ it to inspire people by music _____ with _____ instruments.

    A. possible   B. recycled   C. found   D. played

32 Kate: (5 days ago) Not only do these _____ young people _____ great music, but they also bring _____ environmental problems to our _____.

    A. attention   B. deliver   C. serious   D. talented

---

18 나는 그들의 삶에 긍정적인 무엇인가를 더해 주고 싶어서, 음악에 대한 나의 사랑을 그들과 나누기로 결정했습니다.

19 Lucy White: 왜 당신은 악기를 만들기 위해 쓰레기를 이용했나요?

20 Favio Chávez: 한 사람의 쓰레기는 다른 사람의 보물입니다.

21 그 지역의 쓰레기 줍는 사람인 Nicolás Gámez가 나를 많이 도와주었습니다.

22 그는 쓰레기로 악기를 만들어 줌으로써 어린이들이 음악을 연주하는 것이 가능하도록 만들었습니다.

23 이 악기들의 멋진 점은 어린이들이 악기에 많은 돈을 쓸 것을 걱정하지 않아도 된다는 점이었죠.

24 Lucy White: 당신의 음악을 통해서 사람들이 무엇을 배우기를 원하십니까?

25 Favio Chávez: 나는 가치 없는 것도 영감을 주는 음악을 만들어 낼 수 있다는 것을 사람들이 알게 되기를 원합니다.

26 Chávez를 인터뷰한 후에 나는 사람들이 악기를 연주하는 데 마음을 쏟아붓는 한, 그 사람이 연주하는 악기가 무엇인지는 별로 중요하지 않다는 것을 깨달았다.

27 카테우라의 어린이들은 나에게 오케스트라는 악기에 의해서가 아니라 사람에 의해 이루어지는 것이라는 것을 보여 주었다.

28 감상평

29 Annie: (23초 전) 음악이 삶을 바꿀 수 있다는 것을 보아서 너무 가슴이 뭉클하다.

30 음악의 힘은 끝이 없다!

31 Thomas: (1분 전) 음악회가 끝난 후, 나는 재활용 악기로 연주되는 음악으로 사람들에게 영감을 주는 것이 가능하다는 것을 알았다.

32 Kate: (5일 전) 이 재능 있는 젊은이들은 훌륭한 음악을 전할 뿐만 아니라, 또한 심각한 환경 문제에 우리가 주목하게 한다.

※ 다음 우리말과 일치하도록 빈칸에 알맞은 말을 쓰시오.

1 The _____ Orchestra

2 _____ _____ a _____ _____, Lucy White

3 "The world sends us _____, we _____ _____ _____."

4 This was _____ _____ _____ _____ _____ a concert ticket I _____ _____.

5 The musical group _____ _____ "The Junk Orchestra."

6 They played instruments _____ _____ _____ _____ _____.

7 I could not imagine what kind of sound these instruments would make, so I _____ _____ _____ _____ _____.

8 Before the concert, I _____ that the instruments _____ _____ _____.

9 _____ _____ _____ _____, a group of young people _____ _____ _____ on the stage.

10 _____ _____ _____ _____ _____ was their instruments: a cello _____ _____ _____ a shiny oil tank, a violin made with forks, and a flute made with a water pipe and buttons.

11 The concert began _____ _____ _____ _____ Bach's *Cello Suite No. 1* _____ her _____ _____.

12 I _____ _____ _____ the _____ _____.

13 I _____ so _____ the music that I forgot that they were playing with instruments _____ _____ _____ _____.

14 After the concert, I _____ _____ _____ _____ _____ a story about the orchestra.

15 I met Favio Chávez, _____ _____, and _____ him about the orchestra.

16 **Lucy White**: _____ _____ _____ _____ **The Junk Orchestra?**

17 **Favio Chávez**: When I went to a small town called Cateura in Paraguay _____ _____ _____ a recycling program in 2005, I _____ children _____ in a town that _____ _____ _____ _____ _____.

1 정크 오케스트라
2 음악 블로거 Lucy White 씀
3 "세상이 우리에게 쓰레기를 보내면, 우리는 음악을 돌려준다."
4 이것은 내가 받은 음악회 입장권의 뒷면에 쓰여 있었다.
5 그 음악 그룹은 '정크 오케스트라'라고 불렸다.
6 그들은 완전히 쓰레기로만 만들어진 악기를 연주했다.
7 나는 그런 악기들이 어떤 종류의 소리를 낼지 상상할 수 없었고, 그래서 나는 알아보고 싶어졌다.
8 음악회가 시작되기 전에 나는 그 악기들이 이상한 소리를 낼지도 모른다고 생각했다.
9 몇 분 후에 한 무리의 젊은이들이 무대 위로 걸어 올라오기 시작했다.
10 내가 처음으로 알아차린 것은 그들의 악기였는데, 그것들은 반짝이는 기름통으로 만들어진 첼로, 포크로 만들어진 바이올린, 수도관과 단추로 만들어진 플루트였다.
11 음악회는 한 소녀가 자신의 반짝이는 첼로로 바흐의 〈첼로 모음곡 1번〉을 연주하는 것으로 시작되었다.
12 나는 그 깊은 소리에 충격을 받았다.
13 나는 음악에 너무 심취해서 그들이 재활용된 재료들로 만들어진 악기를 연주하고 있다는 것을 잊었다.
14 음악회가 끝나고, 나는 그 오케스트라에 대한 이야기를 몹시 쓰고 싶었다.
15 나는 지휘자인 Favio Chávez를 만나서 그에게 오케스트라에 대해 물었다.
16 Lucy White: 왜 당신은 정크 오케스트라를 시작하셨나요?
17 Favio Chávez: 2005년에 재활용 프로그램에서 일을 하기 위해서 내가 파라과이의 카테우라라고 불리는 작은 마을에 갔을 때, 나는 대부분이 쓰레기로 가득 차 있는 마을에 살고 있는 어린이들을 보았습니다.

18 I wanted to add _____ _____ to their lives, _____ I decided to _____ my love of music _____ them.

19 **Lucy White: Why did you use garbage** _____ _____ _____?

20 **Favio Chávez**: One person's _____ is _____ _____.

21 Nicolás Gómez, _____ _____ _____ _____, helped me _____ _____.

22 He made _____ possible _____ _____ to play music by making instruments _____ _____ _____.

23 _____ _____ _____ about these instruments was that the children _____ _____ _____ _____ _____ a lot of money on them.

24 **Lucy White: What do you want people** _____ _____ **your music?**

25 **Favio Chávez**: I want people to know that _____ _____ can make _____ _____.

26 After _____ Chávez, I realized that it really _____ _____ what instrument you play with _____ _____ _____ you put your heart _____ playing it.

27 The children of Cateura showed me that an orchestra is _____ _____ people, _____ _____ _____.

28 _____

29 **Annie**: (23 _____ ago) So moving to see _____ music can change _____.

30 The power of music is _____!

31 **Thomas**: (1 minute ago) After the concert, I found it possible to inspire people by music _____ _____ recycled instruments.

32 **Kate**: (5 days ago) _____ _____ _____ these _____ _____ people _____ great music, but they also _____ serious environmental problems _____ _____ _____.

18 나는 그들의 삶에 긍정적인 무엇인가를 더해 주고 싶어서, 음악에 대한 나의 사랑을 그들과 나누기로 결정했습니다.

19 Lucy White: 왜 당신은 악기를 만들기 위해 쓰레기를 이용했나요?

20 Favio Chávez: 한 사람의 쓰레기는 다른 사람의 보물입니다.

21 그 지역의 쓰레기 줍는 사람인 Nicolás Gámez가 나를 많이 도와주었습니다.

22 그는 쓰레기로 악기를 만들어 줌으로써 어린이들이 음악을 연주하는 것이 가능하도록 만들었습니다.

23 이 악기들의 멋진 점은 어린이들이 악기에 많은 돈을 쓸 것을 걱정하지 않아도 된다는 점이었죠.

24 Lucy White: 당신의 음악을 통해서 사람들이 무엇을 배우기를 원하십니까?

25 Favio Chávez: 나는 가치 없는 것도 영감을 주는 음악을 만들어 낼 수 있다는 것을 사람들이 알게 되기를 원합니다.

26 Chávez를 인터뷰한 후에 나는 사람들이 악기를 연주하는 데 마음을 쏟아붓는 한, 그 사람이 연주하는 악기가 무엇인지는 별로 중요하지 않다는 것을 깨달았다.

27 카테우라의 어린이들은 나에게 오케스트라는 악기에 의해서가 아니라 사람에 의해 이루어지는 것이라는 것을 보여 주었다.

28 감상평

29 Annie: (23초 전) 음악이 삶을 바꿀 수 있다는 것을 보아서 너무 가슴이 뭉클하다.

30 음악의 힘은 끝이 없다!

31 Thomas: (1분 전) 음악회가 끝난 후, 나는 재활용 악기로 연주되는 음악으로 사람들에게 영감을 주는 것이 가능하다는 것을 알았다.

32 Kate: (5일 전) 이 재능 있는 젊은이들은 훌륭한 음악을 전할 뿐만 아니라, 또한 심각한 환경 문제에 우리가 주목하게 한다.

※ 다음 문장을 우리말로 쓰시오.

1 The Junk Orchestra
➡ _____

2 written by a music blogger, Lucy White
➡ _____

3 "The world sends us garbage, we send back music."
➡ _____

4 This was written on the back of a concert ticket I was given.
➡ _____

5 The musical group was called "The Junk Orchestra."
➡ _____

6 They played instruments made entirely out of garbage.
➡ _____

7 I could not imagine what kind of sound these instruments would make, so I was eager to find out.
➡ _____

8 Before the concert, I thought that the instruments might sound strange.
➡ _____

9 After a few minutes, a group of young people began to walk on the stage.
➡ _____

10 The first thing I noticed was their instruments: a cello made out of a shiny oil tank, a violin made with forks, and a flute made with a water pipe and buttons.
➡ _____
_____

11 The concert began with a girl playing Bach's *Cello Suite No. 1* on her shiny cello
➡ _____

12 I was shocked by the deep sound.
➡ _____

13 I was so into the music that I forgot that they were playing with instruments made from recycled materials.
➡ _____

14 After the concert, I was eager to write a story about the orchestra.
➡ _____

15 I met Favio Chávez, the conductor, and asked him about the orchestra.
➡ _____

16 Lucy White: Why did you start The Junk Orchestra?
➡ _____

17 Favio Chávez: When I went to a small town called Cateura in Paraguay to work on a recycling program in 2005, I saw children living in a town that was mostly filled with garbage.
➡ _____
_____

18 I wanted to add something positive to their lives, so I decided to share my love of music with them.

➡ _____

19 Lucy White: Why did you use garbage to make instruments?

➡ _____

20 Favio Chávez: One person's garbage is another person's treasure.

➡ _____

21 Nicolás Gómez, a local garbage picker, helped me a lot.

➡ _____

22 He made it possible for children to play music by making instruments out of garbage.

➡ _____

23 The wonderful thing about these instruments was that the children didn't have to worry about spending a lot of money on them.

➡ _____

24 Lucy White: What do you want people to learn through your music?

➡ _____

25 Favio Chávez: I want people to know that even something worthless can make inspiring music.

➡ _____

26 After interviewing Chávez, I realized that it really doesn't matter what instrument you play with as long as you put your heart into playing it.

➡ _____

27 The children of Cateura showed me that an orchestra is formed by people, not by instruments.

➡ _____

28 Comments

➡ _____

29 Annie: (23 seconds ago) So moving to see how music can change lives.

➡ _____

30 The power of music is endless!

➡ _____

31 Thomas: (1 minute ago) After the concert, I found it possible to inspire people by music played with recycled instruments.

➡ _____

32 Kate: (5 days ago) Not only do these talented young people deliver great music, but they also bring serious environmental problems to our attention.

➡ _____

※ 다음 괄호 안의 단어들을 우리말에 맞도록 바르게 배열하시오.

1 (Junk / The / Orchestra)
➡ _____

2 (by / written / music / a / blogger, / White / Lucy)
➡ _____

3 (world / "the / us / sends / garbage, / send / we / music." / back)
➡ _____

4 (was / this / on / written / back / the / a / of / ticket / concert / was / I / given.)
➡ _____

5 (musical / the / was / group / called / Junk / "The / Orchestra.")
➡ _____

6 (played / they / instruments / entirely / made / out / garbage. / of)
➡ _____

7 (could / I / imagine / not / kind / what / sound / of / these / would / instruments / make / I / so / eager / was / to / out. / find)
➡ _____

8 (the / before / concert, / thought / I / the / that / might / instruments / strange. / sound)
➡ _____

9 (a / after / minutes, / few / group / a / young / of / began / people / walk / to / on / stage. / the)
➡ _____

10 (first / the / I / thing / was / noticed / instruments: / their / cello / a / out / made / of / shiny / a / tank, / oil / violin / a / with / made / forks, / a / and / flute / with / made / a / pipe / water / buttons. / and)
➡ _____

11 (concert / the / with / began / girl / a / Bach's / playing / *Cello No. Suite 1* / her / on / cello. / shiny)
➡ _____

12 (was / I / by / shocked / deep / the / sound.)
➡ _____

13 (was / I / so / the / into / music / I / that / forgot / they / that / playing / were / instruments / with / made / recycled / from / materials.)
➡ _____

14 (the / after / concert, / was / I / to / eager / a / write / about / story / orchestra. / the)
➡ _____

15 (met / I / Cháves, / Favio / conductor, / the / and / him / asked / the / about / orchestra.)
➡ _____

16 (Lucy White: / did / why / start / you / Junk / The / Orchestra?)
➡ _____

17 (Favio Chávez: / I / when / to / went / small / a / town / Cateura / called / Paraguay / in / work / to / a / on / program / recycling / 2005, / in / saw / I / children / living / a / in / that / town / mostly / was / with / filled / garbage.)
➡ _____

1 정크 오케스트라
2 음악 블로거 Lucy White 씀
3 "세상이 우리에게 쓰레기를 보내면, 우리는 음악을 돌려준다."
4 이것은 내가 받은 음악회 입장권의 뒷면에 쓰여 있었다.
5 그 음악 그룹은 '정크 오케스트라'라고 불렸다.
6 그들은 완전히 쓰레기로만 만들어진 악기를 연주했다.
7 나는 그런 악기들이 어떤 종류의 소리를 낼지 상상할 수 없었고, 그래서 나는 알아보고 싶어졌다.
8 음악회가 시작되기 전에 나는 그 악기들이 이상한 소리를 낼지도 모른다고 생각했다.
9 몇 분 후에 한 무리의 젊은이들이 무대 위로 걸어 올라오기 시작했다.
10 내가 처음으로 알아차린 것은 그들의 악기였는데, 그것들은 반짝이는 기름통으로 만들어진 첼로, 포크로 만들어진 바이올린, 수도관과 단추로 만들어진 플루트였다.
11 음악회는 한 소녀가 자신의 반짝이는 첼로로 바흐의 〈첼로 모음곡 1번〉을 연주하는 것으로 시작되었다.
12 나는 그 깊은 소리에 충격을 받았다.
13 나는 음악에 너무 심취해서 그들이 재활용된 재료들로 만들어진 악기를 연주하고 있다는 것을 잊었다.
14 음악회가 끝나고, 나는 그 오케스트라에 대한 이야기를 몹시 쓰고 싶었다.
15 나는 지휘자인 Favio Chávez를 만나서 그에게 오케스트라에 대해 물었다.
16 Lucy White: 왜 당신은 정크 오케스트라를 시작하셨나요?
17 Favio Chávez: 2005년에 재활용 프로그램에서 일을 하기 위해서 내가 파라과이의 카테우라라고 불리는 작은 마을에 갔을 때, 나는 대부분이 쓰레기로 가득 차 있는 마을에 살고 있는 어린이들을 보았습니다.

18 (wanted / I / add / to / positive / something / their / to / lives, / I / so / to / decided / my / share / love / music / of / them. / with)
➡ _____

19 (Lucy White: / did / why / use / you / to / garbage / instruments? / make)
➡ _____

20 (Favio Chávez: / person's / one / is / garbage / another / treasure. / person's)
➡ _____

21 (Gómez, / Nicolás / local / a / picker / garbage / me / helped / lot. / a)
➡ _____

22 (made / he / possible / it / children / for / play / to / by / music / instruments / making / of / out / garbage.)
➡ _____

23 (wonderful / the / about / thing / instrements / these / that / was / children / the / have / didn't / to / about / worry / spending / lot / a / of / money / them. / on)
➡ _____

24 (Lucy White: / do / what / want / you / to / people / learn / your / through / music?)
➡ _____

25 (Favio Chávez: / want / I / to / people / that / know / something / even / can / worthless / make / music. / inspiring)
➡ _____

26 (interviewing / after / Chávez, / realized / I / it / that / doesn't / really / what / matter / instrument / play / you / with / long / as / you / as / put / heart / your / into / it. / playing)
➡ _____

27 (children / the / Cateura / of / me / showed / that / orchestra / an / formed / is / people, / by / by / not / instruments.)
➡ _____

28 Coments
29 (Annie: (seconds / (23 / ago) // moving / so / see / to / music / how / change / can / lives.)
➡ _____

30 (power / the / music / of / endless! / is)
➡ _____

31 (Thomas: / minute / (1 / ago) // the / after / concert, / found / I / it / to / possible / inspire / by / people / played / music / recycled / with / instruments.)
➡ _____

32 (Kate: / days / (5 / ago) // only / not / these / do / young / talented / people / deliver / people / music, / great / they / but / bring / also / serious / problems / environmental / out / to / attention.)
➡ _____

18 나는 그들의 삶에 긍정적인 무엇인가를 더해 주고 싶어서, 음악에 대한 나의 사랑을 그들과 나누기로 결정했습니다.

19 Lucy White: 왜 당신은 악기를 만들기 위해 쓰레기를 이용했나요?

20 Favio Chávez: 한 사람의 쓰레기는 다른 사람의 보물입니다.

21 그 지역의 쓰레기 줍는 사람인 Nicolás Gámez가 나를 많이 도와주었습니다.

22 그는 쓰레기로 악기를 만들어 줌으로써 어린이들이 음악을 연주하는 것이 가능하도록 만들었습니다.

23 이 악기들의 멋진 점은 어린이들이 악기에 많은 돈을 쓸 것을 걱정하지 않아도 된다는 점이었죠.

24 Lucy White: 당신의 음악을 통해서 사람들이 무엇을 배우기를 원하십니까?

25 Favio Chávez: 나는 가치 없는 것도 영감을 주는 음악을 만들어 낼 수 있다는 것을 사람들이 알게 되기를 원합니다.

26 Chávez를 인터뷰한 후에 나는 사람들이 악기를 연주하는 데 마음을 쏟아붓는 한, 그 사람이 연주하는 악기가 무엇인지는 별로 중요하지 않다는 것을 깨달았다.

27 카테우라의 어린이들은 나에게 오케스트라는 악기에 의해서가 아니라 사람에 의해 이루어지는 것이라는 것을 보여 주었다.

28 감상평

29 Annie: (23초 전) 음악이 삶을 바꿀 수 있다는 것을 보아서 너무 가슴이 뭉클하다.

30 음악의 힘은 끝이 없다!

31 Thomas: (1분 전) 음악회가 끝난 후, 나는 재활용 악기로 연주되는 음악으로 사람들에게 영감을 주는 것이 가능하다는 것을 알았다.

32 Kate: (5일 전) 이 재능 있는 젊은이들은 훌륭한 음악을 전할 뿐만 아니라, 또한 심각한 환경 문제에 우리가 주목하게 한다.

※ 다음 우리말을 영어로 쓰시오.

1 정크 오케스트라

➡ _____

2 음악 블로거 Lucy White 씀

➡ _____

3 "세상이 우리에게 쓰레기를 보내면, 우리는 음악을 돌려준다."

➡ _____

4 이것은 내가 받은 음악회 입장권의 뒷면에 쓰여 있었다.

➡ _____

5 그 음악 그룹은 '정크 오케스트라'라고 불렸다.

➡ _____

6 그들은 완전히 쓰레기로만 만들어진 악기를 연주했다.

➡ _____

7 나는 그런 악기들이 어떤 종류의 소리를 낼지 상상할 수 없었고, 그래서 나는 알아보고 싶어졌다.

➡ _____

8 음악회가 시작되기 전에 나는 그 악기들이 이상한 소리를 낼지도 모른다고 생각했다.

➡ _____

9 몇 분 후에 한 무리의 젊은이들이 무대 위로 걸어 올라오기 시작했다.

➡ _____

10 내가 처음으로 알아차린 것은 그들의 악기였는데, 그것들은 반짝이는 기름통으로 만들어진 첼로, 포크로 만들어진 바이올린, 수도관과 단추로 만들어진 플루트였다.

➡ _____

_____

11 음악회는 한 소녀가 자신의 반짝이는 첼로로 바흐의 〈첼로 모음곡 1번〉을 연주하는 것으로 시작되었다.

➡ _____

12 나는 그 깊은 소리에 충격을 받았다.

➡ _____

13 나는 음악에 너무 심취해서 그들이 재활용된 재료들로 만들어진 악기를 연주하고 있다는 것을 잊었다.

➡ _____

14 음악회가 끝나고, 나는 그 오케스트라에 대한 이야기를 몹시 쓰고 싶었다.

➡ _____

15 나는 지휘자인 Favio Chávez를 만나서 그에게 오케스트라에 대해 물었다.

➡ _____

16 Lucy White: 왜 당신은 정크 오케스트라를 시작하셨나요?

➡ _____

17 Favio Chávez: 2005년에 재활용 프로그램에서 일을 하기 위해서 내가 파라과이의 카테우라라고 불리는 작은 마을에 갔을 때, 나는 대부분이 쓰레기로 가득 차 있는 마을에 살고 있는 어린이들을 보았습니다.

➡ _____

_____

18 나는 그들의 삶에 긍정적인 무엇인가를 더해 주고 싶어서, 음악에 대한 나의 사랑을 그들과 나누기로 결정했습니다.

➡ _____

19 Lucy White: 왜 당신은 악기를 만들기 위해 쓰레기를 이용했나요?

➡ _____

20 Favio Chávez: 한 사람의 쓰레기는 다른 사람의 보물입니다.

➡ _____

21 그 지역의 쓰레기 줍는 사람인 Nicolás Gámez가 나를 많이 도와주었습니다.

➡ _____

22 그는 쓰레기로 악기를 만들어 줌으로써 어린이들이 음악을 연주하는 것이 가능하도록 만들었습니다.

➡ _____

23 이 악기들의 멋진 점은 어린이들이 악기에 많은 돈을 쓸 것을 걱정하지 않아도 된다는 점이었죠.

➡ _____

24 Lucy White: 당신의 음악을 통해서 사람들이 무엇을 배우기를 원하십니까?

➡ _____

25 Favio Chávez: 나는 가치 없는 것도 영감을 주는 음악을 만들어 낼 수 있다는 것을 사람들이 알게 되기를 원합니다.

➡ _____

26 Chávez를 인터뷰한 후에 나는 사람들이 악기를 연주하는 데 마음을 쏟아붓는 한, 그 사람이 연주하는 악기가 무엇인지는 별로 중요하지 않다는 것을 깨달았다.

➡ _____

27 카테우라의 어린이들은 나에게 오케스트라는 악기에 의해서가 아니라 사람에 의해 이루어지는 것이라는 것을 보여 주었다.

➡ _____

28 감상평

➡ _____

29 Annie: (23초 전) 음악이 삶을 바꿀 수 있다는 것을 보아서 너무 가슴이 뭉클하다.

➡ _____

30 음악의 힘은 끝이 없다!

➡ _____

31 Thomas: (1분 전) 음악회가 끝난 후, 나는 재활용 악기로 연주되는 음악으로 사람들에게 영감을 주는 것이 가능하다는 것을 알았다.

➡ _____

32 Kate: (5일 전) 이 재능 있는 젊은이들은 훌륭한 음악을 전할 뿐만 아니라, 또한 심각한 환경 문제에 우리가 주목하게 한다.

➡ _____

※ 다음 우리말과 일치하도록 빈칸에 알맞은 말을 쓰시오.

After You Read A

1. The _____ _____

2. The world _____ _____ _____, we _____ _____ music.

3. _____ the _____

4. The young people _____ _____ _____ _____ _____ _____.

5. It started _____ _____ _____ _____ made out of _____ _____ _____ _____.

6. I _____ _____ _____ the deep sound.

7. _____ _____ _____ Mr. Chávez

8. He went to Cateura in Paraguay _____ _____ _____ _____ _____ _____.

9. He _____ _____ _____ his love of music _____ the children.

10. A _____ _____ _____ helped him.

11. An orchestra is formed _____ _____, _____ _____ _____.

Grammar in Real Life

1. I _____ a _____ _____.

2. In the news room, I _____ _____ the desk _____ anchors give the news.

3. _____ _____ two screens _____ _____ _____ _____ _____.

4. I could _____ _____ _____ _____ _____ _____ the screen.

5. After I _____ _____ _____ the room, I could see _____ _____ on the TV screen.

6. I really _____ _____ _____ _____ _____ computer graphics.

Wrap Up 2

1. M: Hi, Julie. _____ _____ you _____?

2. W: Hi, Chris. I'm _____ to my guitar lesson. Our band has a concert at the hospital _____ _____.

3. M: This Sunday? _____ you _____ _____ _____ _____ at the Happy Children's Hospital?

4. W: Yes. _____ do you _____ _____ the concert?

5. M: Oh, my sister _____ _____ _____ _____ _____ _____ there, so I'm _____ _____ the concert, _____.

6. W: Great. _____ and _____ our _____!

---

1. 정크 오케스트라
2. 세상이 우리에게 쓰레기를 보내면 우리는 음악을 돌려준다.
3. 음악회에 관해
4. 젊은이들은 쓰레기로 만들어진 악기를 연주했다.
5. 음악회는 한 소녀의 반짝이는 기름통으로 만들어진 첼로 연주로 시작되었다.
6. 나는 그 깊은 소리에 충격을 받았다.
7. Chávez 씨와의 인터뷰
8. 그는 재활용 프로그램에서 일을 하기 위해 파라과이의 카테우라에 갔다.
9. 그는 그의 음악에 대한 사랑을 아이들과 나누기로 결정했다.
10. 그 지역의 쓰레기 줍는 사람이 그를 도와주었다.
11. 오케스트라는 악기에 의해서가 아니라 사람에 의해 이루어지는 것이다.

1. 나는 방송국을 방문했다.
2. 뉴스 룸에서 나는 앵커들이 뉴스를 전하는 책상에 앉았다.
3. 벽에는 두 개의 스크린이 걸려 있었다.
4. 나는 화면을 가로질러 움직이는 문장들을 소리 내어 읽을 수 있었다.
5. 방에서 나온 후 TV 화면에 녹화된 내 모습을 볼 수 있었다.
6. 나는 컴퓨터 그래픽으로 만들어진 배경이 정말 마음에 들었다.

1. M: 안녕, Julie. 어디 가는 길이니?
2. W: 안녕, Chris. 나는 기타 수업에 가는 길이야. 우리 밴드가 이번 주 일요일에 병원에서 공연을 하거든.
3. M: 이번 주 일요일? Happy 아동 병원에서 공연할 계획이니?
4. W: 응. 그 공연에 대해 어떻게 알고 있어?
5. M: 아, 내 여동생이 거기서 피아노를 연주할 거라서 나도 그 공연에 갈 거야.
6. W: 잘됐다. 와서 우리 공연을 봐!

※ 다음 우리말을 영어로 쓰시오.

After You Read A

1. 정크 오케스트라
➡ _____

2. 세상이 우리에게 쓰레기를 보내면 우리는 음악을 돌려준다.
➡ _____

3. 음악회에 관해
➡ _____

4. 젊은이들은 쓰레기로 만들어진 악기를 연주했다.
➡ _____

5. 음악회는 한 소녀의 반짝이는 기름통으로 만들어진 첼로 연주로 시작되었다.
➡ _____

6. 나는 그 깊은 소리에 충격을 받았다.
➡ _____

7. Chávez 씨와의 인터뷰
➡ _____

8. 그는 재활용 프로그램에서 일을 하기 위해 파라과이의 카테우라에 갔다.
➡ _____

9. 그는 그의 음악에 대한 사랑을 아이들과 나누기로 결정했다.
➡ _____

10. 그 지역의 쓰레기 줍는 사람이 그를 도와주었다.
➡ _____

11. 오케스트라는 악기에 의해서가 아니라 사람에 의해 이루어지는 것이다.
➡ _____

Grammar in Real Life

1. 나는 방송국을 방문했다.
➡ _____

2. 뉴스 룸에서 나는 앵커들이 뉴스를 전하는 책상에 앉았다.
➡ _____

3. 벽에는 두 개의 스크린이 걸려 있었다.
➡ _____

4. 나는 화면을 가로질러 움직이는 문장들을 소리 내어 읽을 수 있었다.
➡ _____

5. 방에서 나온 후 TV 화면에 녹화된 내 모습을 볼 수 있었다.
➡ _____

6. 나는 컴퓨터 그래픽으로 만들어진 배경이 정말 마음에 들었다.
➡ _____

Wrap Up 2

1. M: 안녕, Julie. 어디 가는 길이니?
➡ _____

2. W: 안녕, Chris. 나는 기타 수업에 가는 길이야. 우리 밴드가 이번 주 일요일에 병원에서 공연을 하거든.
➡ _____

3. M: 이번 주 일요일? Happy 아동 병원에서 공연할 계획이니?
➡ _____

4. W: 응. 그 공연에 대해 어떻게 알고 있어?
➡ _____

5. M: 아, 내 여동생이 거기서 피아노를 연주할 거라서 나도 그 공연에 갈 거야.
➡ _____

6. W: 잘됐다. 와서 우리 공연을 봐!
➡ _____

※ 다음 영어를 우리말로 쓰시오.

01 seriously _____

02 admit _____

03 critically _____

04 awful _____

05 extremely _____

06 fake _____

07 confess _____

08 critical _____

09 harmful _____

10 citizen _____

11 mislead _____

12 height _____

13 strengthen _____

14 adult _____

15 argument _____

16 publish _____

17 recognize _____

18 incident _____

19 criticize _____

20 prove _____

21 current _____

22 disaster _____

23 escape _____

24 judge _____

25 describe _____

26 nevertheless _____

27 reliable _____

28 wound _____

29 muscle _____

30 support _____

31 mine _____

32 measure _____

33 source _____

34 chest _____

35 be related to _____

36 look into _____

37 make up _____

38 break down _____

39 according to _____

40 draw one's attention to _____

41 think outside the box _____

42 be useful for _____

43 on the loose _____

※ 다음 우리말을 영어로 쓰시오.

01 인정하다, 자백하다		22 믿을 만한, 신뢰할 만한
02 근육		23 끔찍한, 지독한
03 그럼에도 불구하고		24 시민
04 경쟁자, 경쟁 상대		25 판단하다
05 진지하게, 심각하게		26 측정하다, 재다
06 성인, 어른		27 현재의, 지금의
07 잘못 이끌다, 오해하게 하다		28 발행하다, 출판하다
08 광산; 채굴하다		29 위험한, 위독한
09 비난하다		30 알아보다
10 입증하다, 증명하다		31 출처, 자료
11 비판적으로		32 기술하다
12 참사, 재난		33 (사실임을) 입증하다, 뒷받침하다
13 달아나다, 탈출하다		34 상처를 입히다
14 대중, 일반 사람들		35 조사하다, 들여다보다
15 강하게 하다, 더 튼튼하게 하다		36 ~을 찾다
16 가짜의, 거짓의		37 ~와 연관되다
17 고백하다, 인정하다		38 ~의 관심을 ...로 끌다
18 극도로, 극히		39 잠들다
19 해로운, 유해한		40 ~을 부수다, ~을 무너뜨리다
20 사건		41 ~에 따르면
21 논쟁, 언쟁		42 ~에게 유용하다
		43 지어내다, 만들어 내다

※ 다음 영영풀이에 알맞은 단어를 <보기>에서 골라 쓴 후, 우리말 뜻을 쓰시오.

1 _____ : to fire a weapon: _____

2 _____ : not genuine; appearing to be something it is not: _____

3 _____ : a person who lives in a particular city: _____

4 _____ : an event causing great harm, damage, or suffering: _____

5 _____ : to say or write what someone or something is like: _____

6 _____ : to suddenly feel so worried that you cannot be reasonable:
_____

7 _____ : the upper front part of the body of humans: _____

8 _____ : to form words with the letters in the correct order: _____

9 _____ : to express disapproval of someone or something: _____

10 _____ : a place, person, or thing from which something comes: _____

11 _____ : to injure someone or something by cutting or breaking the skin:
_____

12 _____ : an unexpected and usually unpleasant thing that happens: _____

13 _____ : to prepare and produce a book, magazine, etc. for sale: _____

14 _____ : to believe that someone is honest or will not do anything bad or wrong:
_____

15 _____ : to show the existence, truth, or correctness of something by using
evidence, logic, etc.: _____

16 _____ : a conversation or discussion in which two or more people disagree, often
angrily: _____

보기			
trust	publish	fake	citizen
incident	criticize	source	panic
prove	wound	spell	disaster
shoot	argument	chest	describe

※ 다음 우리말과 일치하도록 빈칸에 알맞은 말을 쓰시오.

해석

Listen & Talk 1 A-1

W: I think I _____ _____ _____ _____ I didn't _____ _____ yesterday.

M: Well, I've read an _____ saying that you don't catch a _____ because your _____ _____ is _____ .

W: Really? Can you tell me _____ _____ _____ ?

M: The article said that people catch colds _____ _____ .

W: 어제 옷을 따뜻하게 입지 않아서 감기에 걸린 것 같아.
M: 글쎄, 체온이 낮다고 해서 감기에 걸리지는 않는다고 쓰여 있는 기사를 읽었어.
W: 정말? 그것에 대해 더 말해 줄 수 있니?
M: 기사에서는 사람들이 바이러스 때문에 감기에 걸린다고 했어.

Listen & Talk 1 A-2

W: I usually drink _____ _____ _____ _____ _____ before I go to bed, but it doesn't help me _____ _____ .

M: I saw a show on TV, and a doctor said that a glass of warm milk doesn't actually _____ you _____ _____ .

W: Oh, it doesn't? Can you _____ _____ _____ _____ ?

M: Milk has special _____ that _____ people _____ . But the _____ in a glass is _____ small _____ have any _____ .

W: 나는 보통 잠자리에 들기 전에 따뜻한 우유 한 잔을 마시는데, 그것이 잠드는 데 도움이 되지 않아.
M: 내가 텔레비전 프로그램에서 봤는데, 어떤 의사가 따뜻한 우유 한 잔이 실제로 잠드는 데 도움을 주는 건 아니라고 말했어.
W: 오, 그래? 그것에 대해 더 말해 줄 수 있니?
M: 우유에는 사람들을 졸리게 만드는 특별한 성분이 있어. 하지만 한 잔에 있는 양이 너무 적어서 효과가 없어.

Listen & Talk 2 A-1

W: _____ _____ _____ _____, John?

M: I'm reading a book of _____ .

W: Riddles? Aren't they _____ children?

M: _____, no. Books of riddles are really _____ _____ _____ .

W: Really? Why do you _____ _____ ?

M: They _____ us _____ more _____ . We need to _____ _____ _____ _____ _____ the answers.

W: 무엇을 읽고 있니, John?
M: 나는 수수께끼 책을 읽고 있어.
W: 수수께끼? 그거 아이들용 아니니?
M: 사실은, 그렇지 않아. 수수께끼 책은 어른들에게 굉장히 유용해.
W: 정말? 왜 그렇게 생각해?
M: 그 책들은 우리가 더 창의적으로 생각하도록 도와. 우리는 답을 찾기 위해 고정관념에서 벗어나야 하거든.

Listen & Talk 2 A-2

M: Are these all _____ _____ ?

W: Yeah. These are all poems _____ _____ children.

M: By children?

W: Yeah. I think children _____ _____ _____ than adults.

M: Why do you _____ _____ ?

W: They're really _____ about their _____ and much _____ _____ _____ .

M: 이거 전부 시집이니?
W: 응. 이것들은 모두 아이들이 쓴 시야.
M: 아이들이?
W: 응. 내 생각에 아이들이 어른들보다 더 좋은 시를 쓰는 것 같아.
M: 왜 그렇게 생각해?
W: 아이들은 그들의 감정에 아주 솔직하고 어른들보다 훨씬 더 창의적이거든.

Listen & Talk 2 B

M: Hey, Sandy. Do you think _____ _____ _____ _____ _____? It is said that it can _____ me _____ _____.

W: _____ _____ _____ the _____ more _____. Hmm, it looks a bit _____ to me, David.

M: Why do _____ _____ _____?

W: There isn't _____ _____ about _____ in the _____.

M: Oh, you're _____.

W: Also, it doesn't tell you _____ _____ _____ _____ _____ _____ _____ _____.

Communication

W: There are so many _____ _____ _____ we call "_____" that are _____ _____.

M: Why do you say so?

W: I read a book, and _____ _____ a lot of _____ of these _____ _____ _____ _____.

M: Like _____?

W: Well, most people think _____ are not smart. But, _____ are _____ _____.

M: Really? Can you _____ me _____ about that?

W: They can _____ _____ _____.

M: Oh, I didn't _____ _____.

Wrap Up 2

W: I read an _____ _____ about the Black Sea. Do you know _____ _____ _____?

M: Yes. It's _____ Eastern Europe _____ Western Asia, _____?

W: Right. _____ _____ do you think _____ _____?

M: Well, black, I _____.

M: No, it isn't. It's blue.

M: Really? Then why is it _____ the Black Sea? Can you _____ _____ about it?

W: People call it the Black Sea _____ it is very _____.

M: 안녕, Sandy. 너는 내가 이 음료를 사야 한다고 생각해? 내가 살을 빼는 것을 도와줄 수 있다고 적혀 있어.
W: 라벨을 더 자세히 읽어 볼게. 음, 내가 보기에 좀 이상해, David.
M: 왜 그렇게 생각해?
W: 음료 안에 무엇이 들었는지에 대한 충분한 정보가 없어.
M: 오, 네 말이 맞아.
W: 게다가, 체중을 감량하려면 얼마나 마셔야 하는지도 나와 있지 않아.

W: 우리가 '사실'이라고 말하는 정보 중에 완전히 틀린 것들이 너무 많아.
M: 왜 그렇게 생각해?
W: 내가 책을 읽었는데, 거기에는 이러한 틀린 '사실'의 예시가 많이 있었어.
M: 예를 들면 어떤 것?
W: 음, 대부분의 사람들은 금붕어가 똑똑하지 않다고 생각해. 하지만 금붕어는 사실 똑똑해.
M: 정말? 그것에 대해 더 말해 줄 수 있니?
W: 그들은 그들의 주인을 알아 볼 수 있어.
M: 오, 그건 몰랐어.

W: 나는 흑해에 관한 흥미로운 기사를 읽었어. 너 그게 어디에 있는지 아니?
M: 응. 그것은 동유럽과 서아시아 사이에 있어, 그렇지?
W: 맞아. 그게 무슨 색일 거라고 생각해?
M: 글쎄, 검은색일 것 같아.
W: 아니야, 그렇지 않아. 그것은 파란색이야.
M: 정말? 그럼 왜 흑해라고 불리는 거야? 그것에 대해 더 말해 줄 수 있니?
W: 사람들이 흑해라고 부르는 이유는 그곳이 매우 위험하기 때문이야.

※ 다음 우리말에 맞도록 대화를 영어로 쓰시오.

Listen & Talk 1 A-1

W: _____

M: _____

_____

W: _____

M: _____

해석

W: 어제 옷을 따뜻하게 입지 않아서 감기에 걸린 것 같아.

M: 글쎄, 체온이 낮다고 해서 감기에 걸리지는 않는다고 쓰여 있는 기사를 읽었어.

W: 정말? 그것에 대해 더 말해 줄 수 있니?

M: 기사에서는 사람들이 바이러스 때문에 감기에 걸린다고 했어.

Listen & Talk 1 A-2

W: _____

_____

M: _____

_____

W: _____

M: _____

W: 나는 보통 잠자리에 들기 전에 따뜻한 우유 한 잔을 마시는데, 그것이 잠드는 데 도움이 되지 않아.

M: 내가 텔레비전 프로그램에서 봤는데, 어떤 의사가 따뜻한 우유 한 잔이 실제로 잠드는 데 도움을 주는 건 아니라고 말했어.

W: 오, 그래? 그것에 대해 더 말해 줄 수 있니?

M: 우유에는 사람들을 졸리게 만드는 특별한 성분이 있어. 하지만 한 잔에 있는 양이 너무 적어서 효과가 없어.

Listen & Talk 2 A-1

W: _____

M: _____

W: _____

M: _____

W: _____

M: _____

W: 무엇을 읽고 있니, John?

M: 나는 수수께끼 책을 읽고 있어.

W: 수수께끼? 그거 아이들용 아니니?

M: 사실은, 그렇지 않아. 수수께끼 책은 어른들에게 굉장히 유용해.

W: 정말? 왜 그렇게 생각해?

M: 그 책들은 우리가 더 창의적으로 생각하도록 도와. 우리는 답을 찾기 위해 고정관념에서 벗어나야 하거든.

Listen & Talk 2 A-2

M: _____

W: _____

M: _____

W: _____

M: _____

W: _____

M: 이거 전부 시집이니?

W: 응. 이것들은 모두 아이들이 쓴 시야.

M: 아이들이?

W: 응. 내 생각에 아이들이 어른들보다 더 좋은 시를 쓰는 것 같아.

M: 왜 그렇게 생각해?

W: 아이들은 그들의 감정에 아주 솔직하고 어른들보다 훨씬 더 창의적이거든.

Listen & Talk 2 B

M: _____

_____

W: _____

M: _____

W: _____

M: _____

W: _____

Communication

W: _____

_____

M: _____

W: _____

M: _____

W: _____

M: _____

W: _____

M: _____

Wrap Up 2

W: _____

M: _____

W: _____

M: _____

W: _____

M: _____

W: _____

M: 안녕, Sandy. 너는 내가 이 음료를 사야 한다고 생각해? 내가 살을 빼는 것을 도와줄 수 있다고 적혀 있어.

W: 라벨을 더 자세히 읽어 볼게. 음, 내가 보기에 좀 이상해, David.

M: 왜 그렇게 생각해?

W: 음료 안에 무엇이 들었는지에 대한 충분한 정보가 없어.

M: 오, 네 말이 맞아.

W: 게다가, 체중을 감량하려면 얼마나 마셔야 하는지도 나와 있지 않아.

W: 우리가 '사실'이라고 말하는 정보 중에 완전히 틀린 것들이 너무 많아.

M: 왜 그렇게 생각해?

W: 내가 책을 읽었는데, 거기에는 이러한 틀린 '사실'의 예시가 많이 있었어.

M: 예를 들면 어떤 것?

W: 음, 대부분의 사람들은 금붕어가 똑똑하지 않다고 생각해. 하지만 금붕어는 사실 똑똑해.

M: 정말? 그것에 대해 더 말해 줄 수 있니?

W: 그들은 그들의 주인을 알아 볼 수 있어.

M: 오, 그건 몰랐어.

W: 나는 흑해에 관한 흥미로운 기사를 읽었어. 너 그게 어디에 있는지 아니?

M: 응. 그것은 동유럽과 서아시아 사이에 있어, 그렇지?

W: 맞아. 그게 무슨 색일 거라고 생각해?

M: 글쎄, 검은색일 것 같아.

W: 아니야, 그렇지 않아. 그것은 파란색이야.

M: 정말? 그럼 왜 흑해라고 불리는 거야? 그것에 대해 더 말해 줄 수 있니?

W: 사람들이 흑해라고 부르는 이유는 그곳이 매우 위험하기 때문이야.

※ 다음 우리말과 일치하도록 빈칸에 알맞은 것을 골라 쓰시오.

1 Can You _____ _____ _____?
A. News   B. Spot   C. Fake

2 Every day we _____, _____, or read _____ _____.
A. news   B. hear   C. watch   D. interesting

3 However, have you ever _____ _____ _____ an _____ is really true?
A. article   B. considered   C. seriously   D. whether

4 Everyone likes an interesting news story but _____ _____ it is completely _____ _____?
A. if   B. up   C. what   D. made

5 Fake news can be very _____ in that it can make people _____ _____ or even _____.
A. misled   B. less   C. harmful   D. informed

6 _____, there have been _____ fake news reports _____ _____.
A. various   B. throughout   C. nevertheless   D. history

7 Why have some people _____ _____ _____ _____?
A. written   B. false   C. such   D. information

8 Let's look into some articles _____ about the _____ _____ _____ them.
A. hidden   B. thinking   C. behind   D. motives

9 _____ _____
A. DISATER   B. AWFUL

10 Last night, an angry group of rhinoceroses _____ _____ the walls of the _____ at the zoo and _____.
A. down   B. escaped   C. broke   D. cage

11 They also _____ _____ the walls of the _____ wild animals' _____.
A. other   B. broke   C. cages   D. down

12 These animals _____ _____ the streets and _____ _____ of people.
A. hundreds   B. ran   C. injured   D. down

13 Twelve of the animals are _____ _____ _____ _____.
A. the   B. on   C. still   D. loose

14 Citizens should _____ indoors _____ _____ _____.
A. further   B. stay   C. notice   D. until

15 Not a single act or _____ _____ above has _____.
A. described   B. place   C. incident   D. taken

16 At that time, those who read the _____ carefully _____ _____ _____.
A. out   B. article   C. loud   D. laughed

---

1 당신은 가짜 뉴스임을 알아챌 수 있는가?

2 매일 우리는 흥미로운 뉴스를 보고, 듣고, 읽는다.

3 그러나 당신은 뉴스 기사가 정말로 진실인지 심각하게 고려해 본 적이 있는가?

4 모든 사람이 흥미로운 뉴스 기사를 좋아하지만, 만약 그것이 완전히 지어낸 것이라면 어떻게 할 것인가?

5 가짜 뉴스는 사람들에게 정보를 부족하게 제공하거나 사람들을 잘못 이끌 수 있다는 점에서 매우 해로울 수 있다.

6 그럼에도 불구하고, 역사를 통틀어 다양한 가짜 뉴스 보도들이 존재해 왔다.

7 왜 어떤 사람들은 그러한 거짓 정보를 써 왔던 것일까?

8 그 뒤에 숨겨진 동기를 생각하면서 몇 가지 뉴스 기사를 살펴보자.

9 끔찍한 참사

10 어젯밤, 화가 난 코뿔소 떼가 동물원 우리의 벽을 부수고 도망쳤다.

11 그들은 또한 다른 야생 동물 우리의 벽도 부수었다.

12 이 동물들은 거리를 뛰어다니며 수백 명의 사람들에게 부상을 입혔다.

13 그중 열두 마리의 동물들이 아직 잡히지 않았다.

14 시민들은 추후 안내가 있을 때까지 집 안에 머물러야 한다.

15 위에 기술된 어떤 행동이나 사건도 일어나지 않았다.

16 그 당시 이 기사를 주의 깊게 읽었던 사람들은 크게 웃었다.

17 _____ who didn't read it to the end _____ _____ _____.

 A. worried   B. those   C. got   D. really

18 _____ _____ the news was _____, many people _____.

 A. false   B. knowing   C. panicked   D. not

19 _____ tried to _____ the city while _____ went into the parks with guns to _____ the animals.

 A. others   B. hunt   C. escape   D. some

20 So why did _The Herald_ _____ _____ _____ _____ _____?

 A. such   B. make   C. news   D. up

21 Later, they _____ that they made it _____ so that they could draw the readers' _____ to the _____ conditions at the zoo.

 A. attention   B. confessed   C. unsafe   D. up

22 _____ _____ A FRIEND _____ _____

 A. IN   B. SLAV   C. ARGUMENT   D. SHOOTS

23 Mejk Swenekafew, a Slav worker at the Columbia Coal Mine, was _____ and seriously _____ by John Pecitello _____ the _____ camp Thursday evening.

 A. shot   B. near   C. wounded   D. mining

24 The two men _____ an _____ _____ a meeting.

 A. argument   B. had   C. during

25 The argument _____ to a fight, and Pecitello _____ Swenekafew _____, in the _____ and leg.

 A. twice   B. led   C. chest   D. shot

26 He is now at the hospital _____ _____ _____.

 A. critical   B. in   C. condition

27 Pecitello _____ _____ _____ the _____.

 A. away   B. shooting   C. after   D. ran

28 The police are _____ for him now and are _____ that he is extremely _____.

 A. warning   B. searching   C. dangerous   D. citizens

29 Is _____ _____ _____ about the _____?

 A. article   B. strange   C. anything   D. there

30 _____ the Slav's name _____; it _____, "we-fake-news."

 A. backwards   B. read   C. spells

31 _____ _____ this and _____?

 A. wrote   B. why   C. who

---

17 그것을 끝까지 읽지 않은 사람들은 정말로 걱정하였다.

18 그 기사가 거짓이라는 것을 알지 못했기 때문에 많은 사람이 겁에 질려 어쩔 줄 몰랐다.

19 어떤 사람들은 도시를 빠져나가려고 했고 다른 사람들은 그 동물들을 사냥하기 위해 총을 들고 공원으로 나갔다.

20 그렇다면 왜 헤럴드 사는 이러한 뉴스를 만들어 냈을까?

21 나중에 그들은 동물원의 안전하지 않은 상태에 대해 독자들의 주의를 끌기 위해 그 기사를 지어냈다고 고백했다.

22 슬라브인이 언쟁 중에 친구에게 총을 쏘다

23 목요일 저녁 채굴 야영지 근처에서, 컬럼비아 광산 소속의 슬라브인 노동자 Mejk Swenekafew가 John Pecitello에 의해 총상을 입어 심각하게 다쳤다.

24 그 두 사람은 회의 중에 언쟁을 벌였다.

25 언쟁이 싸움으로 번졌고, Pecitello가 Swenekafew의 가슴과 다리에 두 번 총을 쏘았다.

26 현재 그는 위독한 상태로 입원 중이다.

27 Pecitello는 총격 이후 도주했다.

28 경찰이 지금 그를 찾고 있으며, 그가 극히 위험하다고 시민들에게 경고하고 있다.

29 이 기사에 뭔가 이상한 점이 있는가?

30 그 슬라브인의 이름을 거꾸로 읽어 보아라. 그것의 철자는 "우리는 뉴스를 조작한다."가 된다.

31 누가 이것을 썼고 왜 그랬을까?

32 *The Daily Telegram* published this fake article _____ they could prove if *The Daily News*, their _____, was _____ their articles.

    A. stealing   B. that   C. competitor   D. so

33 *The Daily News* _____ the same _____ about "Swenekafew" the next day and thus got _____ _____.

    A. caught   B. published   C. stealing   D. article

34 The people at *The Daily News* had to _____ their act and were _____ _____ by the _____.

    A. criticized   B. admit   C. harshly   D. public

35 The two articles were _____ _____, but there are many "fake" news _____ _____ every day.

    A. cases   B. published   C. articles   D. special

36 As readers, we need to read _____ and _____ _____ the news is real or _____.

    A. whether   B. fake   C. critically   D. judge

37 _____ _____ _____ fake news!

    A. to   B. how   C. spot

38 _____ the _____

    A. Source   B. Consider

39 Is it _____ a _____ _____?

    A. sources   B. from   C. reliable

40 _____ we _____ the _____?

    A. trust   B. can   C. writer

41 _____ the _____

    A. Date   B. Check

42 Is it a _____ or an _____ _____?

    A. old   B. new   C. story

43 _____ it _____ _____ events?

    A. to   B. is   C. current   D. related

44 Read _____ _____ _____

    A. Headlines   B. the   C. Beyong

45 Does the _____ _____ the _____?

    A. content   B. match   C. headline

46 Find _____ _____

    A. Sources   B. Supporting

47 Do other _____ stories _____ _____ _____?

    A. content   B. related   C. similar   D. provide

---

32 데일리 텔레그램 사는 그들의 경쟁자인 데일리 뉴스 사가 그들의 기사를 훔치는지를 증명하기 위해서 이 거짓 기사를 발행했다.

33 데일리 뉴스 사는 그 다음 날 'Swenekafew'에 대한 동일한 기사를 발행했고 그래서 훔친 것이 발각되었다.

34 데일리 뉴스 사의 사람들은 그들의 행동을 인정해야만 했고 대중들로부터 혹독한 비난을 받았다.

35 이 두 기사는 특별한 경우였지만, 매일 발행되는 '가짜' 뉴스 기사는 많이 있다.

36 독자로서, 우리는 비판적으로 읽고 그 뉴스가 진짜인지 가짜인지 판단될 필요가 있다.

37 가짜 뉴스 판별 방법!

38 출처를 고려하라

39 그것은 믿을 만한 출처에서 온 것인가?

40 우리는 그 필자를 신뢰할 수 있는가?

41 날짜를 확인하라

42 그것은 새로운 이야기인가 혹은 오래된 이야기인가?

43 그것은 현재의 사건들과 관련된 것인가?

44 기사 제목 그 이상을 읽어라

45 기사 제목이 기사 내용과 일치하는가?

46 뒷받침하는 자료를 찾아라

47 다른 관련된 이야기도 비슷한 내용을 제공하는가?

※ 다음 우리말과 일치하도록 빈칸에 알맞은 것을 골라 쓰시오.

1 Can You _____ _____ _____?

2 Every day we watch, hear, or read _____ _____.

3 However, _____ you ever seriously _____ _____ an article is really true?

4 Everyone likes an interesting news story but _____ _____ it is _____ _____ _____?

5 Fake news can be very _____ _____ _____ it can make people _____ _____ or even _____.

6 _____, there have been _____ _____ news reports _____ _____.

7 Why have some people _____ _____ _____ _____ _____?

8 _____ _____ _____ some articles _____ about _____ _____ _____ _____ them.

9 _____ DISASTER

10 Last night, an angry group of rhinoceroses _____ _____ the walls of the cage at the zoo and _____.

11 They also _____ _____ the walls of _____ _____ wild animals' cages.

12 These animals _____ _____ the streets and _____ _____ _____ people.

13 Twelve of the animals are still _____ _____ _____.

14 _____ should stay indoors _____ _____ _____.

15 Not a single act or incident _____ _____ has _____ _____.

16 At that time, those who read the article carefully _____ _____ _____.

1 당신은 가짜 뉴스임을 알아챌 수 있는가?

2 매일 우리는 흥미로운 뉴스를 보고, 듣고, 읽는다.

3 그러나 당신은 뉴스 기사가 정말로 진실인지 심각하게 고려해 본 적이 있는가?

4 모든 사람이 흥미로운 뉴스 기사를 좋아하지만, 만약 그것이 완전히 지어낸 것이라면 어떻게 할 것인가?

5 가짜 뉴스는 사람들에게 정보를 부족하게 제공하거나 사람들을 잘못 이끌 수 있다는 점에서 매우 해로울 수 있다.

6 그럼에도 불구하고, 역사를 통틀어 다양한 가짜 뉴스 보도들이 존재해 왔다.

7 왜 어떤 사람들은 그러한 거짓 정보를 써 왔던 것일까?

8 그 뒤에 숨겨진 동기를 생각하면서 몇 가지 뉴스 기사를 살펴보자.

9 끔찍한 참사

10 어젯밤, 화가 난 코뿔소 떼가 동물원 우리의 벽을 부수고 도망쳤다.

11 그들은 또한 다른 야생 동물 우리의 벽도 부수었다.

12 이 동물들은 거리를 뛰어다니며 수백 명의 사람들에게 부상을 입혔다.

13 그중 열두 마리의 동물들이 아직 잡히지 않았다.

14 시민들은 추후 안내가 있을 때까지 집 안에 머물러야 한다.

15 위에 기술된 어떤 행동이나 사건도 일어나지 않았다.

16 그 당시 이 기사를 주의 깊게 읽었던 사람들은 크게 웃었다.

17 Those who didn't read it to the end _____ _____ _____ .

18 _____ _____ the news was _____ , many people _____ .

19 _____ tried _____ _____ the city while _____ went into the parks with guns _____ _____ the animals.

20 So why did *The Herald* _____ _____ _____ _____ ?

21 Later, they confessed that they _____ _____ _____ _____ _____ they _____ draw the _____ _____ the unsafe conditions at the zoo.

22 SLAV _____ A FRIEND _____ _____

23 Mejk Swenekafew, a Slav worker at the Columbia Coal Mine, _____ _____ and _____ _____ John Pecitello near the mining camp Thursday evening.

24 The two men _____ _____ _____ _____ a meeting.

25 The argument _____ _____ a fight, and Pecitello shot Swenekafew _____ , _____ _____ _____ and leg.

26 He is now at the hospital _____ _____ _____ .

27 Pecitello _____ _____ _____ _____ _____ .

28 The police _____ _____ _____ him now and _____ _____ citizens that he is _____ _____ .

29 Is there _____ _____ about the _____ ?

30 Read the Slav's name _____ ; it spells, "we-fake-news."

31 Who _____ this and _____ ?

17 그것을 끝까지 읽지 않은 사람들은 정말로 걱정하였다.

18 그 기사가 거짓이라는 것을 알지 못했기 때문에 많은 사람이 겁에 질려 어쩔 줄 몰랐다.

19 어떤 사람들은 도시를 빠져나가려고 했고 다른 사람들은 그 동물들을 사냥하기 위해 총을 들고 공원으로 나갔다.

20 그렇다면 왜 헤럴드 사는 이러한 뉴스를 만들어 냈을까?

21 나중에 그들은 동물원의 안전하지 않은 상태에 대해 독자들의 주의를 끌기 위해 그 기사를 지어냈다고 고백했다.

22 슬라브인이 언쟁 중에 친구에게 총을 쏘다

23 목요일 저녁 채굴 야영지 근처에서, 컬럼비아 광산 소속의 슬라브인 노동자 Mejk Swenekafew가 John Pecitello에 의해 총상을 입어 심각하게 다쳤다.

24 그 두 사람은 회의 중에 언쟁을 벌였다.

25 언쟁이 싸움으로 번졌고, Pecitello가 Swenekafew의 가슴과 다리에 두 번 총을 쏘았다.

26 현재 그는 위독한 상태로 입원 중이다.

27 Pecitello는 총격 이후 도주했다.

28 경찰이 지금 그를 찾고 있으며, 그가 극히 위험하다고 시민들에게 경고하고 있다.

29 이 기사에 뭔가 이상한 점이 있는가?

30 그 슬라브인의 이름을 거꾸로 읽어 보아라. 그것의 철자는 "우리는 뉴스를 조작한다."가 된다.

31 누가 이것을 썼고 왜 그랬을까?

본문 Test **53**

32 *The Daily Telegram* _____ this fake article _____ _____ they _____ prove _____ *The Daily News*, their competitor, was stealing _____ _____.

33 *The Daily News* published the same article about "Swenekafew" the next day and thus _____ _____ _____.

34 The people at *The Daily News* _____ _____ _____ their act and _____ _____ _____ by the public.

35 The two articles were _____ _____, but there are many "fake" news articles _____ every day.

36 _____ readers, we need to read _____ and _____ _____ the news is real _____ fake.

37 _____ _____ _____ fake news!

38 _____ the _____

39 Is it from a _____ _____?

40 Can we _____ the _____?

41 _____ the Date

42 Is it a _____ or an _____ _____?

43 _____ it _____ _____ _____ events?

44 Read _____ _____ _____

45 Does the headline _____ _____ _____?

46 Find _____ _____

47 Do other _____ stories provide _____ _____?

32 데일리 텔레그램 사는 그들의 경쟁자인 데일리 뉴스 사가 그들의 기사를 훔치는지를 증명하기 위해서 이 거짓 기사를 발행했다.

33 데일리 뉴스 사는 그 다음 날 'Swenekafew'에 대한 동일한 기사를 발행했고 그래서 훔친 것이 발각되었다.

34 데일리 뉴스 사의 사람들은 그들의 행동을 인정해야만 했고 대중들로부터 혹독한 비난을 받았다.

35 이 두 기사는 특별한 경우였지만, 매일 발행되는 '가짜' 뉴스 기사는 많이 있다.

36 독자로서, 우리는 비판적으로 읽고 그 뉴스가 진짜인지 가짜인지 판단할 필요가 있다.

37 가짜 뉴스 판별 방법!

38 출처를 고려하라

39 그것은 믿을 만한 출처에서 온 것인가?

40 우리는 그 필자를 신뢰할 수 있는가?

41 날짜를 확인하라

42 그것은 새로운 이야기인가 혹은 오래된 이야기인가?

43 그것은 현재의 사건들과 관련된 것인가?

44 기사 제목 그 이상을 읽어라

45 기사 제목이 기사 내용과 일치하는가?

46 뒷받침하는 자료를 찾아라

47 다른 관련된 이야기도 비슷한 내용을 제공하는가?

※ 다음 문장을 우리말로 쓰시오.

1 Can You Spot Fake News?

➡ _____

2 Every day we watch, hear, or read interesting news.

➡ _____

3 However, have you ever seriously considered whether an article is really true?

➡ _____

4 Everyone likes an interesting news story but what if it is completely made up?

➡ _____

5 Fake news can be very harmful in that it can make people less informed or even misled.

➡ _____

6 Nevertheless, there have been various fake news reports throughout history.

➡ _____

7 Why have some people written such false information?

➡ _____

8 Let's look into some articles thinking about the hidden motives behind them.

➡ _____

9 AWFUL DISASTER

➡ _____

10 Last night, an angry group of rhinoceroses broke down the walls of the cage at the zoo and escaped.

➡ _____

11 They also broke down the walls of the other wild animals' cages.

➡ _____

12 These animals ran down the streets and injured hundreds of people.

➡ _____

13 Twelve of the animals are still on the loose.

➡ _____

14 Citizens should stay indoors until further notice.

➡ _____

15 Not a single act or incident described above has taken place.

➡ _____

16 At that time, those who read the article carefully laughed out loud.

➡ _____

17 Those who didn't read it to the end got really worried.

➡ _____

18 Not knowing the news was false, many people panicked.

➡ _____

19 Some tried to escape the city while others went into the parks with guns to hunt the animals.

➡ _____

20 So why did *The Herald* make up such news?

➡ _____

21 Later, they confessed that they made it up so that they could draw the readers' attention to the unsafe conditions at the zoo.

➡ _____

22 SLAV SHOOTS A FRIEND IN ARGUMENT

➡ _____

23 Mejk Swenekafew, a Slav worker at the Columbia Coal Mine, was shot and seriously wounded by John Pecitello near the mining camp Thursday evening.

➡ _____

_____

24 The two men had an argument during a meeting.

➡ _____

25 The argument led to a fight, and Pecitello shot Swenekafew twice, in the chest and leg.

➡ _____

26 He is now at the hospital in critical condition.

➡ _____

27 Pecitello ran away after the shooting.

➡ _____

28 The police are searching for him now and are warning citizens that he is extremely dangerous.

➡ _____

29 Is there anything strange about the article?

➡ _____

30 Read the Slav's name backwards; it spells, "we-fake-news."

➡ _____

31 Who wrote this and why?

➡ _____

32 *The Daily Telegram* published this fake article so that they could prove if *The Daily News*, their competitor, was stealing their articles.

➡ _____

_____

33 *The Daily News* published the same article about "Swenekafew" the next day and thus got caught stealing.

➡ _____

34 The people at *The Daily News* had to admit their act and were harshly criticized by the public.

➡ _____

35 The two articles were special cases, but there are many "fake" news articles published every day.

➡ _____

36 As readers, we need to read critically and judge whether the news is real or fake.

➡ _____

37 How to spot fake news!

➡ _____

38 Consider the Source

➡ _____

39 Is it from a reliable source?

➡ _____

40 Can we trust the writer?

➡ _____

41 Check the Date

➡ _____

42 Is it a new or an old story?

➡ _____

43 Is it related to current events?

➡ _____

44 Read Beyond the Headlines

➡ _____

45 Does the headline match the content?

➡ _____

46 Find Supporting Sources

➡ _____

47 Do other related stories provide similar content?

➡ _____

※ 다음 괄호 안의 단어들을 우리말에 맞도록 바르게 배열하시오.

1 (You / Can / Fake / Spot / News?)
➡ _____

2 (day / every / watch, / we / or / hear, / read / news. / interesting)
➡ _____

3 (have / however, / ever / you / considered / seriously / an / whether / is / article / true? / really)
➡ _____

4 (likes / everyone / an / news / interesting / but / story / if / what / is / it / made / completely / up?)
➡ _____

5 (news / fake / be / can / harmful / very / that / in / can / it / people / make / less / or / informed / misled. / even)
➡ _____

6 (there / nevertheless, / been / have / fake / various / reports / news / history. / throughout)
➡ _____

7 (have / why / people / some / such / written / information? / false)
➡ _____

8 (look / let's / some / into / thinking / articles / the / about / motives / hidden / them. / behind)
➡ _____

9 (DISASTER / AWFUL)
➡ _____

10 (night, / last / angry / an / group / rhinoceroses / of / down / broke / walls / the / the / of / cage / the / at / zoo / escaped. / and)
➡ _____

11 (also / they / down / broke / walls / the / the / of / other / animals' / wild / cages.)
➡ _____

12 (animals / these / down / ran / streets / the / and / hundreds / injured / people. / of)
➡ _____

13 (of / twelve / animals / the / still / are / on / loose. / the)
➡ _____

14 (should / citizens / indoors / stay / further / until / notice.)
➡ _____

15 (a / not / act / single / or / described / incident / has / above / place. / taken)
➡ _____

16 (that / at / time, / who / those / the / read / carefully / article / out / laughed / loud.)
➡ _____

1 당신은 가짜 뉴스임을 알아챌 수 있는가?

2 매일 우리는 흥미로운 뉴스를 보고, 듣고, 읽는다.

3 그러나 당신은 뉴스 기사가 정말로 진실인지 심각하게 고려해 본 적이 있는가?

4 모든 사람이 흥미로운 뉴스 기사를 좋아하지만, 만약 그것이 완전히 지어낸 것이라면 어떻게 할 것인가?

5 가짜 뉴스는 사람들에게 정보를 부족하게 제공하거나 사람들을 잘못 이끌 수 있다는 점에서 매우 해로울 수 있다.

6 그럼에도 불구하고, 역사를 통틀어 다양한 가짜 뉴스 보도들이 존재해 왔다.

7 왜 어떤 사람들은 그러한 거짓 정보를 써 왔던 것일까?

8 그 뒤에 숨겨진 동기를 생각하면서 몇 가지 뉴스 기사를 살펴보자.

9 끔찍한 참사

10 어젯밤, 화가 난 코뿔소 떼가 동물원 우리의 벽을 부수고 도망쳤다.

11 그들은 또한 다른 야생 동물 우리의 벽도 부수었다.

12 이 동물들은 거리를 뛰어다니며 수백 명의 사람들에게 부상을 입혔다.

13 그중 열두 마리의 동물들이 아직 잡히지 않았다.

14 시민들은 추후 안내가 있을 때까지 집 안에 머물러야 한다.

15 위에 기술된 어떤 행동이나 사건도 일어나지 않았다.

16 그 당시 이 기사를 주의 깊게 읽었던 사람들은 크게 웃었다.

17 (who / those / read / didn't / to / it / end / the / got / worried. / really)
➡ _____

18 (knowing / not / news / the / false, / was / people / many / panicked.)
➡ _____

19 (tried / some / escape / to / city / the / others / while / into / went / parks / the / guns / with / hunt / to / animals. / the)
➡ _____

20 (why / so *The* / did / make / *Herald* / up / news? / such)
➡ _____

21 (they / later, / that / confessed / made / they / up / it / that / so / could / they / the / draw / readers' / the / to / attention / conditions / unsafe / at / zoo. / the)
➡ _____

22 (SHOOTS / SLAV / FRIEND / A / ARGUMENT / IN)
➡ _____

23 (Swenekafew, / Mejk / Slave / a / worker / the / at / Columbia / Mine, / Coal / shot / was / and / wounded / seriously / by / Pecitello / John / near / mining / the / camp / evening. / Thursday)
➡ _____

24 (two / the / had / men / an / during / argument / meeting. / a)
➡ _____

25 (argument / the / to / led / fight, / a / and / shot / Pecitello / Swenekafew / twice, / the / in / chest / leg. / and)
➡ _____

26 (is / he / at / now / the / in / hospital / condition. / critical)
➡ _____

27 (Pecitello / away / ran / the / after / shooting.)
➡ _____

28 (police / the / searching / are / him / for / now / are / and / warning / that / citizens / is / he / dangerous. / extremely)
➡ _____

29 (there / is / strange / anything / about / article? / the)
➡ _____

30 (the / read / name / Slav's / backwards; / it / "we-fake-news." / spells,)
➡ _____

31 (wrote / who / why? / and / this)
➡ _____

17 그것을 끝까지 읽지 않은 사람들은 정말로 걱정하였다.

18 그 기사가 거짓이라는 것을 알지 못했기 때문에 많은 사람이 겁에 질려 어쩔 줄 몰랐다.

19 어떤 사람들은 도시를 빠져나가려고 했고 다른 사람들은 그 동물들을 사냥하기 위해 총을 들고 공원으로 나갔다.

20 그렇다면 왜 헤럴드 사는 이러한 뉴스를 만들어 냈을까?

21 나중에 그들은 동물원의 안전하지 않은 상태에 대해 독자들의 주의를 끌기 위해 그 기사를 지어냈다고 고백했다.

22 슬라브인이 언쟁 중에 친구에게 총을 쏘다

23 목요일 저녁 채굴 야영지 근처에서, 컬럼비아 광산 소속의 슬라브인 노동자 Mejk Swenekafew가 John Pecitello에 의해 총상을 입어 심각하게 다쳤다.

24 그 두 사람은 회의 중에 언쟁을 벌였다.

25 언쟁이 싸움으로 번졌고, Pecitello가 Swenekafew의 가슴과 다리에 두 번 총을 쏘았다.

26 현재 그는 위독한 상태로 입원 중이다.

27 Pecitello는 총격 이후 도주했다.

28 경찰이 지금 그를 찾고 있으며, 그가 극히 위험하다고 시민들에게 경고하고 있다.

29 이 기사에 뭔가 이상한 점이 있는가?

30 그 슬라브인의 이름을 거꾸로 읽어 보아라. 그것의 철자는 "우리는 뉴스를 조작한다."가 된다.

31 누가 이것을 썼고 왜 그랬을까?

32 (*Daily* / *The* / *Telegram* / this / published / fake / so / article / that / could / they / if / prove / *Daily* / *The* / *News*, / competitor, / their / stealing / was / articles. / their)

➡ _____

_____

33 (*Daily* / *The* / *News* / the / published / article / same / "Swenekafew" / about / next / the / day / thus / and / caught / got / stealing.)

➡ _____

34 (people / the / at / *News* / *The* / *Daily* / to / had / admit / act / their / and / harshly / were / criticized / the / by / public.)

➡ _____

35 (two / the / were / articles / cases, / special / there / but / many / are / news / "fake" / articles / every / published / day.)

➡ _____

36 (readers, / as / need / we / read / to / and / critically / whether / judge / news / the / real / is / fake. / or)

➡ _____

37 (to / how / fake / spot / news!)

➡ _____

38 (the / consider / Source)

➡ _____

39 (it / is / a / from / source? / reliable)

➡ _____

40 (we / can / the / trust / writer?)

➡ _____

41 (the / check / Date)

➡ _____

42 (it / is / new / a / or / old / an / story?)

➡ _____

43 (is / related / it / current / to / events?)

➡ _____

44 (Beyond / Read / Headlines / the)

➡ _____

45 (the / does / match / headline / content? / the)

➡ _____

46 (Supporting / Find / Sources)

➡ _____

47 (other / do / stories / related / similar / provide / content?)

➡ _____

32 데일리 텔레그램 사는 그들의 경쟁자인 데일리 뉴스 사가 그들의 기사를 훔치는지를 증명하기 위해서 이 거짓 기사를 발행했다.

33 데일리 뉴스 사는 그 다음 날 'Swenekafew'에 대한 동일한 기사를 발행했고 그래서 훔친 것이 발각되었다.

34 데일리 뉴스 사의 사람들은 그들의 행동을 인정해야만 했고 대중들로부터 혹독한 비난을 받았다.

35 이 두 기사는 특별한 경우였지만, 매일 발행되는 '가짜' 뉴스 기사는 많이 있다.

36 독자로서, 우리는 비판적으로 읽고 그 뉴스가 진짜인지 가짜인지 판단할 필요가 있다.

37 가짜 뉴스 판별 방법!

38 출처를 고려하라

39 그것은 믿을 만한 출처에서 온 것인가?

40 우리는 그 필자를 신뢰할 수 있는가?

41 날짜를 확인하라

42 그것은 새로운 이야기인가 혹은 오래된 이야기인가?

43 그것은 현재의 사건들과 관련된 것인가?

44 기사 제목 그 이상을 읽어라

45 기사 제목이 기사 내용과 일치하는가?

46 뒷받침하는 자료를 찾아라

47 다른 관련된 이야기도 비슷한 내용을 제공하는가?

※ 다음 우리말을 영어로 쓰시오.

1 당신은 가짜 뉴스임을 알아챌 수 있는가?

➡ _____

2 매일 우리는 흥미로운 뉴스를 보고, 듣고, 읽는다.

➡ _____

3 그러나 당신은 뉴스 기사가 정말로 진실인지 심각하게 고려해 본 적이 있는가?

➡ _____

4 모든 사람이 흥미로운 뉴스 기사를 좋아하지만, 만약 그것이 완전히 지어낸 것이라면 어떻게 할 것인가?

➡ _____

5 가짜 뉴스는 사람들에게 정보를 부족하게 제공하거나 사람들을 잘못 이끌 수 있다는 점에서 매우 해로울 수 있다.

➡ _____

6 그럼에도 불구하고, 역사를 통틀어 다양한 가짜 뉴스 보도들이 존재해 왔다.

➡ _____

7 왜 어떤 사람들은 그러한 거짓 정보를 써 왔던 것일까?

➡ _____

8 그 뒤에 숨겨진 동기를 생각하면서 몇 가지 뉴스 기사를 살펴보자.

➡ _____

9 끔찍한 심사

➡ _____

10 어젯밤, 화가 난 코뿔소 떼가 동물원 우리의 벽을 부수고 도망쳤다.

➡ _____

11 그들은 또한 다른 야생 동물 우리의 벽도 부수었다.

➡ _____

12 이 동물들은 거리를 뛰어다니며 수백 명의 사람들에게 부상을 입혔다.

➡ _____

13 그중 열두 마리의 동물들이 아직 잡히지 않았다.

➡ _____

14 시민들은 추후 안내가 있을 때까지 집 안에 머물러야 한다.

➡ _____

15 위에 기술된 어떤 행동이나 사건도 일어나지 않았다.

➡ _____

16 그 당시 이 기사를 주의 깊게 읽었던 사람들은 크게 웃었다.

➡ _____

17 그것을 끝까지 읽지 않은 사람들은 정말로 걱정하였다.

➡ _____

18 그 기사가 거짓이라는 것을 알지 못했기 때문에 많은 사람이 겁에 질려 어쩔 줄 몰랐다.

➡ _____

19 어떤 사람들은 도시를 빠져나가려고 했고 다른 사람들은 그 동물들을 사냥하기 위해 총을 들고 공원으로 나갔다.

➡ _____

20 그렇다면 왜 헤럴드 사는 이러한 뉴스를 만들어 냈을까?

➡ _____

21 나중에 그들은 동물원의 안전하지 않은 상태에 대해 독자들의 주의를 끌기 위해 그 기사를 지어냈다고 고백했다.

➡ _____

_____

22 슬라브인이 언쟁 중에 친구에게 총을 쏘다

➡ _____

23 목요일 저녁 채굴 야영지 근처에서, 컬럼비아 광산 소속의 슬라브인 노동자 Mejk Swenekafew가 John Pecitello에 의해 총상을 입어 심각하게 다쳤다.

➡ _____

_____

24 그 두 사람은 회의 중에 언쟁을 벌였다.

➡ _____

25 언쟁이 싸움으로 번졌고, Pecitello가 Swenekafew의 가슴과 다리에 두 번 총을 쏘았다.

➡ _____

26 현재 그는 위독한 상태로 입원 중이다.

➡ _____

27 Pecitello는 총격 이후 도주했다.

➡ _____

28 경찰이 지금 그를 찾고 있으며, 그가 극히 위험하다고 시민들에게 경고하고 있다.

➡ _____

29 이 기사에 뭔가 이상한 점이 있는가?

➡ _____

30 그 슬라브인의 이름을 거꾸로 읽어 보아라. 그것의 철자는 "우리는 뉴스를 조작한다."가 된다.

➡ _____

31 누가 이것을 썼고 왜 그랬을까?

➡ _____

32 데일리 텔레그램 사는 그들의 경쟁자인 데일리 뉴스 사가 그들의 기사를 훔치는지를 증명하기 위해서 이 거짓 기사를 발행했다.

➡ _____

33 데일리 뉴스 사는 그 다음 날 'Swenekafew'에 대한 동일한 기사를 발행했고 그래서 훔친 것이 발각되었다.

➡ _____

34 데일리 뉴스 사의 사람들은 그들의 행동을 인정해야만 했고 대중들로부터 혹독한 비난을 받았다.

➡ _____

35 이 두 기사는 특별한 경우였지만, 매일 발행되는 '가짜' 뉴스 기사는 많이 있다.

➡ _____

36 독자로서, 우리는 비판적으로 읽고 그 뉴스가 진짜인지 가짜인지 판단할 필요가 있다.

➡ _____

37 가짜 뉴스 판별 방법!

➡ _____

38 출처를 고려하라

➡ _____

39 그것은 믿을 만한 출처에서 온 것인가?

➡ _____

40 우리는 그 필자를 신뢰할 수 있는가?

➡ _____

41 날짜를 확인하라

➡ _____

42 그것은 새로운 이야기인가 혹은 오래된 이야기인가?

➡ _____

43 그것은 현재의 사건들과 관련된 것인가?

➡ _____

44 기사 제목 그 이상을 읽어라

➡ _____

45 기사 제목이 기사 내용과 일치하는가?

➡ _____

46 뒷받침하는 자료를 찾아라

➡ _____

47 다른 관련된 이야기도 비슷한 내용을 제공하는가?

➡ _____

※ 다음 우리말과 일치하도록 빈칸에 알맞은 말을 쓰시오.

Wrap Up 3

1. A: Wow! The news _____ _____ "Longer Vacation for
   Students." Hey, we're _____ _____ _____ _____
   _____ _____!

2. B: Wait! We _____ _____ first _____ _____ _____
   _____.

3. A: _____ do you _____ _____?

4. B: Some news _____ _____ _____ _____ but _____
   _____ _____ _____ a different story.

5. A: Oh, I see. I _____ _____ _____ the news title.

1. A: 와! 뉴스 제목이 "학생들을 위한 더 긴 방학"이야. 이봐, 우리 더 긴 방학을 갖나봐!
2. B: 기다려! 우리는 먼저 이게 사실인지를 확인해야 해.
3. A: 왜 그렇게 생각해?
4. B: 어떤 뉴스는 충격적인 제목을 사용하지만 그 내용은 다른 이야기를 할지도 몰라.
5. A: 오, 알았다. 뉴스 제목 너머를 읽어야 하는구나.

Read & Think After You Read B

1. Reporter: Why did *The Herald* _____ the "_____ _____"
   story, Mr. Right?

2. Mr. Right: They just wanted to _____ _____ _____ _____
   to the _____ _____ at the zoo.

3. Reporter: _____, readers _____ _____ _____ _____
   _____ that it was _____. _____ _____ "Slav
   Shoots a Friend in Argument?" What was the _____?

4. Mr. Right: *The Daily Telegram* _____ _____ _____ _____
   The Daily News _____ _____ _____ _____.

1. 기자: 왜 헤럴드 사는 〈끔찍한 참사〉 이야기를 썼을까요, Right 씨?
2. Mr. Right: 그들은 단지 동물원의 안전하지 않은 상태에 대해 독자들의 주의를 끌고 싶었답니다.
3. 기자: 사실, 독자들은 그것이 가짜라는 것을 알고 매우 화가 났어요. 〈슬라브인이 전쟁 중에 친구에게 총을 쏘다〉는 어떤가요? 동기가 무엇이었나요?
4. Mr. Right: 데일리 텔레그램 사는 데일리 뉴스 사가 그들의 기사를 훔치고 있다는 것을 증명하기를 원했어요.

Read & Think After You Read C

1. A: _____ the four tips, which do you _____ _____ _____
   _____ _____, and why?

2. B: I think _____ _____ _____ _____ the most important
   _____ I can check _____ the _____ _____ _____.

1. A: 네 가지 조언 중에서 너는 어떤 것이 가장 중요하다고 생각하며, 그 이유는 무엇이니?
2. B: 나는 뒷받침하는 자료들을 찾는 것이 가장 중요하다고 생각하는데, 그 정보가 올바른지 확인할 수 있기 때문이야.

※ 다음 우리말을 영어로 쓰시오.

Wrap Up 3

1. A: 와! 뉴스 제목이 "학생들을 위한 더 긴 방학"이야. 이봐, 우리 더 긴 방학을 갖나봐!

➡ _____

_____

2. B: 기다려! 우리는 먼저 이게 사실인지를 확인해야 해.

➡ _____

3. A: 왜 그렇게 생각해?

➡ _____

4. B: 어떤 뉴스는 충격적인 제목을 사용하지만 그 내용은 다른 이야기를 할지도 몰라.

➡ _____

5. A: 오, 알았다. 뉴스 제목 너머를 읽어야 하는구나.

➡ _____

Read & Think After You Read B

1. 기자: 왜 헤럴드 사는 〈끔찍한 참사〉 이야기를 썼을까요, Right 씨?

➡ _____

2. Mr. Right: 그들은 단지 동물원의 안전하지 않은 상태에 대해 독자들의 주의를 끌고 싶었답니다.

➡ _____

3. 기자: 사실, 독자들은 그것이 가짜라는 것을 알고 매우 화가 났어요. 〈슬라브인이 언쟁 중에 친구에게 총을 쏘다〉는 어떤가요? 동기가 무엇이었나요?

➡ _____

4. Mr. Right: 데일리 텔레그램 사는 데일리 뉴스 사가 그들의 기사를 훔치고 있다는 것을 증명하기를 원했어요.

➡ _____

Read & Think After You Read C

1. A: 네 가지 조언 중에서 너는 어떤 것이 가장 중요하다고 생각하며, 그 이유는 무엇이니?

➡ _____

2. B: 나는 뒷받침하는 자료들을 찾는 것이 가장 중요하다고 생각하는데, 그 정보가 올바른지 확인할 수 있기 때문이야.

➡ _____

_____

MEMO

MEMO

영어 기출 문제집

적중100

1학기

정답 및 해설

비상 | 김진완

중 3

적중100

Lesson 3

For the Love of Our Country

01 ③	02 ④	03 ⑤	04 ④
05 ②	06 (s)ince	07 ①	

01 rescue: 구하다, 구조[구출/구제]하다 save: 구하다 / 우리는 지나가는 낚싯배에 의해서 가라앉는 배에서부터 구조되었다.

02 fortune: 재산 / 버핏은 영리한 투자를 통해서 큰 돈을 벌었다.

03 ① 그는 학자라기보다는 오히려 작가이다. ② 그녀는 분명히 진실을 말하고 있었다. ③ 병사들은 요새를 방어할 준비가 되어 있었다. ④ 너는 한국 전쟁 기념관에 가 본 적이 있니? ⑤ general: 장군 / 그는 최근에 장군으로 진급했다.

04 horrible: 끔찍한 / 우리의 모든 돈이 도난당했다는 것을 알았을 때 정말로 끔찍했다.

05 ① make, make an arrangement: ~을 결정하다 / 우리의 목적지를 결정하자. ② devote, devote one's life to 명사: ~에 일생을 바치다 / 그녀는 공직에 일생을 바칠 것이라고 말했습니다. ③ try. try on: 입어 보다, 신어 보다 / 입어 볼 만한 재킷 좀 있나요? ④ take, take a look around ~: ~ 주위를 둘러보다 / 이곳은 재미있는 곳이에요. 한번 둘러보시겠어요? ⑤ heard, hear of[about] ~: ~에 대해 듣다 / 너는 차고 세일에 대해 들어 본 적이 있니?

06 since: ~이기 때문에

07 movement: (정치적·사회적) 운동 / 태도, 의견 또는 정책의 점진적인 발전 또는 변화

01 (1) trying to be used to new glasses
    (2) It is said that she has been all over the world.
    (3) I hate talking like this behind his back.
    (4) Is it okay if I take a picture?

02 independence

03 so, that he could

04 (i)nclude (r)uin (s)ave
    (1) ruin (2) save (3) include

05 by

06 (1) article (2) would

01 (1) be used to (동)명사: ~하는 데 익숙하다 (2) It is said that 주어+동사 ~: (사람들이) ~라고 한다 (3) behind one's

back: 등 뒤에서 (4) Is it okay if I ~?: 제가 ~해도 될까요? take a picture: 사진을 찍다

02 depend: 의존하다 independence: 독립 / 그녀는 대한민국 독립을 위한 3.1 운동에 참여했다.

03 so+형용사/부사+that 주어+동사: 너무 ~해서 …하다

04 include: ~을 포함하다 / 사람이나 사물을 어떤 것의 일부로 내포하다 ruin: 망치다, 파산시키다 / 누군가로 하여금 그들의 돈이나 권력을 모두 잃게 만들다 save: 구하다 / 위험, 해로움, 또는 파괴로부터 사람이나 사물을 안전하게 만들다 (1) 어떤 사람들은 스포일러가 이야기를 망친다고 말한다. (2) 안전띠를 매는 것은 너의 생명을 구할 수 있다. (3) 호텔비는 아침식사를 포함한다.

05 be+p.p+by 행위자(수동태) / 그 빌딩은 2004년 화재에 의해 파괴되었다. by 동사ing: ~함으로써 / 그녀는 아이들을 돌봄으로써 여분의 돈을 번다.

06 (1) article: 기사 (2) would: (과거에 있어서의 습관·습성·반복적 동작) ~하곤 했다

1 It is said that there will be a big festival
2 It is said that he is a liar.
3 It is said that purple was
4 Is it okay if I practice the guitar?
5 Is it okay if I sit next to you?

1 F   2 T   3 T   4 F   5 F   6 F   7 F   8 T   9 T

Listen & Talk 1 Get Ready

was / read, it is said / both

Listen & Talk 1 A-1

what, reading / biography / haven't heard / the first female, It is said that, over

Listen & Talk 1 A-2

interesting, detective / scholar / but it is said that he was also, solved / didn't know that

Listen & Talk 1 B

know about / heard / Take a look at, to be included / helped, by building a clinic, that such stories, be included in / to, such

Listen & Talk 2 A-1

can't take, museum / Is it okay / leave, in

Listen & Talk 2 A-2

to, How / is it okay if I take pictures in / don't

Listen & Talk 2 B

How was / were / get the chance to, okay if I / remember that, at / on / Let me know if

Communication Step A

are moving onto, As you can see, many, inventions, is called / musical instrument / It is said that it is, largest / How, Is it okay if

Wrap Up 1

what / watching / Isn't he / It is said that he won / how, possible / general who made creative

Wrap Up 2

Would you like to / I'd like to / Here / is it okay if / if, on, stay

 시험대비 기본평가　　　　　　　　p.18

01 ⑤　　　　02 ②　　　　03 ②, ④, ⑤

04 Is it okay if I open the window?

01 무엇을 읽고 있는지 물어보는 질문에, (C) 권기옥의 자서전을 읽고 있다고 대답한다. (D) 그녀(권기옥)에 대해 들어본 적이 없다고 말하며, 그녀가 누구인지 질문한다. (B) 그녀는 한국 최초의 여자 비행 조종사라고 얘기하며 비행시간이 7,000시간 이상이었다는 사실을 추가해서 말한다. (A) 놀라움을 표현하며, 그러한 사실을 몰랐다고 반응한다.

02 'Is it okay if I ~?'는 '제가 ~해도 될까요?'라는 뜻으로 어떤 행동을 하기 전에 허가를 요청할 때 사용하는 표현이다.

03 빈칸 다음에 접속사 but(하지만)이 나오고 플래시를 사용하지 말라는 내용이 나오는 것으로 보아 미술관 안에서 사진을 찍는 것을 허락하고 당부하는 말을 덧붙인 것으로 볼 수 있다.

04 Is it okay if I ~?: 제가 ~해도 될까요? open: 열다

01 ③	02 ②	03 ③	04 ③, ④
05 ④	06 ③	07 ⑤	08 ①, ③
09 ①	10 ②, ④		

01 주어진 문장은 조선 시대에 그가 학자가 아니었는지 묻는 것으로 여기서 그는 정약용을 말한다. 남자가 정약용이 학자이지만, 또한 형사였다고 말하는 것이 주어진 문장에 대한 대답이 될 수 있으므로 ③에 들어가는 것이 적절하다.

02 밑줄 친 부분은 대략 90개의 사건을 해결했다는 의미이므로, 사건을 해결할 수 있는 detective(형사, 탐정)가 가장 어울린다. ① diplomat: 외교관 ③ reporter: 기자 ④ victim: 피해자 ⑤ painter: 화가

03 주어진 문장에서 she는 여자가 읽고 있는 자서전의 주인공인 권기옥을 의미한다. 남자는 그녀(권기옥)에 대해 들어 본 적이 없다고 말하며 이어서 그녀가 누구인지 여자에게 묻는 것이 어울리므로 ③이 적절하다.

04 ① Lisa는 어떤 종류의 책을 읽고 있는가? (자서전) ② 얼마나 많은 비행 시간을 권기옥은 가지고 있었는가? (7,000시간 이상) ③ 누가 한국에서 최초의 남성 비행사였는가? (최초의 여성 비행사에 대한 정보만 있으므로 알 수 없다.) ④ Lisa는 왜 권기옥에 관한 책을 읽고 있는가? (책을 읽는 이유에 대해서는 언급되어 있지 않다.) ⑤ 남자는 권기옥에 대해서 들어본 적이 있는가? (아니요)

05 ④ 상대방의 핸드폰을 사용할 수 있는지 허락을 묻는 질문에 긍정으로 대답하고 핸드폰을 안 가져왔다고 말하는 것은 어울리지 않는다.

06 한옥 마을이 어땠는지 감상을 묻는 질문에 (C) 좋았다고 대답하며 집들이 예뻤다고 대답한다. (A) 잘 되었다고 말한다. (B) 여자가 저녁을 먹을 기회가 없었다고 하면서, 부엌을 이 시간에 쓰는 것에 대해 허락을 요청하자 (D) 괜찮다고 대답하며, 하지만 부엌이 10시에 닫는다는 사실을 상기시켜 준다.

07 주어진 문장에서 such stories는 여자가 말한 이태석 신부가 병원과 학교를 지음으로써 아이들을 도왔다는 이야기를 의미하므로 그 문장 다음에 나와야 적절하다.

08 남자가 이태석 신부에 대해서 들어 본 적이 있다고 대답하고 있으므로, 이태석 신부에 대해서 들어 본 적이 있는지 아니면 이태석 신부에 대해서 알고 있는지 물어보는 것이 적절하다.

09 take a look at ~: ~을 보다

10 알고 있는 내용을 진술할 때 'It is said that 주어+동사 ~.(~라고 한다)', 'It is believed that 주어+동사 ~. (~라고 믿어진다.)', 'It is thought that 주어+동사 ~. (~라고 생각된다.)'라고 말할 수 있다.

01 who Shin Saimdang is

02 it is said that her paintings were so realistic that birds gathered around the painted tree

03 if

04 Sure / Of course / Certainly / No problem

05 by

06 such

07 built, will be included, South Sudan

08 Is it okay if I try on your hat?

01 간접의문문의 어순은 '의문사+주어+동사'이다.

02 It is said that 주어+동사 ~: (사람들이) ~라고 한다 so+형용사/부사+that 주어+동사: 너무 ~해서 …하다 realistic: 진짜 같은, 사실적인 gather: 모이다

03 Is it okay if I ~?: 제가 ~해도 될까요?

04 사진을 찍어도 되는지 허가를 묻는 말에 허락의 말이 나오고 접속사 but 다음에 카메라의 플래시를 터뜨리지 말라는 말이 나오는 것이 어울린다.

05 by 동사ing: ~함으로써

06 such: (형) 이러한, 그러한 such (a(n))+형용사+명사: 너무 ~한 명사

07 build: 짓다(built-built) include: ~을 포함하다 social studies: 사회 Sudan: 수단 (민주 공화국) / 이태석 신부가 아이들을 돕기 위해서 병원과 학교를 지은 이야기는 남수단의 사회 교과서에 포함될 것이다.

08 Is it okay if I ~?: 제가 ~해도 될까요? try on: 입어[써] 보다, 신어 보다

교과서
Grammar

1 (1) if[whether]   (2) whether   (3) if[whether]

2 (1) had just heard   (2) had lost   (3) heard

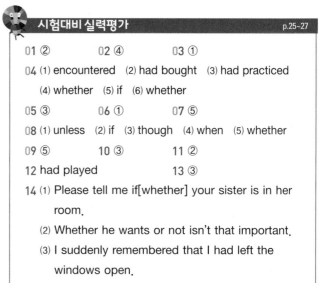

01 ⑤

02 (1) had already left   (2) had broken   (3) if   (4) whether   03 ④

04 (1) My daughter had never been sick until then.

(2) I had just fallen asleep when someone knocked at the door.

(3) She is not sure if she will return in the future.

01 주절의 동사가 remembered로 과거이고 그것들을 탁자 위에 던져 놓은 것은 그 이전의 사실이므로 과거완료(대과거)를 써야 한다.

02 (1) 도착한 것보다 기차가 떠난 것이 앞서는 것이므로 과거완료가 적절하다. (2) 꽃병을 깼음(앞선 사실)을 고백하는 것이므로 과거완료가 적절하다. (3) 내용상 '올 수 있다는 것을 모른다'는 어색하다. 사실의 여부를 확인하거나 불확실함을 나타내는 if가 적절하다. (4) 바로 뒤에 or not이 이어지고 있으므로 whether가 적절하다.

03 asked의 직접목적어가 나와야 하는데 '~인지 (아닌지)'라는 의미로 명사절을 이끄는 접속사 if가 적절하다.

04 (1) 경험을 나타내는 과거완료를 이용한다. (2) 노크하기 전에 잠이 막 든 것이므로 과거완료로 나타낸다. (3) '~인지 (아닌지)'라는 의미의 접속사로 어떠한 사실의 여부를 확인하거나 불확실함을 나타낼 때 쓰이는 if를 이용한다.

01 ②   02 ④   03 ①

04 (1) encountered   (2) had bought   (3) had practiced   (4) whether   (5) if   (6) whether

05 ③   06 ①   07 ⑤

08 (1) unless   (2) if   (3) though   (4) when   (5) whether

09 ⑤   10 ③   11 ②

12 had played   13 ③

14 (1) Please tell me if[whether] your sister is in her room.

(2) Whether he wants or not isn't that important.

(3) I suddenly remembered that I had left the windows open.

(4) I had never been to the big city before.

(5) I found out that someone had broken the lamp.

15 ④   16 ⑤   17 ①, ②

01 When she arrived at the station, the first train had already left.

02 He asked her nicely if he could see her license.

03 첫 번째 빈칸에는 '~인지 (아닌지)'라는 의미의 접속사 if가 적절하다. 두 번째 빈칸에는 잃어버린 것이 우연히 찾은 것보다 앞서므로 과거완료가 적절하다.

04 (1) 과거완료는 'had+과거분사'의 형태이므로 encountered가 적절하다. (2) 산책시킨 시점보다 아빠가 사주신 시점이 앞서므로 had bought가 적절하다. (3) since(~ 이래로)가 있으므로 had practiced가 적절하다. (4) 내용상 '~인지 (아닌지)'라는 의미의 접속사 whether가 적절하다. (5) 내용상 '~인지 (아닌지)'라는 의미의 접속사 if가 적절하나. (6) 뒤에 or not이 바로 이어서 나오고 있으므로 whether가 적절하다.

05 도착했을 때(과거) 이미 극장에 들어간 것이므로 과거완료로 써야 한다.

06 I thought보다 앞선 시제이므로 @의 have been은 had been으로 고쳐야 한다.

07 뒤에 or not이 있고 내용상 '~인지 (아닌지)'라는 의미가 자연스러우므로 if나 whether가 적절하고, 알고 싶어 하는 것보다 가방이 버려진 시점이 앞선 시제이므로 과거완료가 적절하다.

08 (1) 조건의 unless가 적절하다. (2) 조건의 부사절을 이끄는 if가 적절하다. (3) 서로 상반되는 내용이 나오므로 though가 적절하다. (4) 뒤에 '주어+be동사'가 생략된 형태로 when이 적절하다. (5) or not이 바로 뒤에 이어지므로 whether가 적절하다.

09 집에 도착한 것보다 산책을 나간 것이 앞서므로 과거완료가 적절하다.

10 '~인지 (아닌지)'라는 의미의 명사절을 이끄는 if가 적절하다.

11 ask의 목적어로 '~인지 (아닌지)'라는 의미의 명사절을 이끄는 if가 적절하다.

12 6살에 연주하기 시작했으므로 6살 이래로 연주해 왔다고 과거완료로 나타낼 수 있다.

13 <보기>는 계속적 용법이다. ① 완료, ② 경험, ③ 계속, ④ 결과, ⑤ 대과거

14 (1) what이 문장 내에서 하는 역할이 없으므로 '~인지 (아닌지)'라는 의미의 접속사로 쓰이는 if나 whether로 고치는 것이 적절하다. (2) if가 이끄는 명사절은 주어 역할을 할 수 없으므로 whether로 고치는 것이 적절하다. (3) 창문을 열어 놓은 것이 기억하는 시점보다 앞서므로 과거완료로 고치는 것이 적절하다. (4) 완료시제와 어울리는 것은 ago가 아니라 before이다. (5) 누군가 램프를 깨뜨린 것이 발견한 것보다 앞서므로 과거완료가 적절하다.

15 '~인지 (아닌지)'라는 의미의 접속사 if가 적절하며 if 다음에는 or not을 바로 붙여 쓰지 않는다.

16 사기 전에 말했던 것이므로 과거완료로 나타내는 것이 적절하다. 전치사 about을 빠뜨리지 않도록 주의한다.

17 ① He asked me whether or not the book was boring. ② I remembered that I had turned the stove on.

01 (1) had bought for me   (2) she had received

02 (1) had not locked   (2) he had already gone

03 (1) I wonder if these dishes will suit your taste.
  (2) I don't know whether he is at home or at the office.
  (3) We found out that we had been at the same school.
  (4) She seemed astonished that I had never been to Paris.

04 (1) If → Whether   (2) if → whether   (3) if → whether

05 (1) had never learned   (2) if[whether] she forgot

06 (1) The man isn't sure if[whether] he can help her.
  (2) They don't know if[whether] he will be promoted.
  (3) Would you tell me if[whether] he needs surgery or not?

07 (1) He won the contest because he had practiced a lot for the contest.
  (2) I couldn't take the class because it had been canceled.

08 (1) He told me that he had stolen the money the other day.
  (2) No computer had won even one game against a human player until then.
  (3) I found my bag that I had lost on the bus.
  (4) I asked the lady if[whether] I could use the bathroom.
  (5) I'm not sure if Santa will give me a nice gift or not.
  (6) I couldn't decide whether to buy it.

01 각각 과거보다 앞선 시제에 행한 것을 나타내는 과거완료를 이용한다.

02 (1) 과거완료의 대과거 용법을 이용한다. (2) 과거완료의 결과 용법을 이용한다.

03 (1) if가 명사절을 이끌도록 한다. (2) whether가 명사절을 이끌도록 한다. (3), (4) 하나 앞서는 시제에 과거완료를 이용한다.

04 (1) 문두에서 주어를 이끄는 역할을 하고 있으므로 If를 Whether로 고치는 것이 적절하다. (2) 뒤에 or not이 바로 이어서 나오고 있으므로 if를 whether로 고치는 것이 적절하다. (3) whether 다음에 to부정사를 쓸 수 있지만 if는 to부정사와 함께 쓰이지 않는다.

05 (1) 과거보다 앞서는 일이나 상태를 나타내는 과거완료(대과거)를 이용한다. (2) 명사절을 이끄는 if[whether]를 이용한다.

06 명사절을 이끄는 if나 whether를 이용하여 두 문장을 연결한다.

07 시간차가 드러나도록 하라고 했으므로 앞서는 사건을 과거완료 시제로 나타낸다.

5

08 (1) 말했을 때보다 그가 훔친 시점이 앞서므로 과거완료가 적절하다. (2) until then으로 보아 그때까지의 경험을 나타내는 과거완료가 적절하다. (3) 잃어버린 후에 발견한 것이므로 잃어버린 것을 과거완료로 쓰는 것이 적절하다. (4) 명사절을 이끄는 if나 whether를 쓰는 것이 적절하다. (5) if가 이끄는 절이 명사절이므로 미래는 미래시제로 나타내야 한다. (6) whether 다음에 to부정사를 쓸 수 있지만 if는 to부정사와 함께 쓰이지 않는다.

Reading

교과서

확인문제 p.30

1 T 2 F 3 F

확인문제 p.31

1 T 2 T 3 F

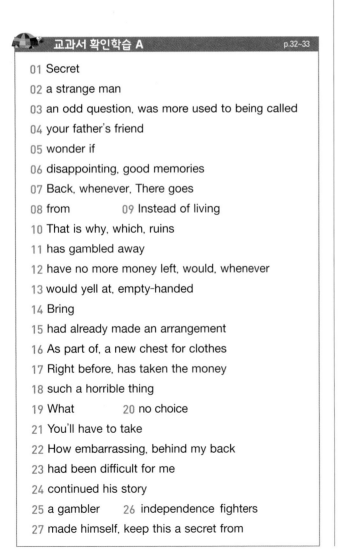

교과서 확인학습 A p.32~33

01 Secret
02 a strange man
03 an odd question, was more used to being called
04 your father's friend
05 wonder if
06 disappointing, good memories
07 Back, whenever, There goes
08 from   09 Instead of living
10 That is why, which, ruins
11 has gambled away
12 have no more money left, would, whenever
13 would yell at, empty-handed
14 Bring
15 had already made an arrangement
16 As part of, a new chest for clothes
17 Right before, has taken the money
18 such a horrible thing
19 What   20 no choice
21 You'll have to take
22 How embarrassing, behind my back
23 had been difficult for me
24 continued his story
25 a gambler   26 independence fighters
27 made himself, keep this a secret from

28 if
29 afterwards, had been wrong
30 had devoted his life to

교과서 확인학습 B p.34~35

1 The Secret of My Father
2 In 1946, a strange man visited me and asked, "Are you Mr. Kim Yonghwan's daughter?"
3 For me, this was an odd question because I was more used to being called the daughter of a *parakho*.
4 "I'm your father's friend.
5 You may wonder if it is true, but your father....," the man said.
6 At that moment, I was expecting disappointing news since I did not have good memories of my father.
7 Back in the 1920's, whenever people saw me in the village, they would say, "There goes the *parakho*'s daughter."
8 My father was a son from a very rich family.
9 Instead of living the life of a seonbi, he was always at the gambling house.
10 That is why he was called a *parakho*, which means someone who ruins his family's fortune.
11 "Your father has gambled away all of the money, and now he's asking for more.
12 Go and tell him that we have no more money left," my mother would tell me whenever she sent me to the gambling house.
13 Then, my father would yell at me angrily, "Why did you come empty-handed?
14 Bring me more money!"
15 When I was sixteen years old, my family had already made an arrangement for me to marry Mr. Seo.
16 As part of the wedding tradition, Mr. Seo's family sent my family some money to buy a new chest for clothes.
17 Right before the wedding day, my mother came into my room and said, "Your father has taken the money for the chest."
18 I asked angrily, "How could he do such a horrible thing?
19 What should we do now?"
20 "We have no choice.

21 You'll have to take your aunt's old chest," my mother said.

22 "How embarrassing for the family," people would whisper behind my back.

23 Since the first day of marriage, life at my husband's house had been difficult for me.

24 "Your father, my dear friend....," my father's friend continued his story.

25 "He was not a gambler.

26 Your father sent the family money to the independence fighters in Manchuria.

27 He made himself look like a gambler to keep this a secret from the Japanese officers."

28 At first, I was not sure if he was telling the truth.

29 But afterwards, I found out the truth about my father and I realized that I had been wrong about him.

30 Ever since that moment, I have been proud to be the daughter of a *parakho* who had devoted his life to the independence movement.

시험대비 실력평가
p.36~39

01 Are you Mr. Kim Yonghwan's daughter?

02 (A) odd   (B) being   (C) if

03 ②, ⑤   04 ②, ④   05 ①   06 ①

07 ②   08 ②   09 ①

10 (A) already   (B) What   (C) Since   11 ⑤

12 ④   13 ④   14 ③   15 ④

16 I was not sure if[whether] he was telling the truth

17 ②   18 ②, ③

19 (A) would   (B) ruins   (C) empty-handed

20 and it

21 we have no more money left

01 낯선 남자가 물어본 내용을 가리킨다.

02 (A) 나는 파락호의 딸이라고 불리는 것이 더 익숙했기 때문에 이것은 나에게 '이상한' 질문이었다고 해야 하므로 odd가 적절하다. familiar: 익숙한, 친숙한, odd: 이상한, 특이한, (B) 나는 파락호의 딸이라고 불리는 것에 더 '익숙했다'고 해야 하므로 being이 적절하다. be used to ~ing: ~하는 데 익숙하다, be used to 동사원형: ~하기 위해 사용되다, (C) wonder if: ~여부를 궁금해 하다, that은 목적어의 내용이 확실할 때 사용한다.

03 ⓑ와 ②, ⑤: [이유를 나타내어] …이므로, …이니까, ①, ③, ④: …부터[이후]

04 ⓐ와 ③, ④: ~인지 아닌지, ①, ②, ⑤: 만약

05 필자의 아버지가 독립운동가들에게 얼마나 많은 돈을 보냈는지는 알 수 없다. ① No. ② To the independence fighters in Manchuria. ③ To keep the fact that he sent the family money to the independence fighters in Manchuria a secret from the Japanese officers. ⑤ Her father's friend told her the truth.

06 ⓐ ask for: 요청하다, ⓑ yell at: ~에게 소리를 지르다

07 ②번 다음 문장의 That에 주목한다. 주어진 문장의 내용을 받고 있으므로 ②번이 적절하다.

08 글쓴이의 아버지는 '선비'의 삶을 사는 대신 항상 도박장에 계셨다.

09 ① (C)의 첫 부분은 (A)의 내용을 가리키므로 (A) 다음에 (C)가 이어지고 (B)의 that moment가 (C)에서 아버지에 대한 사실을 알게 된 다음을 가리키므로 (C) 다음에 (B)가 와야 한다. 그러므로 (A)-(C)-(B)의 순서가 적절하다.

10 (A) 긍정문이므로 already를 쓰는 것이 적절하다. yet: 부정문(아직), 의문문(벌써), (B) do의 목적어를 써야 하므로 What이 적절하다. (C) 결혼 첫날 '이래'라고 해야 하므로 Since가 적절하다. for+기간(~ 동안), since+기점(~부터[이후])

11 ⓐ와 ⑤: [역할·자격·기능·성질 따위를 나타내어] …으로서(전치사), ① …할 때(접속사), ② [비례] …함에 따라(접속사) ③ [보통 as ~ as ...로 형용사·부사 앞에서] …와 같은 정도로(앞의 as는 지시부사, 뒤의 as는 접속사), ④ [상태] …한 대로(접속사)

12 글쓴이의 아버지가 장롱을 살 돈을 어디에 썼는지는 대답할 수 없다. ① Mr. Seo. ② To buy a new chest for clothes. ③ No. ⑤ No.

13 선비의 삶을 사는 '대신에'라고 해야 하므로 instead of가 적절하다. instead of: ~ 대신에, ① ~에도 (불구하고), ② ~ 때문에, ③ ~에 더하여, 게다가, ⑤ ~에 더하여

14 ③의 his는 글쓴이의 아버지가 아니라 일반적인 '파락호'를 지칭한다.

15 ⓑ와 ④: ~하곤 했다(과거의 불규칙적 습관), ① 시제 일치에 의해 will(…일[할] 것이다)을 과거형 would로 쓴 것임. ② 정중히 요청을 할 때 씀, ③ would rather 동사원형(~했으면 좋겠다), ⑤ 정중한 제의·초대를 할 때 씀

16 if[whether]를 보충하면 된다.

17 이 글은 필자의 아버지가 파락호로 신분을 숨기고 독립 운동 자금을 대었다는 내용의 글이므로, 제목으로는 ②번 '파락호가 아니라 비밀 독립운동가'가 적절하다.

18 the reason why는 선행사와 관계부사 중에서 the reason이나 why 어느 한 쪽만 써도 된다.

19 (A) '말하곤 했다'라고 해야 하므로 과거의 불규칙적 습관을 나타내는 would가 적절하다. (B) 집안의 '재산을 탕진하는' 사람

이라고 해야 하므로 ruins가 적절하다. ruin one's fortune: 재산을 탕진하다, (C) 명사에 ed를 붙인 유사분사가 주격보어로 쓰인 것이므로 empty-handed가 적절하다. empty-handed: 빈손인

20 계속적 용법의 관계대명사는 '접속사+인칭대명사'로 바꿔 쓸 수 있다.

21 have no more money left: 남은 돈이 없다

p.40~41

서술형 시험대비

01 left

02 every time 또는 each time

03 Instead of living the life of a *seonbi*, he was always at the gambling house.

04 had devoted

05 Your father sent the independence fighters in Manchuria the family money.

06 whether

07 (A) independence fighters (B) a secret

08 (A) some money (B) new chest

09 (A) clothes (B) horrible (C) embarrassing

10 chest

11 There goes the *parakho's* daughter

12 that → which

13 (A) *parakho* (B) gambled

01 have no more money left: 더 이상 남은 돈이 없다

02 whenever = every time = each time: …할 때는 언제든지

03 앞 문장의 내용('선비의 삶을 사는 대신 그는 항상 도박장에 계셨다.')을 가리킨다.

04 독립 운동에 생애를 바친 것이 먼저 일어난 일이므로 과거완료로 쓰는 것이 적절하다.

05 to를 생략하고 '간접목적어+직접목적어' 순서로 쓰는 것이 적절하다.

06 if = whether: ~인지 아닌지

07 필자는 아버지를 파락호라고 오해했지만, 사실 그의 아버지는 가족의 돈을 만주에 있는 독립운동가들에게 보냈고 그 사실을 일본 순사들에게 비밀로 하기 위해 도박꾼처럼 보이게 했다.

08 신랑측 가족이 신부측 가족에게 옷을 넣을 새 장롱을 살 약간의 돈을 보내 주었다.

09 (A) '옷'을 넣을 장롱이라고 해야 하므로 clothes가 적절하다. cloths: cloth(옷감, 천)의 복수 clothes: 옷, 의복, (B) 그런 '끔찍한' 일이라고 해야 하므로 horrible이 적절하다. horrible: 끔찍한, terrific: 아주 좋은, 멋진, (C) 감정을 나타내는 동사는 감정을 유발할 때 현재분사를 쓰는 것이 적절하므

로 embarrassing이 적절하다.

10 chest: (보통 나무로 만든) 상자, 장롱, 물건을 보관하기 위해 사용되는 크고 무거운 상자

11 There+동사+명사 주어

12 관계대명사 that은 계속적 용법으로 쓸 수 없기 때문에, which로 고치는 것이 적절하다.

13 gamble away one's fortune: 노름으로 가산을 탕진하다

p.43~47

영역별 핵심문제

01 ③, ④   02 marriage   03 of
04 keeping   05 (A) is called (B) if   06 fortress
07 ④   08 ①   09 ①
10 wooden   11 (A) Right. (B) who (C) made
12 general   13 ⑤   14 ④
15 if[whether] he would forgive his fault
16 ⓑ, ⓓ, ⓔ   17 ③
18 (1) I was not sure if[whether] he was telling the truth.
   (2) Rob wants to know if[whether] more men than women like gardening.
   (3) I asked her if[whether] I could have a drink.
19 ⑤   20 ⑤
21 because → why   22 ①   23 ②
24 (A) her father (B) new chest
25 (A) himself (B) keep (C) At first
26 ②, ④, ⑤   27 ④   28 had been 또는 was
29 ②   30 ④

01 ① 이상한 것은 그가 나를 못 알아본다는 점이었다. ② 이 나라는 독립 이후로 많은 발전을 이룩했다. ③ movement: (정치적·사회적) 운동 / 그는 인상주의 운동을 추종했다. ④ leave: 맡기다, 남기다 / 너는 아이들을 토요일에 할머니한테 맡겼니? ⑤ 옆 사람과 속삭이지 마세요.

02 주어진 단어는 동사와 명사의 관계이다. marry는 뒤에 –age를 붙여 명사형을 만든다. solve: 해결하다, 풀다 solution: 해결 marry: 결혼하다 marriage: 결혼

03 hear of ~: ~에 대해 듣다 / Big Star라고 불리는 밴드에 대해 들어 본 적 있니? instead of: ~ 대신에 / 내가 햄 대신에 참치를 먹어도 되나요?

04 keep a secret: 비밀을 지키다 / 대부분의 사람들은 비밀을 지키는 것을 잘하지 못한다. keep: (~한 상태를) 유지하다 awake: 깨어 있는 / Paul은 강한 블랙 커피를 많이 마심으로써 깨어 있었다.

05 (A) call이 5형식으로 사용하여 '[사람·물건을] (어떤 이름으로) 부르다, 이름을 붙이다'로 쓰일 수 있다. 원래는 'People call this the Geojunggi.'인 문장을 수동태로 바꿨으므로 is

called가 적절하다. (B) 어떤 일을 하기 전에 해도 되는지 허가 여부를 물을 때 'Is it okay if I ~?(제가 ~해도 될까요?)'라고 질문한다.

06 fortress: 요새 / 중요한 장소를 방어하기 위해 사용되는 크고 튼튼한 건물

07 ⓐ 거중기는 화성 요새를 지을 때 사용되었다.(○) ⓑ B는 화성 요새를 더 가까이 보기를 원했다. (화성 요새가 아닌 거중기를 더 가까이 보고 싶어 했다.) ⓒ 화성 요새는 28개월 동안에 지어졌다.(○) ⓓ 거중기는 기계의 일종이다. (○) ⓔ A는 거중기가 무엇인지 알고 있다.(○)

08 'How was ~?'는 상대방의 경험에 대해 묻는 표현으로, 대답 'It was wonderful.(좋았어요.)'과 어울리므로 ①이 적절하다.

09 ⓐ to, the chance to 동사원형: ~할 기회, to부정사가 the chance를 꾸며주고 있다. ⓑ if, Is it okay if I ~?: 제가 ~해도 될까요? ⓒ that, that은 remember의 목적어 자리에 들어가는 명사절을 이끄는 접속사로 사용됐다. ⓓ at, 시간 앞에는 전치사 at을 사용한다. ⓔ if, if: (접) ~한다면

10 ships를 수식하는 형용사가 들어갈 자리이다. wood: 나무, 목재 wooden: 나무로 된, 목재의

11 (A) (사람들이) 그가 12척의 나무 배로(목선으로) 전쟁을 이겼다고 말했으므로, 긍정의 대답이 나와야 한다. (B) 여기서 general은 '장군'이므로 사람을 선행사로 하는 주격 관계대명사 who[that]가 적절하다. (C) 목적어 creative plans가 있으므로 능동이 어울린다.

12 general: 장군 / 육군이나 공군에서 높은 계급을 가진 장교

13 명사절을 이끄는 접속사 if는 whether로 바꿔 쓸 수 있다.

14 When Megan arrived at the station, the train had already left for London. 도착하기 전에 이미 출발한 것이므로 도착한 것은 과거로, 출발한 것은 과거완료로 써야 한다.

15 명사절을 이끄는 접속사 if나 whether를 이용하고 주절이 과거 시제이므로 will을 would로 써야 하는 것에 유의한다.

16 ⓐ has → had ⓒ had eaten → ate, made → had made ⓕ which → if[whether] ⓖ that → if[whether]

17 already로 보아 had already eaten과 같은 과거완료가 나와야 한다.

18 명사절을 이끄는 접속사 if[whether]를 이용한다.

19 ⑤번은 believe의 목적어를 이끄는 접속사 that이 적절하고 나머지는 모두 '~인지 (아닌지)'라는 의미의 명사절을 이끄는 접속사 if[whether]가 적절하다.

20 win a lot of money by gambling: 노름으로 돈을 많이 따다

21 '그것이 그가 파락호라고 불린 이유이다'라고 해야 하므로, because를 why로 고치는 것이 적절하다.

22 ①번 다음 문장의 the money에 주목한다. 주어진 문장의 some money를 받고 있으므로 ①번이 적절하다.

23 ⓐ와 ② 꼭, 바로(부사), ① 권리(명사), ④ 옳은(형용사) ④ 제

대로 된(형용사), ⑤ (상태가) 좋은(형용사)

24 글쓴이는 Mr. Seo와 결혼하게 되었지만, '그녀의 아버지' 때문에 옷을 넣을 '새 장롱'을 살 수 없었다.

25 (A) 주어와 목적어가 같으므로 재귀대명사 himself가 적절하다. (B) '일본 경찰들로부터 이것을 비밀로 지키려'라고 해야 하므로 keep이 적절하다. keep+O+O.C.+from A: A로부터 ~을 …로 지키다, stop A from B: A가 B하는 것을 막다, (C) '처음에는'이라고 해야 하므로 At first가 적절하다. for the first time: 처음으로

26 ⓐ와 ①, ③: 계속 용법, ② 경험 용법, ④ 결과 용법, ⑤ 완료 용법

27 'I realized that I had been wrong about him'을 통해 'ashamed'를, 'I have been proud'를 통해 'respectful'을 찾을 수 있다. ① ashamed: 부끄러운, ② respectful: 존경심을 보이는, ③ disappointed: 실망한

28 after가 있을 때는 시간의 전후관계가 분명하므로, 과거완료를 과거로 쓸 수 있다.

29 ② 위 글은 '전기'이다. ④ (신문•잡지의) 글, 기사, ⑤ 자서전

30 석방된 직후에 죽었다.

단원별 예상문제 p.48~51

01 ② 　　02 (1) so (2) such 　　03 ④
04 (1) (g)eneral (2) marriages (3) (o)bject (4) (s)ince
05 ① 　　06 ④
07 is it okay if I use the bathroom now?
08 (A) What are you reading? (B) Who is she?
09 ⓐ female ⓑ is said ⓒ that
10 biography 11 ⑤ 　　12 inventions
13 if[whether] she could go out 　　14 ④
15 ④ 　　16 ③, ⑤ 　　17 gambling house
18 ⓑ such a horrible thing ⓒ behind my back
19 has → had 　　20 ④ 　　21 ⑤
22 ①, ④ 　　23 (A) look like (B) Japanese officers
24 to look → look like
25 He sent the family money to the independence fighters in Manchuria.

---

01 ②번을 제외한 보기들은 뒤에 -ward(s)를 붙여 부사를 만들 수 있다. ① inward: 안으로 ③ afterwards: 후에, 나중에 ④ backwards: 뒤로 ⑤ forwards: 앞으로

02 (1) so+형용사/부사+that 주어 동사: 너무 ~해서 …하다 / 모든 것이 너무 변해서 나는 그 장소를 알아차리지 못했다. (2) such (a(n))+형용사+명사: 너무 ~한 명사 / 그는 너무 갑작스럽게 멈춰서 우리가 거의 그를 칠 뻔 했다.

03 (A) unwilling: 꺼려하는, 싫어하는 ask for: 청구하다, 청

9

하다 / 그는 항상 다른 사람에게 부탁하기를 꺼려한다. (B) devote one's life to 명사: ~에 일생을 바치다 / 그녀는 예술에 자신의 일생을 바치겠다고 발표했다.

04 (1) general: 장군 (2) marriage: 결혼, 혼인 (3) object: 물체, 물건 (4) since: ~이기 때문에

05 주어진 문장은 카레랑 비빔밥 중 무엇을 먹을지 묻는 질문이다. 이에 대한 대답으로 'I'd like to have *bibimbap*, please.'가 어울리므로 ①이 적절하다.

06 마지막 부분에서 여자가 좌석 불이 켜지면 좌석에 앉아야 한다고 말하는 것을 볼 때 대화는 항공기 안에서 이뤄지고 있다.

07 Is it okay if I ~?: 제가 ~해도 될까요? if 다음에는 주어와 동사 순으로 나온다. use: 사용하다 bathroom: 화장실

08 (A) Lisa가 권기옥에 대한 책을 읽고 있는 중이라고 대답하였으므로 무엇을 하고 있는지 묻는 질문이 어울린다. (B) Lisa가 권기옥에 대한 설명을 하고 있으므로, 그녀(권기옥)가 누구인지 물어보는 질문이 적절하다

09 ⓐ She가 주어이므로 female이 어울린다. male: 남성; 남성의 female: 여자; 여자의, 여성의 ⓑ, ⓒ It is said that 주어+동사 ~: (사람들이) ~라고 한다.

10 biography: 전기 / 누군가가 다른 누군가의 삶에 대해 쓴 책

11 남자는 조선 시대로 넘어가자고 얘기하면서 조선 시대의 유물들을 보여주며 그 중 하나인 자격루를 소개하고 있는 상황이다. As you can see: 보시다시피

12 invent: 발명하다 invention: 발명품, 발명

13 명사절을 이끄는 접속사 if나 whether를 이용하고 주절이 과거 시제이므로 will을 would로 써야 하는 것에 유의한다.

14 ④번은 '만약 ~한다면'의 의미로 부사절을 이끄는 접속사로 쓰였지만 나머지는 모두 '~인지 아닌지'라는 의미로 명사절을 이끄는 접속사로 쓰였다.

15 ① I told the story that I had read in the book. ② I couldn't find the pen which Dad had given to me. ③ After she had been[was] in prison for 6 months, she was released and died short after. ⑤ It was proved that the officials had taken bribes from him months before. bribe: 뇌물

16 ⓐ와 ①, ②, ④: 동명사, ③, ⑤: 현재분사

17 선비의 삶을 사는 대신 항상 '도박장'에 계셨기 때문이다.

18 ⓑ 'such a 형용사+명사'의 순서로 쓰는 것이 적절하다. ⓒ behind one's back: ~ 몰래

19 기준 시점보다 더 이전에 일어난 일이므로, 과거완료로 쓰는 것이 적절하다.

20 '결혼식 직전'에 돈을 가져갔다.

21 ⓐ keep+O+O.C.+from A: A로부터 ~을 …로 지키다, ⓑ devote A to B: A를 B에 바치다

22 (A)와 ②, ③, ⑤: 부사적 용법, ① 형용사적 용법, ④ 명사적

용법

23 필자의 아버지는 파락호가 아니라 가족의 돈을 만주에 있는 독립운동가들에게 보내는 사실을 '일본 순사들'에게 비밀로 하기 위해 그 자신을 도박꾼처럼 보이게 했다.

24 사역동사(made)+목적어+원형부정사, look like+명사: ~처럼 보이다

25 '그가 가족의 돈을 만주에 있는 독립 운동가들에게 보냈다.'는 것을 가리킨다.

🦉 서술형 실전문제
p.52~53

01 ⓐ Why? ⓒ He is going to be included in the social studies textbook in South Sudan.
　ⓔ It is good to hear that students will learn about such a great person.

02 It is said that such stories will be included in the textbook. / People say that such stories will be included in the textbook.

03 (1) had left　(2) had been closed

04 Is it okay if I bring in my water bottle? / Can I bring in my water bottle?

05 (1) It was the most interesting game that I had ever played.
　(2) His wife was surprised to learn that he had already been fired without any warning.
　(3) He could not decide if[whether] this was a fairy tale or a nightmare.
　(4) I'm considering whether to accept his offer.

06 (1) I want to know if[whether] he can give her a recommendation.
　(2) She could not open the door because she had left the key at school.

07 not, but

08 Bring more money to me!

09 marry with → marry

10 글쓴이의 아버지가 장롱을 살 돈을 가지고 간 것

11 her father, money

---

01 ⓐ 남자가 그 사람에 대해서 들어본 적이 있다고 했는데, 그 사람이 누구인지 묻는 것은 앞뒤가 맞지 않는다. 여자가 이태석 신부의 이야기가 교과서에 실린다는 말을 하고 있으므로 남자는 이태석 신부를 아는지 물어본 이유에 대해서 질문하는 것이 적절하다. ⓒ 그의 이야기가 교과서에 포함되어지는 것이므로 수동태로 써야 한다. ⓔ 학생들이 훌륭한 사람에 대해서 배우는 일은 듣기 좋은 것이므로 bad를 good으로 바꿔야 한다.

02 알고 있는 내용을 진술할 때 'It is said that 주어+동사 ~.'나

'They[People] say (that) 주어+동사 ~.'을 쓸 수 있다.

03 (1) 기억하는 시점보다 앞선 시점에 문을 열어 놓은 것이므로 과거완료를 이용한다. (2) 도착한 시점보다 앞선 시점에 문이 닫힌 것이므로 과거완료를 이용한다. 수동태로 써야 하는 것에 주의한다.

04 'Is it okay if I ~?'는 '제가 ~해도 될까요?'라는 뜻으로 어떤 행동을 하기 전에 허가를 요청할 때 사용하는 표현이다. 이외의 허가를 구하는 다른 표현으로 'Can I ~?'가 있다.

05 (1) 과거의 어느 시점까지 게임을 해 본 것이므로 과거완료로 나타내는 것이 적절하다. (2) 해고된 것이 앞선 일이고 already가 있으므로 과거완료로 나타내는 것이 적절하다. (3) 뒤에 or a nightmare가 나오므로 that을 if나 whether로 고치는 것이 적절하다. (4) if는 to부정사와 함께 쓰이지 않으므로 if를 whether로 고치는 것이 적절하다. nightmare: 악몽

06 (1) '~인지 (아닌지)'라는 의미의 명사절을 이끄는 접속사 if[whether]를 이용한다. (2) 열쇠를 두고 온 것이 문을 열지 못하는 시점보다 앞서므로 과거완료로 써야 한다.

07 not A but B = instead of A, B = B instead of A

08 bring은 to를 사용하여 3형식으로 고친다.

09 marry는 타동사이므로 전치사 with 없이 목적어를 쓰는 것이 적절하다.

10 글쓴이의 어머니가 말한 "Your father has taken the money for the chest."를 가리킨다.

11 '그녀의 아버지'가 장롱을 살 '돈'은 가져갔기 때문이다.

창의사고력 서술형 문제   p.54

|모범답안|

01 A: Is it okay if I borrow your bicycle? / Can[May] I borrow your bicycle? / I'm wondering if I can borrow your bicycle.
    B: I'm sorry. It's broken.

02 (1) if[whether] she is reading
     (2) had memorized

03 (A) female independence fighter
     (B) to fight for independence
     (C) built schools and educated women
     (D) six months   (E) an award

01 'Is it okay if I ~?'는 '제가 ~해도 될까요?'라는 뜻으로 어떤 행동을 하기 전에 허가를 요청할 때 사용하는 표현이다. if 다음에는 허락을 구하는 내용을 쓴다. 허가를 묻는 다른 표현으로는 'Can I ~?' 등이 있다. borrow: 빌리다 broken: 고장 난

단원별 모의고사   p.55~59

01 ⓑ to spend → to spending   02 at
03 (1) biography   (2) female   (3) locker   (4) detective
04 (1) movement   (2) inventions   (3) getting
05 ②   06 ④
07 (A) is called   (B) it   08 ③
09 It is said that it is the oldest and the largest water clock in Korea.
10 ①   11 scholar
12 It is said that he was also a detective.
13 ④   14 ③
15 (1) if[whether] the school lunch is delicious
     (2) if[whether] it's all right to sit next to her
     (3) had already eaten
16 (1) Would you please check if[whether] I filled out this card right?
     (2) I don't know if[whether] my mom likes potato pizza.
     (3) I am not sure if[whether] Mike will meet Judy at 3 o'clock.
     (4) He insisted that he had never heard a girl crying that night.
     (5) I decided to come home earlier than I had planned.   17 ⑤
18 (1) had been sold out   (2) had never met
19 ①, ②, ③   20 good memories
21 they called him a parakho   22 ①
23 ④   24 ②, ④   25 himself   26 ②
27 who[that] had devoted his life to the independence movement   28 ③

01 ⓐ so+형용사/부사+that 주어+동사: 너무 ~해서 …하다 / 땅의 표면이 너무 뜨거워서 녹았다. ⓑ be used to 동명사: ~하는 데 익숙하다 / 아이들은 그들의 많은 자유 시간을 TV 보는 데 쓰는 것에 익숙하다. ⓒ by 동사ing: ~함으로써 / 나는 내 집을 팔아서 새 차를 사기를 바랐다.

02 at that moment: 그 순간에 / 바로 그 순간, 당신은 나에게 다가와서 내게 설명할 기회도 주지 않고 딱지를 끊었어요. yell at: ~에게 고함치다 / 나에게 그렇게 소리치지 마.

03 (1) biography: 전기 / 나는 아브라함 링컨의 전기를 읽었다. (2) female: 여자; 여자의, 여성의 / 오은선은 한국의 여성 등반가이다. (3) locker: 사물함 / 제 사물함 열쇠를 어디서 받을 수 있나요? (4) detective: 형사, 탐정 / 그 탐정은 약간의 증거를 찾았다.

04 (1) movement: (정치적·사회적) 운동 (2) invention: 발명품, 발명 (3) be used to 동명사 ~하는 데 익숙하다

05 ⓐ take ⓑ know ⓒ bring ⓓ leave

06 ① 남자가 물병을 박물관 안에 가지고 들어갈 수 있나요? (네) ② 남자는 지금 어디에 있는가? (박물관) ③ 박물관에 사물함이 있나요? (네) ④ 박물관 안에서 사진을 찍을 수 있나요?(답할 수 없음) ⑤ 남자가 가방을 박물관 안에 가지고 들어갈 수 있나요? (아니요)

07 (A) 이것이 '자격루'라고 불리는 것이므로 수동태를 사용해야 한다. (B) *Jagyeongnu*를 가리키고 있으므로 'it'으로 받아야 한다.

08 actually: 사실은, 실제로 in fact: 사실은

10 주어진 문장의 it은 남자가 본 영화를 의미이므로 ①번이 적절하다.

11 scholar: 학자 / 특히 과학적인 주제가 아닌 특정한 주제에 대해 공부하고 많이 아는 사람

12 It is said that 주어+동사 ~: (사람들이) ~라고 한다 also: 또한 detective: 형사, 탐정

13 동사 know 뒤에 목적어 자리로 명사절을 이끄는 접속사 that이 어울린다.

14 if는 'if or not'의 형태로 쓰이지 않으므로 if만 쓰거나 or not 을 '~ it or not.'의 형태로 문장의 뒷부분에 써야 한다.

15 (1) 의문사가 없는 간접의문에 쓰인 if[whether]이다. (2) 명사절을 이끄는 접속사 if[whether]를 이용한다. (3) 점심을 먹은 것이 앞선 시점이고 already가 있으므로 과거완료로 쓰는 것이 적절하다.

16 (1) 명사절을 이끄는 접속사 if[whether]를 이용한다. (2) 의문사가 없는 간접의문문에 쓰인 if[whether]이다. (3) I am not sure의 목적어로는 접속사 if[whether]를 이용하는 것이 적절하다. (4) 주장하는 시점보다 듣지 못한 시점이 앞서므로 과거완료로 쓰는 것이 적절하다. (5) 결정하는 시점보다 계획한 시점이 앞서므로 과거완료로 쓰는 것이 적절하다.

17 ⑤ I'm not sure if she made a mistake or not.

18 과거의 어느 시점보다 먼저 일어난 일이나 상태를 나타낼 때 과거완료를 사용한다.

19 ⓐ와 ①, ②, ③: 동명사, ④, ⑤: 현재분사

20 아버지에 대한 '좋은 기억'을 가지고 있지 않았기 때문이다.

21 they를 주어로 하여 능동태로 고치는 것이 적절하다.

22 ⓐ와 ①, ②, ③, ⑤: 관계대명사, ④: 의문대명사

23 신랑 집에서 장롱을 사라고 준 돈을 신부의 아버지가 결혼식 전에 가져가 버렸기 때문에, '난처한'이 적절하다. ② 만족스러운, ⑤ (감탄스럽도록) 놀라운

24 ⓐ와 ②, ④: 완료 용법, ① 결과 용법, ③ 계속 용법, ⑤ 경험 용법

25 주어와 목적어가 같은 사람이므로 재귀대명사를 써야 한다.

26 at first: 처음에

27 devote A to B: A를 B에 바치다

28 필자의 아버지는 '일본 순사들'로부터 자신의 신분을 비밀로 지키려고 도박꾼처럼 보이기를 원했다.

Lesson 4

Music to My Ears!

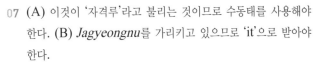
시험대비 실력평가   p.64

01 positive   02 ①   03 ①   04 ②
05 (1) treasure (2) shocked (3) thumb (4) pure
    (5) recommend
06 (1) We had dinner at a local restaurant.
    (2) He worked as a cherry picker.
    (3) My life would be worthless without music.

01 주어진 단어는 반의어 관계이다. positive: 긍정적인, negative: 부정적인

02 '오케스트라나 합창단의 공연을 지휘하는 사람'을 가리키는 말은 'conductor(지휘자)'이다.

03 주어진 문장에서 beat은 박자를 나타내며 이와 같은 의미로 쓰인 것은 ①번이다. 나머지는 모두 '때리다, 두드리다'를 나타낸다.

04 entirely: 전적으로, 완전히

05 thumb: 엄지손가락, shocked: 충격을 받은, pure: 깨끗한, 순수한, treasure: 보물, recommend: 추천하다

06 local: 현지의, picker: 채집자, worthless: 가치 없는

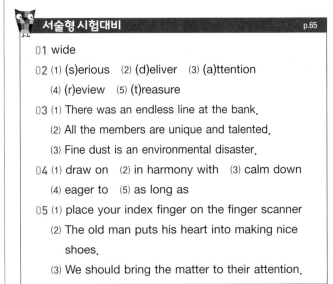
서술형 시험대비   p.65

01 wide
02 (1) (s)erious (2) (d)eliver (3) (a)ttention
    (4) (r)eview (5) (t)reasure
03 (1) There was an endless line at the bank.
    (2) All the members are unique and talented.
    (3) Fine dust is an environmental disaster.
04 (1) draw on (2) in harmony with (3) calm down
    (4) eager to (5) as long as
05 (1) place your index finger on the finger scanner
    (2) The old man puts his heart into making nice shoes.
    (3) We should bring the matter to their attention.

01 주어진 단어는 반의어 관계이다. wide: 넓은, narrow: 좁은

02 serious: 심각한, deliver a speech: 연설하다 attention: 관심, review: 복습하다, treasure: 보물

03 endless: 끝없는, talented: 재능 있는, environmental: 환경의, fine dust: 미세 먼지

04 as long as: ~하는 한, be eager to: ~하고 싶어 하다, in harmony with: ~와 조화를 이루어, calm down: 진정하다, draw on: ~을 활용하다

05 index finger: 집게손가락, put one's heart into: ~에 정열을 쏟다, ~에 열중하다, bring ~ to one's attention: ~에 …가 주목하게 하다

Conversation

핵심 Check
p.66~67

1 Do you find it interesting to sing in the choir?
2 (C) → (B) → (A)

교과서 대화문 익히기

Check(√) True or False
p.68

1 T 2 F 3 T 4 F

교과서 확인학습
p.70~71

Listen & Talk 1 A-1

won, competition, Congratulations / compete, find it helpful / keeps, awake

Listen & Talk 1 A-2

off / choir practice / forgot, choir, find, interesting / in harmony with

Listen & Talk 1-B

you recorded / find it easy to write them / beginning, draw on, keep a journal / No pain, no gain

Listen & Talk 2 A-1

sign up for / Are you planning to / perform / violin, cello

Listen & Talk 2 A-2

sign up for / take the class / planning, offer / another one, Both / sign up

Listen & Talk 2-B

musical instrument, recommend, is similar to, Playing, thumb nails

---

Communication

something / up / which seat I should choose / orchestra / orchestra / get the seats, various musical instruments / from the second floor / find it better

Wrap Up

been / I've read / have you / for visiting / find / post, latest / spread

시험대비 기본평가
p.72

01 Do you find it interesting to sing in the choir?
02 ⑤   03 (E) → (D) → (C) → (A) → (B)

02 Chris는 동생의 연주를 보러 콘서트에 갈 것이다.

03 (E) 장기 자랑 등록 기한 질문 → (D) 대답 및 계획 질문 → (C) 장기 자랑 계획 대답 → (A) 반응 및 구체적 계획 질문 → (B) 구체적 계획 대답

시험대비 실력평가
p.73~74

01 Do you find it easy to write them?   02 ①
03 ⓒ → compete   04 ⑤
05 She should sign up for the talent show by Friday.
06 Her plan is to play K-pop music with the violin and cello with a couple of people
07 It is a small African musical instrument.
08 It is similar to the sound of a music box.
09 I should use my thumb nails to play the *kalimba*.
10 ③   11 ③   12 ④

02 수진이 '다시 만나 반갑습니다.'라고 인사한 것으로 보아 Jason을 처음 만난 것이 아님을 알 수 있다.

03 접속사 뒤에 절이 이어지므로 동사 compete가 적절하다.

04 Jake가 일에 집중하기 위해 수영할 필요가 있다는 설명은 대화의 내용과 일치하지 않는다.

05 Megan은 금요일까지 장기 자랑 등록을 마쳐야 한다.

06 Megan은 몇 사람과 함께 공연을 할 것이다.

07 칼림바는 아프리카의 작은 악기이다.

08 칼림바는 음악 상자의 소리와 비슷하다.

09 칼림바를 연주하기 위해 엄지손톱을 사용해야 한다.

10 'Yes, I do.'라는 대답이 적절하다.

11 주어진 문장은 수업을 주중에 들을 건지 주말에 들을 건지에 대한 대답으로 적절하므로 (C)에 와야 한다.

12 주중 드럼 수업은 정각 6시로 서로 같다.

01 Are you planning to sign up for it
02 Her team is going to play the violin and cello.
03 Are you planning to learn a musical instrument?
04 (B) is   (C) Playing
05 (A) winning the swimming   (B) he competes
   (C) it keeps him awake and it helps him focus
06 Do you find it interesting to post the latest pop news?

02 Megan의 팀은 바이올린과 첼로를 연주할 것이다.

04 (B) 주어가 3인칭 단수이므로 'is', (C)는 주어로 동명사 'Playing'이 적절하다.

05 Anna는 Jake에게 어제 수영대회에서 우승한 것을 축하했다. 그녀는 왜 Jake가 항상 경기 전에 음악을 듣는지 알고 싶었다. Jake는 이것이 그를 깨어 있게 하고 집중하는 데 도움을 준다고 말했다.

교과서
Grammar

1 (1) written   (2) singing   (3) rolling
2 (1) it   (2) to

01 ⑤
02 (1) smiling   (2) hidden   (3) wearing   (4) planted
03 ③
04 (1) The concert began with a girl playing Bach's Cello Suite No. 1 on her shiny cello.
   (2) He bought a car made in Korea.
   (3) Anna finds it fun to play the piano.

01 to부정사구가 목적어로 쓰일 때, to부정사를 문장의 맨 뒤에 쓰고 목적어 자리에 가목적어 it을 쓴 것이다.

02 (1) 소녀가 웃고 있는 것이므로 능동의 의미를 갖는 현재분사가 적절하다. (2) 비용이 감춰진 것이므로 수동의 의미를 갖는 과거분사가 적절하다. (3) 소녀가 안경을 끼는 것이므로 능동의 의미를 갖는 현재분사가 적절하다. (4) 나무들이 심겨진 것이므로 수동의 의미를 갖는 과거분사가 적절하다.

03 목적격보어가 있는 5형식 문장에서 길이가 긴 to부정사구가 목적어로 쓰일 때, 보통 목적어 자리에 가목적어 it을 쓰고 to부정사는 문장의 맨 뒤에 쓴다. 이때 진목적어는 to 이하이다.

04 (1) 'playing Bach's *Cello Suite No. 1* on her shiny cello'가 a girl을 뒤에서 수식하도록 영작한다. (2) 차가 만들어지는 것이므로 수동의 의미를 갖는 과거분사를 이용한다. (3) it을 가목적어로 하고 to부정사를 진목적어로 하여 영작한다.

01 ②   02 ③   03 ①
04 (1) for (2) it (3) to achieve (4) talking (5) frightened
   (6) complaining
05 ⑤   06 ⑤   07 ③   08 ④
09 ②   10 ④   11 ①   12 ③
13 ④   14 ①   15 ②   16 ④, ⑤
17 (1) An autograph is something that[which] is written by a person, not a machine.
   (2) The image of a girl who[that] is playing chess with the statue was taken on Jan. 7.
18 ②, ③

01 make 동사는 to부정사가 목적어로 나올 때 반드시 가목적어 it을 써야 한다. The new law made it possible for teenagers to drive.

02 '게시된' 결과이므로 현재분사가 아니라 과거분사가 되어야 한다.

03 첫 번째 빈칸에는 노래를 하는 것이므로 진행의 뜻을 갖는 현재분사가 적절하다. 두 번째 빈칸에는 가목적어 역할을 하는 it이 적절하다.

04 (1) 전체 문장과 to부정사구의 행위의 주체가 다르므로 의미상의 주어로 to부정사구의 주체를 나타내야 하며, 주로 'for+목적격'의 형태로 to부정사 앞에 쓴다. (2) 가목적어이므로 it이 적절하다. (3) 진목적어이므로 to부정사가 적절하다. (4) '말을 하는' 것이므로 능동의 뜻을 갖는 현재분사가 적절하다. (5) 아이가 '놀라게 된' 것이므로 수동의 뜻을 갖는 과거분사가 적절하다. (6) 고객이 '불평하는' 것이므로 능동의 뜻을 갖는 현재분사가 적절하다. 현재분사가 앞에서 수식하는 경우이다.

05 ⑤번은 현재완료에 쓰였고 나머지는 모두 앞에 나오는 명사를 수식하는 형용사적 용법이다.

06 앞에 의미상의 주어로 'for+목적격'이 나왔으므로 'to sing'이 적절하다.

07 '어린 왕자'가 쓰여진 것이므로 수동의 뜻을 갖는 과거분사가 적절하다.

08 ④번은 가목적어로 쓰였지만 나머지는 모두 시간이나 날씨, 거리 등을 나타내는 비인칭 주어이다.

09 분사에 다른 어구(여기서는 a letter)가 함께 있을 때는 뒤에서 명사를 수식한다.

10 think 동사의 경우 to부정사구가 목적어로 나올 때 가목적어 it을 쓰고 to부정사구를 진목적어로 문장의 뒷부분에 쓴다.

11 노래가 불리어지고 사랑받는 것이므로 수동의 의미를 나타내는 과거분사가 적절하며 이것은 '주격 관계대명사+be동사'가 생략된 것으로 볼 수 있다.

12 ① 가주어 ② 대명사 ③ 가목적어 ④ 비인칭 주어 ⑤ 인칭대명사 *goose bumps: 소름

13 책을 읽고 있는 것이므로 진행의 의미를 가지는 현재분사 reading이 되어야 한다. 접속사 없이 동사 reads와 is 두 개가 나올 수 없음에 유의한다.

14 ① 접속사 that ② It was ~ that 강조 구문 ③, ⑤ 가목적어 it ④ 가주어 It

15 첫 번째 빈칸에는 회의가 개최한 것이 아니라 '개최된' 것이므로 수동의 뜻을 갖는 과거분사가 적절하다. 두 번째 빈칸에는 음식이 무엇을 제공하는 것이 아니라 '제공되는' 것이므로 수동의 뜻을 갖는 과거분사가 적절하다.

16 지각동사 see의 목적격보어로 동사원형이나 현재분사가 적절하다. 또 쓰레기로 가득 차 있는 것이므로 수동의 의미를 갖는 과거분사가 적절하며 분사가 명사를 뒤에서 수식하는 경우에는 그 앞에 '주격 관계대명사+be동사'가 생략된 것으로 생각할 수 있다.

17 분사가 명사를 뒤에서 수식하는 경우에는 그 앞에 '주격 관계대명사+be동사'가 생략된 것으로 생각할 수 있다.

18 ② 가목적어로 that이 아니라 it을 쓴다. ③ 누워 있는 것이므로 능동의 의미를 갖는 현재분사 lying이 적절하다.

서술형 시험대비 p.82~83

01 (1) it (2) for (3) to

02 (1) I want people to know that even something worthless can make inspiring music.
   (2) The teacher made it clear for the students to do their homework.
   (3) Stravinsky considered it helpful to stand on his head for 15 minutes every morning.

03 (1) There is an old family photo which[that] is hanging on the wall.
   (2) Only the people who[that] are invited to the meeting can attend the meeting.

04 (1) to draw pictures using his imagination
   (2) to do experiments at a science lab
   (3) to memorize all the poems in the book

05 (1) painting (2) painted (3) wearing (4) written

06 (1) playing (2) satisfied, written (3) playing

07 (1) it, to play
   (2) it, to listen

08 (1) walked → walking (2) lain → lying
   (3) calling → called (4) that → it
   (5) of → for (6) visiting → to visit
   (7) to carry out our design at once necessary → it necessary to carry out our design at once

09 (1) to support (2) for you to do it

01 (1) 가목적어이므로 it을 쓴다. (2) 의미상의 주어로 for를 쓴다. (3) 의미상의 주어로 'for+목적격'이 나와 있으므로 진목적어로 to부정사를 쓴다.

02 (1) 영감을 주는 것이므로 능동의 뜻을 갖는 현재분사를 이용한다. (2), (3) '가목적어(it)+의미상의 주어(for목적격)+진목적어(to부정사)' 구문을 이용한다.

03 분사가 명사를 뒤에서 수식하는 경우에는 그 앞에 '주격 관계대명사+be동사'가 생략된 것으로 생각할 수 있다.

04 가목적어 it은 긴 to부정사구가 목적어로 쓰일 때 to부정사구를 문장의 맨 뒤로 보내고 그 목적어 자리에 it을 쓴 것이고, 가주어 It은 주어 역할을 하는 to부정사구를 뒤로 보내고 가짜 주어인 it을 그 자리에 쓴 것이다.

05 (1) 그녀의 모습을 그리는 것이므로 현재분사를 이용한다. (2) 초콜릿 꽃이 그려진 것이므로 과거분사를 이용한다. (3) 모자를 쓰고 있는 것이므로 현재분사를 이용한다. (4) 편지가 씌여진 것이므로 과거분사를 이용한다.

06 (1) 학생들이 축구를 하는 것이므로 진행의 뜻을 갖는 현재분사를 이용한다. (2) 선생님이 만족해하고, 편지가 쓰여지는 것이므로 수동의 뜻을 갖는 과거분사를 이용한다. (3) 기타를 치고 있는 것이므로 진행의 뜻을 갖는 현재분사를 이용한다.

07 '가목적어(it)+목적격보어+진목적어(to부정사)' 구문을 이용한다.

08 (1) 진행의 의미를 나타내므로 현재분사로 고친다. (2) 남자가 누워 있는 것이므로 현재분사로 고친다. lie-lay-lain, lying (3) 음악 그룹이 "The Junk Orchestra"라고 불리는 것이므로 과거분사로 고친다. (4) 가목적어로는 that이 아니라 it을 쓴다. (5) 의미상의 주어로 for를 쓴다. (6) 의미상의 주어로 'for us'가 나와 있으므로 to부정사가 진목적어가 되어야 한다. (7)

think, find, believe 등의 동사는 to부정사구가 목적어로 나오면 반드시 가목적어 it을 써야 한다.

09 '가목적어(it)+목적격보어+진목적어(to부정사)' 구문을 이용하여 같은 뜻의 문장으로 고쳐 쓸 수 있다.

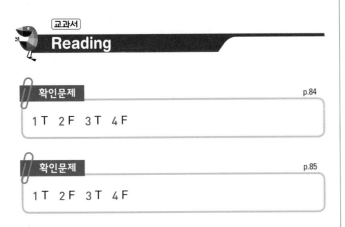

Reading

확인문제 p.84

1 T 2 F 3 T 4 F

확인문제 p.85

1 T 2 F 3 T 4 F

교과서 확인학습 A p.86~87

01 Junk 02 written by
03 garbage, music
04 on the back of
05 was called 06 made entirely out of
07 was eager to find out
08 sound strange
09 After a few minutes
10 The first thing I noticed
11 with a girl playing, on
12 was shocked by
13 was, into, made from recycled materials
14 was eager to write
15 the conductor
16 Why did you start
17 to work on, was mostly filled with
18 something positive, share, with
19 to make instruments
20 garbage, treasure
21 a local garbage picker
22 out of garbage
23 The wonderful thing, didn't have to worry about
24 through 25 worthless, inspiring music
26 as long as, into
27 not by instruments
29 how 30 endless
31 played with
32 Not only do, bring, to our attention

교과서 확인학습 B p.88~89

1 The Junk Orchestra
2 written by a music blogger, Lucy White
3 "The world sends us garbage, we send back music."
4 This was written on the back of a concert ticket I was given.
5 The musical group was called "The Junk Orchestra."
6 They played instruments made entirely out of garbage.
7 I could not imagine what kind of sound these instruments would make, so I was eager to find out.
8 Before the concert, I thought that the instruments might sound strange.
9 After a few minutes, a group of young people began to walk on the stage.
10 The first thing I noticed was their instruments: a cello made out of a shiny oil tank, a violin made with forks, and a flute made with a water pipe and buttons.
11 The concert began with a girl playing Bach's *Cello Suite No. 1* on her shiny cello.
12 I was shocked by the deep sound.
13 I was so into the music that I forgot that they were playing with instruments made from recycled materials.
14 After the concert, I was eager to write a story about the orchestra.
15 I met Favio Chávez, the conductor, and asked him about the orchestra.
16 Lucy White: Why did you start The Junk Orchestra?
17 Favio Chávez: When I went to a small town called Cateura in Paraguay to work on a recycling program in 2005, I saw children living in a town that was mostly filled with garbage.
18 I wanted to add something positive to their lives, so I decided to share my love of music with them.
19 Lucy White: Why did you use garbage to make instruments?
20 Favio Chávez: One person's garbage is another person's treasure.
21 Nicolás Gómez, a local garbage picker, helped me a lot.
22 He made it possible for children to play music by making instruments out of garbage.

23 The wonderful thing about these instruments was that the children didn't have to worry about spending a lot of money on them.

24 Lucy White: What do you want people to learn through your music?

25 Favio Chávez: I want people to know that even something worthless can make inspiring music.

26 After interviewing Chávez, I realized that it really doesn't matter what instrument you play with as long as you put your heart into playing it.

27 The children of Cateura showed me that an orchestra is formed by people, not by instruments.

28 Comments

29 Annie: (23 seconds ago) So moving to see how music can change lives.

30 The power of music is endless!

31 Thomas: (1 minute ago) After the concert, I found it possible to inspire people by music played with recycled instruments.

32 Kate: (5 days ago) Not only do these talented young people deliver great music, but they also bring serious environmental problems to our attention.

시험대비 실력평가 p.90~93

01 into → out of   02 ②, ⑤

03 ③   04 ⑤   05 ③   06 ②

07 ③   08 ①, ④   09 have   10 ②

11 with a girl playing Bach's *Cello Suite No. 1*

12 ④   13 ②   14 children

15 the orchestra   16 ① of → for

17 ⑤   18 ③   19 important

20 ①, ⑤   21 touching   22 recycling → recycled

23 Not only do these talented young people deliver great music

01 '쓰레기로만 만들어진' 악기라고 해야 하므로 into를 out of 로 고치는 것이 적절하다. 재료 be made into 제품, 제품 be made out of 재료, (made 앞에 which were가 생략됨.)

02 be eager to=be anxious to = long to: ~하기를 갈망하다 ③ be likely to: ~할 것 같다, ④ pay attention to: ~에 유의 하다

03 '나는 이런 악기들이 어떤 종류의 소리를 낼지 상상할 수 없었고, 그래서 나는 알아보고 싶어졌다.'라고 했으므로 뒤에 올 내용으로

는 '이런 악기들의 소리를 알아보기'가 적절하다.

04 ⓐ begin with: ~으로 시작하다, ⓑ on: ('수단'을 나타내어) ~으로[~에]

05 이 글은 '재활용된 재료들로 만들어진 악기로 멋진 연주를 한 음 악회에 관한' 내용의 글이므로, 제목으로는 ③번 '믿을 수 없어! 재활용된 재료들로 만들어진 악기에서 이런 깊은 소리가 난다 고?'가 적절하다.

06 전반부의 'I thought that the instruments might sound strange.'를 통해 'anxious'를, 후반부의 'I was shocked by the deep sound.'를 통해 'satisfied'를 찾을 수 있 다. anxious: 불안해하는, 염려하는, ① nervous: 초조한, disappointed: 실망한

07 Favio Chávez는 파라과이의 카테우라라고 불리는 작은 마을 어 린이들의 삶에 긍정적인 무엇인가를 더해 주고 싶어서, 음악에 대 한 그의 사랑을 그들과 나누기로 결정했다고 했으므로, 빈칸에 들 어갈 질문으로는 ③번 '왜 당신은 정크 오케스트라를 시작하셨나 요?'가 적절하다.

08 ⓑ와 ①, ④: 부사적 용법, ②, ⑤: 명사적 용법, ③: 형용사적 용법

09 have something in common (with somebody): (관심사·생각 등을) 공통적으로 지니다

10 악기의 재료에 '숟가락'은 속하지 않는다.

11 begin with+명사: ~로 시작하나, 소녀가 첼로를 연주하고 있 는 주체이므로 능동이나 진행의 의미를 가지는 현재분사구를 써 서 a girl을 후치 수식하도록 하는 것이 적절하다.

12 음악회의 첫 번째 음악은 '첼로'곡이었다.

13 쓰레기로 가득 차 있는 마을에 살고 있는 어린이들의 삶에 '긍정 적인' 무엇인가를 더해 주고 싶었다고 하는 것이 적절하다. ① 수동적인, ③ 일시적인, 임시의, ④ 일반[보편/전반]적인, ⑤ 영 구[영속]적인

14 '어린이들'을 가리킨다.

15 '그 오케스트라'에 대한 이야기를 몹시 쓰고 싶었기 때문이다.

16 진목적어인 to play의 의미상의 주어이므로 for children으로 쓰는 것이 적절하다.

17 ⓐ와 ⑤: 가목적어, ① 비인칭 주어, ② [3인칭 단수 중성 목적 격](인칭대명사), ③ 가주어, ④ It is[was] ~ who[that] … 강조 구문에 쓰이는 It

18 Nicolás Gómez가 왜 Favio Chávez를 많이 도왔는지는 알 수 없다. ① Because one person's garbage is another person's treasure. ② He was a local garbage picker. ④

The children didn't have to worry about spending a lot of money on them. ⑤ He wants people to know that even something worthless can make inspiring music.

19 matter = be important: 중요하다

20 as long as = as far as = so long as: ~하는 한, ② ~에 더하여, 게다가, ③ ~만큼, ~ 못지 않게, ④ ~하자마자

21 moving = touching: 감동적인

22 재활용되어진 악기이므로, recycling을 과거분사 recycled로 고치는 것이 적절하다.

23 'do'를 보충하면 된다. not only라는 부사가 문장 맨 앞에 쓰였기 때문에, 조동사 do가 주어 these talented young people보다 앞에 쓰여 도치가 되도록 쓰는 것이 적절하다.

서술형 시험대비   p.94~95

01 was given
02 (a) garbage   (b) music
03 I could not imagine what kind of sound these instruments would make
04 (A) strange   (B) shocked   (C) recycled
05 instruments
06 a shiny oil tank
07 the instrument
08 not, but
09 called
10 I saw children living in a town mostly filled with garbage.
11 (A) his love of music   (B) something positive
12 need
13 priceless → worthless 또는 valueless

---

01 나에게 '주어진'(내가 받은) 음악회 입장권이라고 해야 하므로, 수동태로 쓰는 것이 적절하다.

02 우리는 '쓰레기'를 재활용해서 악기를 만들고, 그 악기를 연주해서 '음악'을 공연한다.

03 동사 imagine의 목적어 역할을 하는 간접의문문이 되도록, '의문사+주어+동사'의 순서로 쓰는 것이 적절하다.

04 (A) 감각동사 sound 뒤에 형용사 보어를 써야 하므로 strange가 적절하다. (B) 감정을 나타내는 동사는 감정을 느끼게 되는 대상과 함께 쓰일 경우에는 과거분사를 써야 하므로 shocked가 적절하다. (C) '재활용된' 재료들이라고 해야 하므로 recycled가 적절하다.

05 글쓴이가 처음으로 알아차린 것은 그들의 '악기'였다.

---

06 음악회는 한 소녀가 '반짝이는 기름통'으로 만들어진 자신의 첼로로 바흐의 <첼로 모음곡 1번>을 연주하는 것으로 시작되었다.

07 '악기'를 가리킨다.

08 not A but B = B, not A: A가 아니라 B

09 카테우라라고 '불리는' 작은 마을이라고 해야 하므로 과거분사로 쓰는 것이 적절하다.

10 'that was(주격 관계대명사+be동사)'를 생략할 수 있다.

11 Favio Chávez가 2005년에 재활용 프로그램에서 일을 하기 위해서 파라과이의 카테우라에 갔을 때, 그는 대부분이 쓰레기로 가득 차 있는 마을에 살고 있는 어린이들의 삶에 '긍정적인 무엇인가'를 더해 주고 싶어서, '음악에 대한 그의 사랑'을 그들과 나누기로 결정했다.

12 didn't have to = didn't need to

13 '가치 없는' 것도 영감을 주는 음악을 만들어 낼 수 있다는 것을 사람들이 알게 되기를 원한다고 해야 하므로 priceless를 worthless 또는 valueless로 고치는 것이 적절하다. priceless: 값을 매길 수 없는, 대단히 귀중한, worthless = valueless: 가치 없는, 무가치한

영역별 핵심문제   p.97~101

01 survival   02 ③
03 (1) stand on your head   (2) keep, awake
   (3) sign up for   (4) work out
04 ⑤   05 ⑤   06 ⑤   07 ③
08 ③   09 ③   10 ①   11 ⑤
12 ⓐ → I should   13 ⑤   14 ①, ③
15 ⑤   16 it, to sew
17 (1) who[that] were   (2) who[that] was, which[that] was
18 ②   19 ⓐ, ⓒ, ⓔ
20 The deep sound shocked me.
21 a group of young people
22 two thousand (and) five   23 ③
24 It was that the children didn't have to worry about spending a lot of money on them.
25 ⑤
26 even something worthless can make inspiring music
27 be cheered up   28 up me → me up

---

01 주어진 단어는 동사와 명사의 관계를 나타낸다. survive: 살아남다, survival: 생존

02 '다른 목적으로 무언가를 다시 사용하다'를 가리키는 말은 'recycle(재활용하다)'이다.

04 mostly 주로, 대부분

05 notice는 동사로 '알아차리다', 명사로는 '공지, 알림, 통지'를 뜻한다.

06 주어진 문장에서 touch는 '감동시키다'를 나타내며 이와 같은 의미로 쓰인 것은 ⑤번이다. 나머지는 모두 '만지다'를 뜻한다.

07 이어지는 대답에서 Jake가 음악의 장점을 설명하고 있으므로 도움이 되는지 여부를 묻는 질문이 적절하다.

08 (A) be off to: ~로 떠나다, (B) 목적어를 이끄는 접속사 that이 적절하다. (C) '흥미로운'을 뜻하는 interesting이 적절하다.

09 주어진 문장은 곡을 쓰는 것이 쉬운지 묻는 질문에 대한 대답으로 적절하므로 (C)가 적합하다.

10 위 대화를 통해 수진과 Jason은 인터뷰 진행자와 래퍼임을 알 수 있다.

11 위 대화를 통해 수진이 Jason의 새 랩 노래를 몇 번이나 들었는지는 알 수 없다.

12 간접의문문으로 '의문사+주어+동사'의 어순이 되어야 하므로 'I should' 형태가 알맞다.

13 위 대화에는 Anthony가 공연을 보았다는 내용은 나오지 않고 있다.

14 ① Fallen leaves are under the trees. ③ This is the newest smartphone made in Korea.

15 to부정사(구)가 목적어로 쓰인 경우 가주어로 it을 쓰고 to부정사(구)는 문장이 뒤로 보낸다.

16 빈칸에 맞추어 가목적어 it과 to부정사를 쓴다.

17 분사가 명사를 뒤에서 수식하는 경우에는 그 앞에 '주격 관계대명사+be동사'가 생략된 것으로 생각할 수 있다.

18 ②번의 it은 가주어로 사용되었고, 나머지는 모두 가목적어로 사용되었다.

19 ⓑ stealing → stolen ⓓ run → running ⓕ to exercise every Sunday a rule → it a rule to exercise every Sunday

20 The deep sound를 주어로 해서 능동태로 고치는 것이 적절하다.

21 '한 무리의 젊은이들'을 가리킨다.

22 2005년을 두 부분으로 나눠 twenty five로 읽으면 25처럼 들리기 때문에, 2001년부터 2009년까지는 two thousand (and) ~로 읽는 것이 적절하다.

23 '파라과이의 카테우라라고 불리는 작은 마을의 어린이들이' 대부분이 쓰레기로 가득 차 있는 마을에 살고 있었다.

24 이 악기들의 멋진 점은 '어린이들이 악기에 많은 돈을 쓸 것을

걱정하지 않아도 된다'는 점이었다.

25 이 글은 Favio Chávez가 악기를 만들기 위해 쓰레기를 이용한 이유와 자신의 음악을 통해서 사람들이 배우기를 원하는 것에 관한 내용의 글이므로, 주제로는 ⑤번 '쓰레기를 사용하여 악기를 만드는 이유와 목표'가 적절하다.

26 현재분사 inspiring이 music을 앞에서 꾸며주게 하는 것이 적절하다.

27 '힘을 얻을' 필요가 있는 사람들이라고 해야 하므로 be cheered up으로 쓰는 것이 적절하다. be cheered up: 힘을 얻다

28 'cheer up'이 '동사+부사'로 이루어졌으므로, 목적어가 인칭대명사일 경우, 동사와 부사 사이에 목적어를 쓰는 것이 적절하다.

단원별 예상문제   p.102~105

01 do you find it better to hear the performance from the second floor?   02 ⑤

03 (A) seat   (B) the second floor
  (C) hear the performance from the second floor
  (D) the beautiful sounds of various musical instruments

04 He won the swimming competition.

05 He always listens to music before he competes.

06 It keeps him awake and it helps him focus.

07 Do you have a plan to learn a musical instrument?

08 thumb nails   09 ③

10 (C) → (D) → (A) → (B)   11 ③

12 (1) Can you tell me a name beginning with M?
  (2) There was a small boy called "Mr. Big" in my school.
  (3) The dog lying under the table is Mike's.

13 (1) to have breakfast every day
  (2) to write lyrics   (3) to exercise every day

14 (1) The man beating the drums is a famous musician.
  (2) I went to a small town called Cateura.
  (3) My mom made it possible for me to play the violin.
  (4) The girl thinks it hard to learn foreign languages.

15 The world sends us garbage, we send back music.

16 as → so   17 with   18 a recycling program

19 ④   20 ②   21 ③

22 as long as you put your heart into playing it

23 is → isn't

02 Emma가 오케스트라 콘서트를 누구와 보러 가는지는 대화를 통해 알 수 없다.

03 나는 오케스트라 콘서트를 보러 갈 계획이었다. 그러나 나는 어떤 좌석을 선택해야 할지 혼란스러웠다. 나는 Anthony에게 자리를 선택하는 데 도움을 요청했다. Anthony는 2층 좌석을 추천했다, 왜냐하면 그는 2층에서 공연을 듣는 것이 더 낫다고 생각하기 때문이었다. 그는 내가 다양한 악기 소리를 더 잘 들을 수 있다고 말했다. 그것은 내게 매우 유용한 정보였다. 나는 곧 콘서트를 보는 것이 기대된다.

04 Jake는 어제 수영대회에서 우승했다.

05 Jake는 경기 전에 항상 음악을 듣는다.

06 음악을 듣는 것은 Jake를 깨어 있게 하고 집중하는 데 도움을 준다.

07 Are you planning to ~? = Are you going to ~? = Do you have a plan to ~?

09 ⑤ 단 한 번의 lesson으로 배울 수 있다고 언급되어 있다.

10 (C) 수영대회의 우승을 축하 → (D) 감사 표현 → (A) 상대방의 의견 묻기 → (B) 대답 및 설명

11 ① The book borrowed from the library is heavy. ② These talented young people deliver great music and bring serious environmental problems to our attention. ④ She made it possible for us to sing in the talent show. ⑤ She thinks it more relaxing to sleep.

12 분사에 다른 어구(목적어, 수식어구 등)가 함께 있을 때는 뒤에서 명사를 수식한다. (1) M으로 '시작하는' 능동의 의미이므로 현재분사를 이용한다. (2) "Mr. Big"으로 '불리는' 수동의 의미이므로 과거분사를 이용한다. (3) '누워 있는'으로 진행의 의미로 현재분사를 이용한다.

13 (1), (2) 가목적어 it은 진목적어인 to부정사(구) 대신 쓰인 것이다. (3) 가주어 it은 진주어인 to부정사(구) 대신 쓰인 것이다.

14 (1) '드럼을 치고 있는' 능동의 의미로 현재분사를 이용한다. (2) Cateura라고 '불리는' 수동의 의미로 과거분사를 이용한다. (3) make 동사는 to부정사(구)가 목적어로 나올 때 it을 가목적어로 써야 한다. (4) think 동사는 to부정사(구)가 목적어로 나올 때 it을 가목적어로 써야 한다.

15 앞 문장의 내용을 가리킨다.

16 '나는 그런 악기들이 어떤 종류의 소리를 낼지 상상할 수 없었고, 그래서 나는 알아보고 싶어졌다.'고 해야 하므로, as를 so로 고치는 것이 적절하다.

17 ⓐ be filled with: ~로 가득 차다, ⓑ share A with B: A를 B와 공유하다

18 '재활용 프로그램'에서 일을 하기 위해서 갔다.

19 Favio Chávez가 쓰레기를 이용해 악기를 만든 이유를 설명하고 있으므로, 빈칸에 들어갈 질문으로는 ④번 '왜 당신은 악기를 만들기 위해 쓰레기를 이용했나요?'가 적절하다.

20 ⓑ와 ②: 가치 없는, ① 값을 헤아릴 수 없는, 평가 못할 만큼의, 매우 귀중한, ③, ④ 가치가 있는, ⑤ 값을 매길 수 없는, 대단히 귀중한

21 Nicolás Gómez helped Favio Chávez a lot.

22 as long as+주어+동사: '~하는 한'

23 사람들이 악기를 연주하는 데 마음을 쏟아 붓는 한, 그 사람이 연주하는 악기가 무엇인지는 별로 '중요하지 않다.'

서술형 실전문제   p.106~107

01 She thinks that it is really cool.

02 He draws on his experiences and keeps a journal.

03 She uses the proverb 'No pain, no gain.'

04 (1) Einstein considered it fun to solve math problems.
　(2) We found it enjoyable to sing the song written by children.
　(3) The woman making a cake is my mother.
　(4) We studied at desks made out of trees from the nearby mountain.

05 (1) The girl playing the piano on the stage is my sister.
　(2) The box carried into the building is very big.
　(3) I found it possible to inspire people by music played with recycled instruments.
　(4) Rebecca thought it difficult to sing in front of others even though she is a great singer.

06 interested

07 It was made with forks.

08 (A) strange　(B) deep sound

09 One person's garbage is another person's treasure.

10 these instruments

11 (A) worthless　(B) inspiring

01 수진은 Jason이 녹음한 새로운 랩 노래가 정말로 멋지다고 생각한다.

02 Jason은 그의 경험을 활용해서 일기를 쓰고 있다.

03 수진은 Jason의 노력을 묘사하기 위해 '고통이 없으면 얻는 것도 없다.'는 속담을 사용했다.

04 (1) 보통 5형식 문장에서 to부정사(구)가 목적어로 나올 때 it을 가목적어로 쓴다. (2) find 동사는 to부정사(구)가 목적어로 나올 때 it을 가목적어로 써야 한다. 또한 노래가 '쓰여지는' 것이므로 수동의 의미로 과거분사로 써야 한다. (3) 케이크를 '만드는'

것이므로 진행의 의미를 갖는 현재분사 making이 되어야 한다. (4) 책상이 '만들어진' 것이므로 수동의 의미를 갖는 과거분사 made가 되어야 한다.

05 (1) 분사에 다른 어구가 함께 있을 때는 뒤에서 명사를 수식하며 피아노를 치는 것이므로 현재분사가 적절하다. (2) 상자가 '옮겨지는' 수동의 의미이므로 과거분사가 적절하다. (3) 가목적어로는 that을 사용하지 않고 it을 사용한다. (4) think 동사는 to부정사(구)가 목적어로 나올 때 it을 가목적어로 쓴다.

06 'be into+명사 : ~에 관심이 많다, ~을 매우 좋아하다'

07 바이올린은 '포크'로 만들어졌다.

08 음악회가 시작되기 전에 글쓴이는 그 악기들의 소리가 '이상하게' 들릴지도 모른다고 생각했지만, 음악회가 한 소녀가 자신의 반짝이는 첼로로 바흐의 <첼로 모음곡 1번>을 연주하는 것으로 시작되었을 때 그 '깊은 소리'에 충격을 받았다.

09 주격보어 another person's treasure가 주어 One person's garbage의 의미를 보충해 주도록 쓰는 것이 적절하다.

10 '(쓰레기로 만든) 악기들'을 가리킨다.

11 자신의 음악을 통해서, Favio Chávez는 '가치 없는' 것도 '영감을 주는' 음악을 만들어 낼 수 있다는 것을 사람들이 알게 되기를 원한다.

창의사고력 서술형 문제 p.108

|모범답안|

01 (A) hard   (B) easier   (C) experiences
   (D) keeps a journal

02 (A) be cheered up   (B) Allan Hamilton
   (C) bright side   (D) in the hospital
   (E) gave me hope

01 래퍼 Jason은 새로운 곡, 'Young and Wild'를 발매했다. 그의 노래는 너무 좋았다. 그는 곡을 쓰는 것은 처음에는 어렵지만 점점 쉬워지고 있다고 말했다. 곡을 쓰기 위해, 그는 경험을 활용하며 일기를 쓴다. 나는 그에게 행운을 빌었다.

단원별 모의고사 p.109~113

01 ⑤   02 ①

03 (1) in harmony with   (2) in the beginning
   (3) sent back   (4) keep a journal

04 (1) His room is filled with books and documents.
   (2) My bag is similar to yours, but mine is bigger.

05 It's because she has choir practice.

06 She thinks that it's great to sing in harmony with

others.

07 ⑤   08 ⑤   09 (D) → (B) → (A) → (C)

10 She is planning to sign up for a drum class.

11 She is going to take it at 6 o'clock on Tuesdays.

12 ③

13 (1) to play the guitar   (2) for everybody to come
   (3) to clarify the objectives of the listening task

14 ⑤

15 (1) made   (2) making

16 (1) Sally finds it boring to sing in the choir.
   (2) She thinks it a key factor to success to make good friends.
   (3) He made it possible for children to play music by making instruments out of garbage.
   (4) The singer wore a T-shirt designed by an artist. 또는 The singer wore a T-shirt which [that] was designed by an artist.
   (5) The man is taking pictures of people posing in front of the monuments.

17 ⑤

18 It was made with a water pipe and buttons.

19 making → made   20 ⑤

21 bring serious environmental problems to our attention, deliver great music   22 writing

23 I saw children living in a town that was mostly filled with garbage.   24 ④

25 to, could

26 ②번 played → playing   27 ⑤

01 '더 이상 쓸모가 없어 버려지는 것들'을 가리키는 말은 'garbage(쓰레기)'이다.

02 nail: 손톱, 못

05 Sally는 합창단 연습을 하러 음악실에 가는 중이다.

06 Sally는 다른 사람들과 조화를 이루어 노래하는 것이 좋다고 생각한다.

07 ⑤번을 제외한 나머지는 모두 계획을 묻는 표현이다.

08 Megan은 바이올린과 첼로로 케이팝을 연주할 것이다.

09 (D) 노래 칭찬에 대한 감사 표현 → (B) 곡을 쓰는 것에 대해 의견 질문 → (A) 대답 및 노력 설명 → (C) 대답 및 행운을 기원함

10 Sue는 드럼 수업에 등록할 계획이다.

11 Sue는 화요일 6시 수업을 들을 것이다.

12 계획을 묻는 질문에 네가 노래 대회에 참가할 것이라는 대답은 어색하다.

13 (1), (2) 가목적어 it은 진목적어인 to부정사구 대신 형식상 쓰

인 것이다. 의미상의 주어가 있는 경우 빠뜨리지 않도록 주의한다. (3) 가주어 it은 진주어인 to부정사구 대신 형식상 쓰인 것이다.

14 두 문장을 관계대명사를 이용하여 한 문장으로 쓰면 'I received a letter which was written by the student.'이고 여기서 '관계대명사+be동사'를 생략하면 분사가 뒤에서 수식하는 문장이 된다.

15 (1) 포도주가 '만들어진' 것이므로 수동의 뜻을 갖는 과거분사를 이용한다. (2) 치즈를 '만드는' 것이므로 능동의 뜻을 갖는 현재분사를 이용한다.

16 (1) 가목적어로는 that을 사용하지 않고 it을 사용하며, '노래하는 것(to sing)'이 '지루하게 하는 것'이므로 현재분사를 써야 한다. (2) think 동사는 to부정사(구)가 목적어로 나올 때 it을 가목적어로 쓴다. (3) 'for children'이라는 의미상의 주어가 있으므로 playing을 to play로 고쳐야 하며, think 동사는 to부정사(구)가 목적어로 나올 때 it을 가목적어로 쓴다. (4) 현재분사가 뒤에서 명사를 수식하도록 하거나 '주격 관계대명사+be동사'가 되도록 해야 한다. (5) 사람들이 '자세를 취하는' 것이므로 능동의 의미인 현재분사가 적절하다.

17 첫 번째 빈칸에는 여자가 '서 있는' 것이므로 현재분사가 적절하고 두 번째 빈칸에는 꽃으로 '덮인' 것이므로 과거분사가 적절하다.

18 플루트는 '수도관과 단추'로 만들어졌다.

19 수동의 의미이므로 made가 적절하다.

20 ⓐ와 ⑤: 감동적인, 가슴[마음]을 뭉클하게[아프게] 하는, ①, ②, ③: 움직이는, ④ 이사하는[용의]

21 not only A but also B = B as well as A: 'A뿐만 아니라 B도'

22 be eager to부정사 = be eager for ~ing: ~하기를 갈망하다

23 living 이하가 앞의 children을 수식하고, 주격 관계대명사 that 이하가 선행사인 a town을 수식하도록 쓰는 것이 적절하다.

24 ⓐ와 ②: 부사적 용법, ①, ④: 명사적 용법, ③, ⑤: 형용사적 용법

26 '첼로 연주를 하는' 소녀라고 해야 하므로, played를 playing으로 고치는 것이 적절하다.

27 '그 지역의 쓰레기 줍는 사람의 이름이 무엇인지'는 대답할 수 없다. ① It was made out of a shiny oil tank. ② It made the deep sound. ③ To work on a recycling program. ④ He decided to share his love of music with the children.

Critical Minds

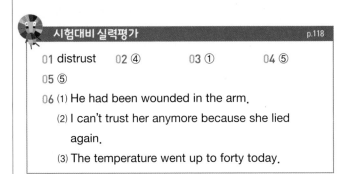

시험대비 실력평가   p.118

01 distrust   **02** ④   **03** ①   **04** ⑤

05 ⑤

06 (1) He had been wounded in the arm.

   (2) I can't trust her anymore because she lied again.

   (3) The temperature went up to forty today.

01 주어진 관계는 반의어 관계이다. trust: 신뢰하다, distrust: 불신하다

02 '해, 손상, 고통을 초래하는 사건'을 나타내는 말은 disaster(재난)이다.

03 trust는 명사로 '신뢰', 동사로 '신뢰하다'를 의미한다.

04 mine: 광산

05 보기에 주어진 judge는 '판단하다'를 의미한다. ⑤번은 '판사'를 뜻한다.

06 wound: 상처를 입히다, trust: 신뢰하다, temperature: 온도

서술형 시험대비   p.119

01 realize

02 (1) competitors   (2) condition   (3) confessed

   (4) critical

03 (1) on the loose   (2) think outside the box

   (3) search for   (4) catch a cold   (5) got caught

04 (1) Don't you think the restaurant is extremely loud?

   (2) Eating too much sugar is harmful for your teeth.

   (3) He is almost the same height as my sister.

05 (1) She admitted that she had made mistakes.

   (2) I had an argument with my boyfriend yesterday.

   (3) Adults should pay an entrance fee, but children get in free.

01 형용사에 접미사 '-ize'를 붙여 동사를 만들 수 있다. realize: 실현하다, regularize: 합법화하다

02 competitor: 경쟁자, condition: 상태, confess: 고백하다, critical: 위독한

03 catch a cold: 감기에 걸리다, got caught -ing: ~하다가 걸리다, on the loose: 잡히지 않은, search for: ~을 찾다, think outside the box: 고정관념에서 벗어나다

04 extremely: 극도로, 극히, harmful: 해로운, height: 키

05 admit: 인정하다, argument: 논쟁, entrance fee: 입장료, adult: 어른

Conversation

핵심 Check   p.120~121

1 (C) - (A) - (B)   **2** makes you say so

교과서 대화문 익히기

Check(√) True or False   p.122

1 T **2** T **3** T **4** F

교과서 확인학습   p.124~125

Listen & Talk 1 A-1
caught a cold, warmly / article, body temperature / more about it / because of viruses

Listen & Talk 1 A-2
a glass of warm milk, fall asleep / help, fall / tell me more about it / chemicals, amount, too, to, effect

Listen & Talk 2 A-1
What are you reading / riddles / for / Actually, useful for adults / say so / creatively, think outside the box

Listen & Talk 2 A-2
poetry books / written / write better / say so / honest, feelings, more creative

Listen & Talk 2 B
I should buy this drink, lose weight / label, closely, strange / you say so / enough information, what's, drink / right / how much you have to drink

Communication
information, facts, completely wrong / examples, facts that are wrong / what / goldfish, goldfish /

recognize their owners / know that

Wrap Up 2
interesting article, where it is / between, and / What color / guess / called / dangerous

시험대비 기본평가   p.126

01 ⓓ → make 02 ⑤   03 ⓓ → because of
04 (A) their low body temperature   (B) viruses

01 관계대명사의 선행사가 chemicals로 복수이므로 make가 적절하다.

02 우유 한 잔에 있는 특별한 성분의 양이 너무 적어서 효과가 없다.

03 뒤에 명사가 이어지므로 because of가 알맞다.

04 기사에 따르면 사람들은 체온이 낮아서가 아니라 바이러스 때문에 감기에 걸린다.

시험대비 실력평가   p.127~128

01 ⓔ → which   02 ⑤
03 She drinks a glass of warm milk.
04 They make people sleepy.
05 It's because the amount in a glass is too small to have any effect.
06 (C) → (A) → (D)→ (B) → (E)   07 ⑤
08 ⑤
09 We need to think outside the box to find the answers.
10 written   11 ⑤   12 children

01 관계대명사의 계속적 용법으로 which가 적절하다.

03 수지는 자기 전에 따뜻한 우유 한 잔을 마신다.

04 우유에 있는 화학물질이 사람들을 졸리게 만든다.

05 우유 한 잔에 들어 있는 화학물질의 양이 너무 적어 효과가 없다.

06 (C) 시집에 대한 설명 → (A) 확인 → (D) 자신의 의견 표현 → (B) 이유 질문 → (E) 이유 설명

07 사실을 알고 있는지 묻는 질문에 '무슨 말인지 알겠다.'라는 대답은 어색하다.

08 ⑤번을 제외한 나머지는 모두 이유를 묻는 표현이다.

10 어린이들에 의해 쓰여진 시로 과거분사 written이 알맞다.

11 ⑤번을 제외한 나머지는 모두 이유를 묻고 있다.

12 They는 아이들(children)을 가리킨다.

01 Can you tell me more about it

02 She thinks (that) she caught a cold because she didn't dress warmly yesterday.

03 (A) Napoleon   (B) height   (C) the French measuring system   (D) the English one

04 Why do you say so?

05 They were written by children.

06 It is because they're really honest about their feelings and much more creative than adults.

02 여자는 어제 따뜻하게 옷을 입지 않았기 때문에 감기에 걸렸다고 생각한다.

03 나폴레옹은 정말 키가 작았을까? 우리는 나폴레옹의 키에 대해 잘못 알았다. 오해는 프랑스의 측정 체계와 영국의 측정 체계와의 차이에서 비롯되었다. 그는 실제로 약 168 cm였다.

05 시집에 있는 시들은 아이들에 의해 쓰여졌다.

06 어린이들은 감정에 매우 솔직하고 어른들보다 훨씬 더 창의적이기 때문에 Sue는 어른들보다 어린이들이 시를 더 잘 쓴다고 생각한다.

교과서
Grammar

1 (1) Living   (2) Listening
2 (1) that   (2) so that

01 ②

02 (1) Having   (2) Not knowing   (3) so that   (4) so that

03 ①

04 (1) Mom's face darkened looking at the report card.
   (2) We are going to the library so that we can borrow books.

01 'so that'은 '~하기 위해', '~하고자', '~하도록'의 의미로 '목적'이나 '의도'를 나타낸다.

02 (1) 접속사가 없으므로 '접속사+주어+동사'의 역할을 할 수 있는 분사구문 Having이 적절하다. (2) 분사구문의 부정은 분사

앞에 'not'이나 'never'를 쓴다. (3) '내 동생이 야생 동물들을 볼 수 있을지라도 동물원에 갔다'는 말은 어색하다. '목적'이나 '의도'를 나타내는 'so that'이 적절하다. (4) 'so that' 앞에 콤마(,)가 있고, '결과'의 부사절을 이끄는 '그래서, 그러므로'의 의미의 'so that'이 적절하다.

03 접속사 없이 '주어+동사'가 이어지고 있으므로 빈칸에는 '접속사+주어+동사'의 역할을 할 수 있는 분사구문이 되어야 한다.

04 (1) looking을 '접속사+주어+동사'의 역할을 하는 분사구문으로 하여 알맞게 배열한다. (2) 일반적으로 '주절+so that+주어+can/will(조동사)+동사원형 ~'의 형태로 쓰여, 'so that'은 '~하기 위해', '~하고자', '~하도록'의 의미로 '목적'이나 '의도'를 나타낸다.

01 ③   02 ③   03 ①

04 (1) that   (2) as   (3) order   (4) Neglecting
   (5) processing   (6) Not knowing

05 ⑤   06 ③   07 ①   08 ⑤

09 Crossing   10 ②   11 ②

12 (1) he was   (2) she was   13 ④

14 (1) Don't throw trash in the sea in order that animals can live safely.
   (2) Look for hidden ideas so that you can see what the writer really means.
   (3) Swimming in the pond, she was wearing her swimming cap.
   (4) It being fine, we went for a walk to the beach.
   (5) Seen from high above, the cars looked tiny.

15 ⑤   16 ②, ③

17 They confessed that they made it up so that they could draw the readers' attention to the unsafe conditions at the zoo.

01 Aaron danced on the stage listening to the music.

02 The bird practiced flying hard so as to fly up high.

03 첫 번째 빈칸에는 접속사가 없으므로 '접속사+주어+동사'의 역할을 할 수 있는 reading이 적절하다. 두 번째 빈칸에는 '~하기 위해', '~하도록'이라는 의미의 '목적'이나 '의도'를 나타내는 'so that'의 so가 적절하다.

04 (1) '~하기 위해', '~하도록'이라는 의미의 '목적'을 나타내도록 that이 적절하다. (2) '목적'을 나타내는 'so that ~ can ...'은 주절과 종속절의 주어가 같은 경우, 'so as to부정사'로 바꿔 쓸 수 있다. (3) '목적'을 나타내는 'so that ~ can ...'은 'in order

that ~ can ...'으로 바꿔 쓸 수 있다.' (4) 접속사가 없으므로 '접속사+주어+동사'의 역할을 할 수 있는 분사구문으로 써야 한다. (5) 분사구문의 뜻을 명확히 하기 위해 접속사 When을 생략하지 않고 남겨둔 경우이다. (6) 분사구문의 부정은 분사 앞에 'not'이나 'never'를 쓴다.

05 '접속사+주어+동사'의 부사절을 분사구문으로 바꾸어 쓸 수 있다. 이때, 분사구문의 뜻을 명확히 하기 위해 접속사를 생략하지 않기도 한다.

06 (A) 'so that ~ can ...'은 주절과 종속절의 주어가 같은 경우 'so as to부정사'로 바꿔 쓸 수 있다. (B) 'so+형용사[부사]+that+주어+can ...(매우 ~해서 …할 수 있는)'은 '형용사+enough to ...(…할 정도로 충분히 ~한)'로 바꿔 쓸 수 있다.

07 접속사가 없으므로 분사구문 thinking으로 만들어야 한다. 분사구문이 문장의 중간에 삽입된 형태이다.

08 'so that ~ can ...'은 'in order that ~ can ...'으로 바꿔 쓸 수 있으며, 주절과 종속절의 주어가 같은 경우 '(in order[so as]) to부정사'로 바꿔 쓸 수 있다.

09 한 문장으로 쓰면 'When you cross the street, you should be careful.'이고, 분사구문으로 바꾸면 'When you cross'를 현재분사 Crossing으로 써야 한다.

10 일반적으로 '주절+so that+주어+can/will(조동사)+동사원형 ~'의 형태로 쓰여, '~하기 위해', '~하고자', '~하도록'의 의미로 '목적'이나 '의도'를 나타낸다.

11 주어진 문장과 ②번은 '양보'를 나타낸다. ① 이유, ③ 시간, ④ 동시동작, ⑤ 조건

12 부사절에서 주어가 주절의 주어와 같을 때 '주어+be동사'를 생략할 수 있으며 이것은 분사구문으로 고쳤을 때 being을 생략하고 접속사를 남겨둔 것과 같다.

13 'so+형용사[부사]+that+주어+can't'는 '너무 ~해서 …할 수 없다'라는 의미이며, 'too+형용사[부사]+to부정사'(…하기에 너무 ~한)로 바꿔 쓸 수 있다.

14 (1) for 뒤에 절이 오므로 for를 that으로 고쳐 'in order that'으로 쓰는 것이 적절하다. (2) 'so as to+부정사' 형태나 'so that+절'의 형태로 써야 하므로 as를 삭제해야 한다. (3) 수영을 하고 있는 '진행'의 의미이므로 Swum을 Swimming으로 고치는 것이 적절하다. (4) 'As it is fine, we went out.'을 분사구문을 이용해서 쓴 문장으로 주절의 주어와 부사절의 주어가 다르므로 독립분사구문으로 써야 한다. (5) Being이 생략된 분사구문으로 '보는' 것이 아니라 '보이는' 것이므로 Seeing을 Seen으로 고쳐야 한다.

15 'Though she had heard their names, Kathryn couldn't recognize them.'을 분사구문으로 바꾼 것이므로 'Though she had heard' 대신에 'Having heard'로 쓰는 것이 적절하다.

16 ② I was stupid enough to believe him. ③ Come early so as to have plenty of time. 또는 Come early so that you can have plenty of time.

17 'so that'은 '~하기 위해', '~하고자', '~하도록'의 의미로 '목적'이나 '의도'를 나타낸다.

서술형 시험대비

p.136~137

01 (1) Catching a bad cold, my mom couldn't get to work.

(2) Finishing breakfast, I took a taxi to school.

(3) Mixing blue and yellow, you get green.

(4) Being nervous, she said it was a good experience.

(5) Not knowing what happened, I called my friend, Sam.

(6) If it being fine tomorrow, I will go hiking.

02 (1) Read the book carefully so that you can find hidden ideas.

(2) Sally bought a camera so that she could take great pictures.

03 (1) Not knowing the news was false, many people panicked.

(2) Leaving early, he was late for the meeting.

(3) He worked so hard that he finally became a lawyer.

(4) He got up early, so that he could catch the first bus.

04 (1) Exhausting → Exhausted

(2) Failing → Having failed

05 (1) so that she can

(2) in order to

(3) so as to

06 (1) It being

(2) Watching

07 (1) Turning to the left, you will find the house. / If you turn to the left, you will find the house.

(2) Being sick, she was absent from school. / Because[As, Since] she was sick, she was absent from school.

(3) Lisa bought some oranges so[in order] that her mother could make orange juice.

08 (1) Judy practices playing the piano in order that she can win the top prize.

25

(2) I got up early so that I could go jogging. 또는 I got up early so as to go jogging.

(3) Arriving late at the station, I saw the train leaving.

01 '접속사+주어+동사'로 이루어진 부사절의 주어가 주절의 주어와 일치할 때 접속사와 주어를 생략하고 동사를 분사(동사원형+-ing)로 만든다. (1) '이유', (2) '시간' (3) '조건' (4) '양보' (5) 분사구문의 부정은 분사 앞에 'not'이나 'never'를 쓴다. (6) 주절의 주어와 부사절의 주어가 다르므로 주어를 생략하면 안 된다.(독립분사구문)

02 so that은 '~하기 위해', '~하고자', '~하도록'의 의미로 '목적'이나 '의도'를 나타낸다. 일반적으로 '주절+so that+주어+can/will(조동사)+동사원형 ~'의 형태로 쓰인다.

03 (1), (2) 현재분사가 분사구문을 이끌도록 한다. 부정은 분사 앞에 'not'이나 'never'를 쓴다. (3) so와 that 사이에 수식어가 오면, '너무 ~해서 결국 …하다'라는 뜻이 된다. (4) 'so that'은 '결과'의 부사절을 이끌어 '그래서, 그러므로'의 의미를 갖는 접속사로 쓰이기도 하는데, 대개 앞에 쉼표(,)가 온다.

04 (1) '지친'의 뜻으로 '수동'의 의미가 되어야 하므로 Exhausting을 Exhausted로 고쳐 써야 한다. (2) 부사절의 시제가 주절보다 앞선 경우에는 완료분사구문(having+과거분사)으로 쓴다.

05 'so that ~ can …'은 'in order that ~ can …'으로 바꿔 쓸 수 있으며, 주절과 종속절의 주어가 같은 경우 '(in order[so as]) to부정사'로 바꿔 쓸 수 있다.

06 (1) 'Because it is rainy, ~'를 부사구문으로 고쳐 쓴다. 주절의 주어와 부사절의 주어가 다르므로 주어를 생략하면 안 된다.(독립분사구문) (2) 'While they are watching the rain, ~'을 부사구문으로 고쳐 쓴다.

07 (1), (2) '접속사+주어+동사'로 이루어진 부사절의 주어가 주절의 주어와 일치할 때 접속사와 주어를 생략하고 동사를 분사(동사원형+-ing)로 만들어서 분사구문으로 바꿔 쓴다. (3) so[in order] that은 '~하기 위해', '~하고자', '~하도록'의 의미로 '목적'이나 '의도'를 나타낸다. 일반적으로 '주절+so [in order] that+주어+can/will(조동사)+동사원형 ~'의 형태로 쓰인다.

08 (1), (2) 'so that ~ can …'은 'in order that ~ can …'으로 바꿔 쓸 수 있으며, 주절과 종속절의 주어가 같은 경우 '(in order[so as]) to부정사'로 바꿔 쓸 수 있다. (3) 내가 도착하는 능동의 의미이므로 현재분사를 쓰는 것이 적절하다.

Reading

확인문제   p.138

1 T   2 F   3 T   4 F

확인문제   p.139

1 T   2 F   3 T   4 F   5 T   6 F

확인문제   p.140

1 T   2 F   3 T   4 F   5 T   6 F

교과서 확인학습 A   p.141~143

01 Spot Fake News
02 interesting news   03 whether
04 what if, made up
05 in that, less informed, misled
06 Nevertheless, throughout history
07 such false information
08 thinking, the hidden motives
09 AWFUL   10 broke down
11 the other   12 hundreds of   13 on the loose
14 until further notice
15 described above
16 laughed out loud
17 got really worried
18 Not knowing, panicked   19 Some, others
20 make up such news
21 made it up so that, could
22 IN ARGUMENT
23 was shot, wounded
24 had an argument
25 led to, in the chest
26 in critical condition
27 after the shooting
28 are searching for, are warning
29 anything strange   30 backwards
31 why   32 so that, could, if
33 got caught stealing
34 admit, were harshly criticized   35 published
36 As, whether, or   37 How to spot
38 Source   39 reliable   40 trust
41 Check   42 new, old
43 Is, related to current
44 Beyond the Headlines

45 match the content　　　　　46 Supporting

47 related, similar

1 Can You Spot Fake News?

2 Every day we watch, hear, or read interesting news.

3 However, have you ever seriously considered whether an article is really true?

4 Everyone likes an interesting news story but what if it is completely made up?

5 Fake news can be very harmful in that it can make people less informed or even misled.

6 Nevertheless, there have been various fake news reports throughout history.

7 Why have some people written such false information?

8 Let's look into some articles thinking about the hidden motives behind them.

9 AWFUL DISASTER

10 Last night, an angry group of rhinoceroses broke down the walls of the cage at the zoo and escaped.

11 They also broke down the walls of the other wild animals' cages.

12 These animals ran down the streets and injured hundreds of people.

13 Twelve of the animals are still on the loose.

14 Citizens should stay indoors until further notice.

15 Not a single act or incident described above has taken place.

16 At that time, those who read the article carefully laughed out loud.

17 Those who didn't read it to the end got really worried.

18 Not knowing the news was false, many people panicked.

19 Some tried to escape the city while others went into the parks with guns to hunt the animals.

20 So why did *The Herald* make up such news?

21 Later, they confessed that they made it up so that they could draw the readers' attention to the unsafe conditions at the zoo.

22 SLAV SHOOTS A FRIEND IN ARGUMENT

23 Mejk Swenekafew, a Slav worker at the Columbia Coal Mine, was shot and seriously wounded by John Pecitello near the mining camp Thursday evening.

24 The two men had an argument during a meeting.

25 The argument led to a fight, and Pecitello shot Swenekafew twice, in the chest and leg.

26 He is now at the hospital in critical condition.

27 Pecitello ran away after the shooting.

28 The police are searching for him now and are warning citizens that he is extremely dangerous.

29 Is there anything strange about the article?

30 Read the Slav's name backwards; it spells, "we-fake-news."

31 Who wrote this and why?

32 *The Daily Telegram* published this fake article so that they could prove if *The Daily News*, their competitor, was stealing their articles.

33 *The Daily News* published the same article about "Swenekafew" the next day and thus got caught stealing.

34 The people at *The Daily News* had to admit their act and were harshly criticized by the public.

35 The two articles were special cases, but there are many "fake" news articles published every day.

36 As readers, we need to read critically and judge whether the news is real or fake.

37 How to spot fake news!

38 Consider the Source

39 Is it from a reliable source?

40 Can we trust the writer?

41 Check the Date

42 Is it a new or an old story?

43 Is it related to current events?

44 Read Beyond the Headlines

45 Does the headline match the content?

46 Find Supporting Sources

47 Do other related stories provide similar content?

01 ④	02 ③	03 ④	
04 they → it	05 ②	06 ⑤	07 ②, ③, ⑤
08 ③	09 ①	10 ④	

11 (A) shot　(B) are　(C) are

12 Swenekafew　　　　　13 ②

14 (A) in that　(B) misled　(C) such　　　　15 ①, ④

16 ①　　　　　17 published　18 ④　　　　19 ②

20 forward → backwards　21 ③, ⑤　　　　22 ③

27

01 ④ 앞에 나오는 내용과 상반되는 내용이 뒤에 이어지므로 However가 가장 적절하다. ① 게다가, 더욱이, ② 다시 말해서, ③ 그러므로

02 주어진 문장의 Nevertheless에 주목한다. 비록 ③번 앞 문장의 내용이 사실이지만, 그럼에도 불구하고, 역사를 통틀어 다양한 가짜 뉴스 보도들이 존재해 왔다는 내용이므로 ③번이 적절하다.

03 가짜 뉴스는 사람들에게 정보를 '부족하게' 제공할 수 있다. well-informed: 사정에 정통한, 박식한, ① day after day: 매일, ③ damaging: 손해를 끼치는, 해로운

04 news는 단수로 취급하기 때문에, they를 it으로 고치는 것이 적절하다.

05 ⓐ on the loose 잡히지 않은, 탈주 중인, ⓑ until: ~까지(계속), by: ~까지는(완료)

06 ⑤ 그 중 열두 마리의 동물들이 아직 잡히지 않았다. on the loose 잡히지 않은, 탈주 중인

07 happen = occur = arise: (사고·일·문제 등이) 발생하다, 일어나다, be held = be hosted: 개최되다

08 ⓐ와 ②, ⑤: 이유, ①, ④: 양보, ③: 조건

09 ⓑ와 ①: (이야기 등을) 지어내다, 만들어 내다, ② (잃어버린 것) ~을 대신하다; ~에 대해 보상하다, ③ (~와) 화해하다, ④ (각 부분이) ~을 구성[형성]하다, ⑤ 화장하다, 분장하다

10 이 글은 '동물원의 안전하지 않은 상태에 대해 독자들의 주의를 끌기 위해 헤럴드사가 기사를 지어냈다'는 것이므로, 주제로는 ④번 '독자들의 주의를 끌기 위한 거짓 뉴스가 적절하다.

11 (A) '총상을 입었다'고 해야 하므로 shot이 적절하다. shoot-shot-shot: (총 등을) 쏘다, shut-shut-shut: (문 등을[이]) 닫다[닫히다], (눈을) 감다, (B) 'The police'는 복수 취급하므로 are가 적절하다. (C) 'The police'가 주어이므로 are가 적절하다.

12 'Swenekafew'를 가리킨다.

13 그가 왜 John Pecitello와 언쟁을 벌였는지는 알 수 없다. ① He worked at the Columbia Coal Mine. ③ He was shot on Thursday evening. ④ He was shot twice. ⑤ He is now at the hospital.

14 (A) '가짜 뉴스는 사람들을 잘못 이끌 수 있다는 점에서 매우 해로울 수 있다'고 해야 하므로 in that이 적절하다. in that: ~이

므로, ~라는 점에서, (B) 목적어인 people이 '잘못 이끌어질 수 있다'는 수동의 의미이므로, 과거분사 misled가 적절하다. (C) such+(a)+형용사+명사

15 ⓐ와 ①, ④: 경험 용법, ② 결과 용법, ③ 계속 용법, ⑤ 완료 용법

16 '매일 우리가 얼마나 많은 흥미로운 뉴스를 보거나 듣고, 읽는지'는 대답할 수 없다. ② Everyone likes an interesting news story. ③ Yes. ④ Yes. ⑤ Yes.

17 앞에 나온 명사 articles를 수식하도록 과거분사 published로 쓰는 것이 적절하다.

18 ⓑ와 ④: 현재의, the current year: 올해, ① 통용되는, ② (물·공기의) 흐름, 해류(명사), ③ 전류(명사), direct current: 직류, ⑤ 때의 흐름(course), 경향, 풍조(명사), swim against the current: 세상 풍조[천하대세]에 거스르다

19 가짜 뉴스 판별 방법 중의 하나인 'Read Beyond the Headlines(기사 제목 그 이상을 읽어라)'는 단순히 기사 제목만 읽고 뉴스의 내용을 짐작하여 판단하지 말고 그 기사의 내용까지 모두 읽으라는 의미이므로, ②번의 '제목으로 내용을 짐작하기'는 가짜 뉴스 판별 방법에 해당하지 않는다.

20 그 슬라브인의 이름을 '거꾸로' 읽어 보라고 하는 것이 적절하다. forward: 앞으로

21 ⓑ와 ③, ⑤: ~인지 아닌지, ①, ②, ④: (가정적 조건을 나타내어) (만약) ~이라면

22 ③ 그 다음 날 'Swenekafew'에 대한 동일한 기사를 발행한 것은 '데일리 뉴스 사'이다.

23 fake: 가짜의, 거짓된, genuine: 진짜의, 진품의

24 nevertheless: 그럼에도 불구하고(부사), even so, still, nonetheless 등과 바꿔 쓸 수 있다. ① despite ~: ~에도 불구하고(전치사), ② therefore: 그러므로(부사) ④ otherwise: (만약) 그렇지 않으면[않았다면](부사)

25 '몇 가지 뉴스 기사'를 가리킨다.

26 이 글은 '가짜 뉴스는 매우 해로울 수 있지만, 역사를 통틀어 다양한 가짜 뉴스 보도들이 존재해 왔다'는 내용의 글이므로, 제목으로는 ④번 '해로운 그러나 계속되는 가짜 뉴스 보도들'이 적절하다. continuous: 계속되는, 지속적인, ⑤ faithful: 충실한, from now on: 이제부터

27 '어떤 사람들은', '다른 사람들은'이라고 해야 하므로, Some, others가 적절하다. some: 처음 지칭하는 어떤 것[사람]들, others: 다른 것[사람]들, ① one: 2개 이상의 대상 중 불특정한 한 개를 처음으로 지칭할 때 사용하는 대명사, the other: 2개 중 나머지 한 개, ② the others: 앞에 지칭한 것들을 제외한 나머지 전부들, ③ another: 3개 이상의 대상에서 두 번째로 불특

정한 한 개를 지칭할 때 사용하는 대명사, ④ the first: 전자, the second: 후자

28 주격 관계대명사절 'who didn't read it to the end'가 선행사 those를 수식하도록 쓰는 것이 적절하다.

29 구동사의 목적어가 인칭대명사이므로 부사의 앞에 목적어를 쓰는 것이 적절하다

서술형 시험대비
p.152~153

01 (A) if   (B) harmful   (C) informed
02 Why have some people written such false information?
03 while we think about the hidden motives behind them
04 on the loose
05 has been taken place → has taken place
06 (A) No   (B) escape
07 in order that[so that], could[might]
08 such news
09 ②번 near from → near
10 (A) had an argument   (B) critical
11 Whether
12 The Daily News published the same article about "Swenekafew" the next day

01 (A) '만약 그것이 완전히 가짜인 것이라면 어떻게 될 것인가?'라고 해야 하므로 if가 적절하다. What if ~?: ~라면 어떻게 될까? (B) '가짜 뉴스는 사람들을 잘못 이끌 수 있다는 점에서 매우 해로울 수 있다'고 해야 하므로 harmful이 적절하다. harmless: 해가 없는, 무해한, (C) 목적어인 people이 '정보를 부족하게 제공받거나'라고 수동의 의미이므로, 과거분사 informed가 적절하다.

02 현재완료 시제의 의문문은 'Have+주어+p.p.'의 순서로 쓰는 것이 적절하다. such+(a)+형용사+명사

03 위 글의 밑줄 친 ⓑ는 동시동작을 나타내는 분사구문으로, '~하는 동안에'라는 의미의 접속사 while을 사용하여 부사절로 고치는 것이 적절하다.

04 on the loose: 잡히지 않은; 탈주 중인

05 take place는 '(사고·일·문제 등이) 발생하다, 일어나다'라는 뜻으로 수동태로 쓸 수 없다.

06 실제로는 어젯밤 동물들이 동물원에서 '도망치지' 않았기 때문에, 동물원에서 탈출한 동물들에 의해 '아무도' 다치지 않았다.

07 목적을 나타내는 부사적 용법의 to부정사는 복문으로 전환할 때 'in order that[so that]+주어+can[may]+동사원형'으로 고

치는 것이 적절하다.

08 '이러한 뉴스'를 가리킨다.

09 전치사 near 뒤에 바로 목적어를 쓰는 것이 적절하다. ① by+수동태의 행위자, ③ be shot in the ~: ~에 총을 맞다, ④ in critical condition: 위독한 상태로, ⑤ search for: ~를 찾다

10 Mejk Swenekafew는 John Pecitello와 회의 중에 '언쟁을 벌였고', Pecitello가 Swenekafew에게 총을 쏘았다. Swenekafew는 지금 입원 중이고, 그의 상태는 '위독하다.'

11 if는 '~인지 아닌지'라는 의미의 명사절을 이끄는 접속사로 whether와 바꾸어 쓸 수 있으며, if가 이끄는 명사절이 동사 prove의 목적어이다.

12 '데일리 뉴스사가 그 다음 날 'Swenekafew'에 대한 동일한 기사를 발행한 것'을 가리킨다.

영역별 핵심문제
p.155~159

01 misunderstand   02 ②
03 (1) reliable   (2) riddle   (3) seriously   (4) shoot
   (5) source   04 ①   05 ⑤
06 (1) break down   (2) According to   (3) made up
07 (1) She described what happened last night.
   (2) This is one of the worst natural disasters.
   (3) A lion escaped from the zoo an hour ago.
08 (C) · (D) · (B) · (C) · (A)   09 ①
10 ⑤
11 It's because they help adults think more creatively.
12 We need to think outside the box.
13 ⑤   14 ⑤
15 (1) Linda was stupid enough to make a big mistake.
   (2) Bill is too poor to buy the house.
16 ①   17 ⑤
18 (1) Though[Although] the two articles were special cases
   (2) and[while] he smiled brightly
   (3) Because[As, Since] I was tired from the work
19 ②   20 ②   21 ⑤   22 ⑤
23 ③   24 ④
25 (A) the other   (B) further   (C) described
26 Twelve of the animals are still on the loose.
27 John Pecitello   28 ②   29 ④
30 ⓐ To draw the readers' attention to the unsafe conditions at the zoo.
   ⓑ To prove that The Daily News was stealing their articles.

01 접두사 'mis'는 '잘못된, 나쁜'을 의미한다. misunderstand: 오해하다, 잘못 이해하다

02 nevertheless: 그럼에도 불구하고

03 riddle: 수수께끼, seriously: 심하게, 진지하게, reliable: 믿을 만한, source: 출처, shoot: 쏘다

04 '갑자기 너무 걱정이 되어서 이성적일 수 없다고 느끼다'를 가리키는 말은 panic이다.

05 보기에 주어진 current는 '현재의'를 뜻한다. ⑤번은 '흐름, 해류'를 의미한다.

06 break down: 부수다, 무너뜨리다, according to: ~에 따르면, make up: 지어내다, 만들다

07 describe: 기술하다, disaster: 재난, escape: 탈출하다

08 (C) TV 뉴스를 보는 이유 질문 → (D) 이유 설명 → (B) TV가 가장 유용하다고 생각하는 이유 질문 → (E) 이유 설명 → (A) 반응 및 이해 표현

09 위 대화에서 Sandy는 '주의 깊은, 신중한' 성격임을 알 수 있다.

10 Sandy에 따르면 음료수가 무엇으로 만들어졌는지에 대한 정보가 없다.

11 John은 수수께끼 책들이 어른들이 좀 더 창의적으로 생각하도록 도와주기 때문에 유익하다고 생각한다.

12 수수께끼의 답을 찾기 위해 고정관념에서 벗어날 필요가 있다.

13 ⑤번을 제외한 나머지는 모두 자세한 설명을 요청하는 표현이다.

14 여자는 체온이 낮아서 감기에 걸렸다는 설명은 대화의 내용과 일치하지 않는다.

15 (1) 'so+형용사[부사]+that+주어+can ...'은 '형용사+enough to ...'로 바꿔 쓸 수 있다. (2) 'so+형용사[부사]+that+주어+can't ...'은 'too+형용사[부사]+to부정사'로 바꿔 쓸 수 있다.

16 'so that ~ can ...'은 'in order that ~ can ...'으로 바꿔 쓸 수 있다.

17 As she didn't hand out the report, she is responsible for the result.를 분사구문으로 쓴 것이므로 handing을 'having handed'로 고쳐야 한다.

18 (1) 내용상 '양보'가 적절하고, 주어가 다른 독립분사구문이므로 다른 주어를 써 주고, having been이 있으므로 한 시제 앞선 양보의 부사절로 쓴다. (2) 내용상 '동시동작'이나 '시간'의 부사절이 적절하다. (3) 내용상 '이유'의 부사절이 적절하다.

19 전치사 with는 '~한 채'의 뜻으로 부대 상황을 나타낸다.

20 앞에 나오는 내용과 상반되는 내용이 뒤에 이어지므로 Nevertheless가 가장 적절하다. ① 뿐만 아니라, 더욱이, ③ 똑같이, 비슷하게, ④ 즉[말하자면], ⑤ 따라서, 그러므로

21 ① every day = each day: 매일, ② whether = if: ~인지 아닌지, ③ what if는 회화에서 자주 쓰이는 줄임말로, 본래 표현은 'what would happen if'이며 '~한다면 어쩌지?'라는 뜻으로 사용된다. ④ in the sense that: ~라는 점에서, ⑤ motive: 동기, 이유, theme: 주제, 테마

22 look into: ~을 조사하다

23 문장 끝에서 '왜 어떤 사람들은 그러한 거짓 정보를 써 왔던 것일까? 그 뒤에 숨겨진 동기를 생각하면서 몇 가지 뉴스 기사를 살펴보자.'라고 했으므로, 뒤에 올 내용으로는 '그 뒤에 숨겨진 동기에 대해 생각할 수 있는 몇 가지 가짜 뉴스 기사'가 적절하다.

24 ⓐ와 ④: 부수다, ① 실패하다, 결렬되다, ②와 ⑤: (기계·차량이) 고장 나다, ③ 아주 나빠지다

25 (A) 뒤에 복수 명사가 이어지므로 the other가 적절하다. another+단수 명사, (B) '추후 안내가 있을 때까지'라고 해야 하므로 further가 적절하다. farther: (공간, 시간상으로) 더 멀리, further: 더 이상의, 추가의, (C) '위에 기술된 어떤 행동이나 사건도'라고 해야 하므로 described가 적절하다.

26 on the loose: 잡히지 않은, 탈주 중인

27 Mejk Swenekafew에게 총을 쏜 John Pecitello를 가리킨다.

28 주어진 문장의 The argument에 주목한다. ②번 앞 문장의 an argument를 받고 있으므로 ②번이 적절하다.

29 위 글은 '인터뷰'이다. ① (신문·잡지의) 글, 기사, ② 수필, ③ (책·연극·영화 등에 대한) 논평[비평], 감상문, ⑤ 요약, 개요

30 ⓐ: 동물원의 안전하지 않은 상태에 대해 독자들의 주의를 끌기 위해서. ⓑ: 데일리 뉴스 사가 그들의 기사를 훔치고 있다는 것을 증명하기 위해서

단원별 예상문제 p.160~163

01 ⑤

02 Can you give me more information about it?

03 ⑤   04 ②   05 ④   06 riddle

07 ⑤   08 ⓐ → where it is   09 ⑤

10 ③

11 (1) As[Because, Since] I was driving my car, I couldn't reply to your text message.
  (2) While[When, As] I was walking down the street, I met my friend.
  (3) Although[Though] there was no work to do, he remained at his office until late.

12 playing the guitar   13 ④   14 ②, ④

15 ②, ③, ⑤   16 ⑤   17 panicked

18 Because[As/Since] they didn't know the news was false   19 ④

20 ⑤

21 (A) *The Daily Telegram*
   (B) The people at *The Daily News*
22 the public harshly criticized the people at *The Daily News*

01 '알맞은 순서로 문자를 가지고 단어를 형성하다'를 가리키는 말은 spell이다.

03 수지가 잠을 잘 자기 위해 몇 잔의 우유를 마셔야 하는지는 대화를 통해 알 수 없다.

04 주어진 문장은 기사에 대한 구체적인 설명을 요청하므로 (B)에 들어가는 것이 적절하다.

05 왜 프랑스의 1인치가 영국과 달랐는지는 대화를 통해 알 수 없다.

06 '이해하기 힘든 질문으로 놀라운 답을 갖고 있고 게임으로 다른 사람에게 묻는 질문'을 가리키는 것은 riddle(수수께끼)이다.

07 think outside the box: 고정관념에서 벗어나다

08 간접의문문으로 '의문사+주어+동사'의 순서가 적절하다.

10 ③ She was too tired to think straight. 'so+형용사[부사]+that+주어+can't …'는 '너무 ~해서 …할 수 없다'라는 의미이며, 'too+형용사[부사]+to부정사'(…하기에 너무~한)로 바꿔 쓸 수 있다.

11 (1), (2) 분사구문의 분사(동사원형+-ing)를 의미에 맞게 '접속사+주어+동사'로 이루어진 부사절로 만든다. (3) 분사구문의 주어가 주절의 주어가 일치하지 않으므로 부사절의 주어를 따로 써 주어야 한다.

12 '접속사+주어+동사'로 이루어진 부사절의 주어가 주절의 주어와 일치할 때 접속사와 주어를 생략하고 동사를 현재분사(동사원형+-ing)로 만든다.

13 Don't waste water in order to prevent water shortages.

14 ⓐ와 ②, ④: (신문·잡지 따위의) 기사, ①, ⑤: (종류가 같은 것의) 한 개, 한 가지(item), ③ 관사, a definite article: 정관사(the)

15 ⓑ와 ②, ③, ⑤: 현재분사, ①, ④: 동명사

16 이 글은 '가짜 뉴스는 매우 해로울 수 있지만, 역사를 통틀어 다양한 가짜 뉴스 보도들이 존재해 왔다'는 내용의 글이므로, 주제로는 ⑤번 '해로운 영향들에도 불구하고, 다양한 가짜 뉴스 보도들이 존재해 왔다'가 적절하다. ④ faithfully: (내용이 틀리지 않게) 충실히, 정확히

17 'panic'의 과거형은 끝에 '-ked'를 붙이는 것이 적절하다. 'paniced'로 쓰지 않도록 주의해야 한다. panic 겁에 질려 어쩔 줄 모르다

18 '이유'를 나타내는 부사절로 고치는 것이 적절하다.

19 헤럴드 사는 사람들에게 '겁주기 위하여' 이러한 뉴스를 만들어 낸 것이 아니라, '동물원의 안전하지 않은 상태에 대해 독자들의 주의를 끌기 위해' 그 기사를 지어냈다.

20 앞의 내용의 결과가 나오고 있으므로 thus가 가장 적절하다. ① 게다가, ② 그 대신에, 그렇지 않으면(둘째 대안을 소개할 때 씀), ③ 다른 한편으로는, 반면에, ④ 게다가, 더욱이

21 (A) 데일리 텔레그램 사, The Daily Telegram과 같이 특정 회사를 지칭할 때는 그 회사를 이루는 구성원 전체를 받아 they로 복수 취급하기도 한다. (B) 데일리 뉴스 사의 사람들을 가리킨다.

22 the public을 주어로 해서 능동태로 고치는 것이 적절하다.

서술형 실전문제

p.164~165

01 It says that Napoleon was actually fairly tall.
02 A French doctor wrote it down according to the French measuring system.
03 An inch in France was longer than an inch in England.
04 (1) Because[As, Since] Jenny won the first prize, she was so happy.
   (2) If you walk with Wing Walker, you burn more calories and get slimmer.
   (3) Using the hidden board technology, they strengthen leg muscles.
   (4) She studied very hard, passing the exam.
05 (1) in order that   (2) in[so] order[as] to
   (3) enough to   (4) too hot, to
06 that → whether[if]
07 what if it is completely made up?
08 (A) fake news   (B) fake news
09 the article
10 (in order/so as) to draw the readers' attention to the unsafe conditions at the zoo
11 (A) escape the city   (B) went into the parks

01 기사에 따르면 나폴레옹은 꽤 키가 컸다.

02 프랑스 의사가 나폴레옹의 키를 적었고 프랑스 측정 체계에 따라 적었다.

03 프랑스의 1인치는 영국의 1인치보다 더 길었다.

04 (1) 의미상 '이유'를 나타내는 분사구문이다. (2) 의미상 '조건'을 나타내는 분사구문이다. (3) 의미상 '이유'를 나타내는 분사구문으로 바꾼다. (4) 의미상 '연속상황'을 나타내는 분사구문으로 바꾼다.

05 (1), (2) 'so that ~ can ...'은 'in order that ~ can ...'으로 바꿔 쓸 수 있으며, 주절과 종속절의 주어가 같은 경우 '(in order[so as]) to부정사'로 바꿔 쓸 수 있다. (3), (4) 'so+형용사[부사]+that+주어+can ...'은 '형용사+enough to ...'로 바꿔 쓸 수 있으며, 'so+형용사[부사]+that+주어+can't ...'는 'too+형용사[부사]+to부정사'로 바꿔 쓸 수 있다. (4)번의 경우 주절과 종속절의 주어가 다르지만 일반인이 주어이므로 따로 밝혀 쓰지 않아도 된다.

06 '뉴스 기사가 정말로 진실인지 심각하게 고려해 본 적이 있는가?'라고 해야 하므로, that을 whether로 고치는 것이 적절하다. that을 쓰면, '뉴스 기사가 정말로 진실이라는 것을 심각하게 고려해 본 적이 있는가?'라는 뜻이 되어 어색하다.

07 what if: ~라면 어떻게 될까?, make up 지어내다, 만들어 내다

08 '가짜 뉴스'때문에 사람들에게 정보가 부족하게 제공되거나 사람들이 잘못 이끌릴 수 있지만, 역사를 통틀어 다양한 '가짜 뉴스' 보도들이 존재해 왔다.

09 '그 기사'를 가리킨다.

10 so that+주어+can+동사원형 = (in order/so as) to+동사원형: ~하기 위하여(목적)

11 어떤 사람들은 '도시를 빠져나가려고 했고' 다른 사람들은 그 동물들을 사냥하기 위해 총을 들고 '공원으로 나갔다.'

창의사고력 서술형 문제   p.166

|모범답안|

01 (A) I drank a glass of warm milk
　(B) a glass of warm milk doesn't actually help me fall asleep
　(C) make people sleepy
　(D) amount
02 (A) the walking shoes, Wing Walker
　(B) burn more calories and get slimmer
　(C) the hidden board technology
　(D) scientifically proven
　(E) what materials

01 최근에 나는 잠을 잘 잘 수 없어서 잠들기 전에 따뜻한 우유를 한 잔 마셨다. 하지만 효과가 없었다. 나는 이에 대해 민수에게 이야기했다. 그는 한 잔의 따뜻한 우유가 실제로는 잠을 잘 자는 데 도움이 되지 않는다고 설명했다. 의사에 따르면 우유에는 사람들을 졸리게 만드는 특별한 화학물질이 있지만 우유 한 잔에 있는 양은 너무 적었다. 나는 잠을 잘 자기 위해 다른 방법을 찾아야겠다고 생각했다.

01 (D) → (C) → (A) → (B)
02 (1) awful　(2) chemicals　(3) chest　(4) citizen
03 (1) poems　(2) prove　(3) public　(4) published
　(5) recognize
04 ③　　　　05 ④　　　　06 ⑤
07 She reads the label of the drink closely.
08 It's because the label on the drink looks a bit strange.
09 What's in the drink and how much one has to drink to lose weight are not shown.　　10 ②
11 ⑤
12 (1) Think critically and don't believe everything (that) they tell you.
　(2) Do not criticize or make fun of your classmates.
　(3) Is this your current address?
　(4) It's difficult to judge whether it's true or not.
13 (1) Sam saved some money so that he could buy a new backpack. 또는 Sam saved some money so as to buy a new backpack.
　(2) You must follow the rules in order for everyone to enjoy the experience. 또는 You must follow the rules in order that everyone may[can] enjoy the experience.
　(3) She saw Thomas entering[enter] the classroom.
　(4) Very embarrassed, she didn't tell us that news.
14 (1) Having no work to do, he goes fishing.
　(2) Susan spoke quietly so that other people couldn't hear her voice.
15 ③　　　　16 ①, ③, ④
17 (1) 해석: Jinho는 외국인과 영어로 말할 수 있도록 영어를 열심히 공부했다.
　차이: so that은 '~하기 위해', '~하고자', '~하도록'의 의미로 '목적'이나 '의도'를 나타낸다. 일반적으로 '주절+so that+주어+can/will(조동사)+동사원형 ~'의 형태로 쓰인다.
　(2) 해석: Jinho는 영어를 열심히 공부해서 외국인과 영어로 말할 수 있었다.
　차이: so와 that 사이에 형용사나 부사가 오면, '너무 ~해서 결국 …하다'라는 뜻이 된다.
18 ①　　　　19 an interesting news story
20 ③　　　21 ③　　　22 ④　　　23 ⑤
24 The two men had an argument during a meeting.
25 ③　　　　26 ④

01 (D) 감기에 걸린 것 같다며 이유 설명 → (C) 기사 내용 설명 → (A) 구체적인 설명 요청 → (B) 감기에 걸리는 이유에 대해

구체적인 설명

02 awful: 끔찍한, 지독한, chemical: 화학 물질, chest: 흉부, 가슴, citizen: 시민

03 public: 대중, recognize: 알아보다, publish: 출판하다, prove: 증명하다, poem: 시

04 mine은 명사로 '광산', 동사로 '채굴하다', 대명사로 '나의 것'을 의미한다.

05 주어진 문장은 금붕어가 사실은 똑똑하다는 말 앞에 오는 것이 자연스러우므로 (D)가 적절하다.

06 위 대화를 통해 금붕어가 어떻게 주인을 알아보는지 알 수 없다.

07 Sandy는 음료의 라벨을 자세히 읽는다.

08 음료수의 라벨이 조금 이상해 보이기 때문에 Sandy는 David가 음료수를 사지 말아야 한다고 생각한다.

09 음료수에 무엇이 있는지 살을 빼기 위해 얼마나 마셔야 하는지 볼 수 없다.

10 (A) useful: 유용한, useless: 무익한, (B) ordinarily: 평범하게, creatively: 창의적으로, (C) think outside the box: 고정관념에서 벗어나다

11 위 대화를 통해 John의 상자 밖에 무엇이 있는지 알 수 없다.

12 critically: 비판적으로, criticize: 비판하다, current: 현재의, judge: 판단하다

13 (1) 'so that+절' 또는 'so as to부정사'가 되어야 한다. (2) 'for everyone to enjoy'로 의미상의 주어를 쓰거나 'in order that+절'이 되어야 한다. (3) entered를 entering[enter]로 바꾸어 목적보어로 만든다. (4) 주어가 embarrassed되는 수동의 관계이므로 being이 생략된 과거분사 embarrassed로 시작하는 문장으로 바꾼다.

14 (1) 분사구문을 이용하고 'no work to do'를 분사 Having의 목적어로 이용한다. (2) 일반적으로 '주절+so that+주어+can/will(조동사)+동사원형 ~'의 형태로 so that은 '목적'이나 '의도'를 나타낸다.

15 Wear a swimming cap in order for the pool to be kept clean. 주절과 부사절의 주어가 다른 경우 서로 다른 주어를 나타내야 하는데 to부정사의 경우 'for+목적격'으로 쓴다.

16 ② Pass → Passing ⑤ Feeling not → Not feeling ⑥ Meeting → Having met

17 'so that+주어+can ...'과 'so+형용사[부사]+that+주어+can ...'의 차이를 구별한다.

18 ⑥와 ③: 계속 용법, ①: 결과 용법, ②, ④: 완료 용법, ⑤: 경험 용법

19 '흥미로운 뉴스 기사'를 가리킨다.

20 ⓐ to the end: 끝까지, ⓑ draw one's attention to ~: ~에 대해 …의 주의를 끌다

21 ③ 잠깐, 잠시(명사), ③을 제외한 나머지: [반대·비교·대조를 나타내어] 그런데, 한편(접속사)

22 주어진 문장의 such news에 주목한다. ④번 앞 단락에서 말한 '거짓 뉴스'를 가리키므로 ④번이 적절하다.

23 이 글은 '컬럼비아 광산 소속의 슬라브인 노동자 두 명이 언쟁을 벌이다가 한 명이 총상을 입어 심각하게 다쳤다'는 내용의 글이므로, 제목으로는 ⑤번 '슬라브인이 언쟁 중에 친구를 쏘다'가 적절하다. ④ criminal: 범인

24 had an argument: 언쟁을 벌였다

25 run away: 도망치다

26 경찰이 찾고 있는 것은 'Pecitello'이다.

교과서 파헤치기

Lesson **3**

단어 TEST Step 1   p.02

01 끔찍한	02 기사	03 자서전, 전기
04 망치다, 파산시키다		05 남편
06 형사, 탐정	07 요새	
08 도박하다, ~을 도박으로 잃다		09 실망시키는
10 나중에, 그 뒤에	11 재산, 행운	12 장군
13 ~을 포함하다	14 사물함	
15 ~할 때마다, ~하면		16 독립, 광복
17 (정치적·사회적) 운동		18 나무로 된, 목재의
19 이상한	20 경찰관, 장교	21 진짜 같은, 사실적인
22 발명품, 발명	23 부끄러운, 당황스러운	
24 낯선, 모르는	25 여자; 여자의, 여성의	
26 속삭이다, (사람·일에 대하여) 소곤소곤 이야기하다		
27 결혼, 혼인	28 서랍장, 큰 상자, 장롱	
29 ~이기 때문에, ~ 이래로		30 상인
31 병원, 진료소	32 해결하다, 풀다	33 진실, 사실
34 학자	35 ~ 대신에	36 ~에게 고함치다
37 ~하는 데 익숙하다		38 ~에 일생을 바치다
39 그 순간에	40 ~을 결정하다	41 비밀을 지키다
42 ~ 몰래, ~의 등 뒤에서		
43 (사람들이) ~라고 한다		

단어 TEST Step 2   p.03

01 afterwards	02 merchant	03 biography
04 chest	05 movement	06 ruin
07 disappointing	08 embarrassing	09 independence
10 odd	11 fortune	12 gamble
13 social studies	14 general	15 whisper
16 include	17 machine	18 scholar
19 invention	20 horrible	21 article
22 marriage	23 female	24 wonder
25 object	26 fortress	27 clinic
28 realistic	29 detective	30 save
31 husband	32 wooden	33 locker
34 strange	35 keep a secret	36 yell at
37 take a look at ~		38 ask for
39 at that moment		40 instead of
41 try on	42 make an arrangement	
43 be used to 동(명사)		

단어 TEST Step 3   p.04

1 female, 여자의, 여성의   2 fortune, 재산
3 husband, 남편   4 chest, 서랍장, 큰 상자, 장롱
5 ruin, 망치다, 파산시키다   6 general, 장군
7 include, ~을 포함하다   8 biography, 자서전, 전기
9 merchant, 상인   10 save, 구하다   11 fortress, 요새
12 independence, 독립   13 article, 기사
14 movement, (정치적·사회적) 운동   15 locker, 사물함
16 scholar, 학자

대화문 TEST Step 1   p.05~07

Listen & Talk 1 Get Ready

was a painter / read, it is said, scholar / fight, both right

Listen & Talk 1 A-1

what, reading / reading, biography / haven't heard / the first female, It is said that, over, flying time

Listen & Talk 1 A-2

interesting, detective / scholar / but it is said that he was also, solved, cases / didn't know that, detective

Listen & Talk 1 B

know about / heard / Take a look at, to be included, social studies / helped, by building a clinic, that such stories, be included in / It, to, that, such

Listen & Talk 2 A-1

can't take, museum / Is it okay, water bottle / leave, in

Listen & Talk 2 A-2

welcome to, How / is it okay if I take pictures in / don't use

Listen & Talk 2 B

How was / were / get the chance to, okay if I / remember that, closes at / on, 5th floor / Let me know if

Communication Step A

are moving onto, As you can see, many, inventions, is called / musical instrument / water clock, It is said that it is, oldest, the largest / How, Is it okay if, picture of

Wrap Up 1

what, watching / watching / Isn't he, saved / It is said that he won, wooden ships / how, possible / wise general who made creative

Wrap Up 2

Would you like to / I'd like to / Here / is it okay if, bathroom / if, on, stay, your seat

Listen & Talk 1 Get Ready

A: Kim Deuksin was a painter.

B: No! I read a book and it is said that he was a scholar.

C: Don't fight. You are both right.

Listen & Talk 1 A-1

M: Lisa, what are you reading?

W: I'm reading a biography of Gwon Giok.

M: I haven't heard about her. Who is she?

W: She was the first female pilot in Korea. It is said that she had over 7,000 hours of flying time.

M: Wow, I didn't know that.

Listen & Talk 1 A-2

M: I watched an interesting movie yesterday. Jeong Yakyong was a detective in it.

W: Jeong Yakyong? Wasn't he a scholar in the Joseon Dynasty?

M: Yeah, but it is said that he was also a detective. He solved about 90 cases.

W: Oh, I didn't know that he was also a detective.

Listen & Talk 1 B

W: Hey, Mark, do you know about Father Lee Taeseok?

M: Yeah, I've heard of him. Why?

W: Take a look at this article. He is going to be included in the social studies textbook in South Sudan.

M: Wow, that's great.

W: Yeah, he helped the children by building a clinic and a school. It is said that such stories will be included in the textbook.

M: It is good to hear that students will learn about such a great person.

Listen & Talk 2 A-1

W: Excuse me, you can't take your backpack inside the museum.

M: Oh, I didn't know that. Is it okay if I bring in my water bottle?

W: Yes, that's fine. You can leave your bag in the locker.

M: Okay, thank you.

Listen & Talk 2 A-2

W: Hi, welcome to the National Museum. How can I help you?

M: Hi, is it okay if I take pictures in the museum?

W: Yes, but please don't use a flash.

M: Oh, I see. Thank you.

Listen & Talk 2 B

M: Hello, Ms. Jackson. How was your tour of the Hanok Village?

W: It was wonderful. The houses were really beautiful.

M: That's great.

W: Actually, I didn't get the chance to have dinner. Is it okay if I cook in the kitchen at this hour?

M: Yes, but please remember that the kitchen closes at 10 p.m.

W: Okay. The kitchen is on the 5th floor, right?

M: Yes, it is. Let me know if you need anything.

Communication Step A

M: All right, everyone! This way, please. Now, we are moving onto the Joseon Dynasty. As you can see, there were many interesting inventions. This one is called the *Jagyeongnu*.

W: Is it a musical instrument?

M: Actually, this is a water clock. It is said that it is the oldest and the largest water clock in Korea.

W: How amazing! Is it okay if I take a picture of it?

M: Sure.

Wrap Up 1

W: James, what are you watching?

M: Oh, I'm watching a video about Yi Sunsin.

W: Isn't he the one that saved Joseon from Japan?

M: Right. It is said that he won the war only with twelve wooden ships.

W: Wow, how can that be possible?

M: He was a wise general who made creative plans.

Wrap Up 2

W: Excuse me, sir. Would you like to have curry or *bibimbap*?

M: I'd like to have *bibimbap*, please

W: Here you are.

M: Thank you. Oh, is it okay if I use the bathroom now?

W: Sure, but if the seat light is on, you should stay in your seat.

M: Okay, thank you.

01 Secret, My Father

02 strange, visited, asked, daughter

03 odd, used to being

04 your father's friend

05 wonder if, true

06 moment, expecting disappointing, memories

07 Back, whenever, There goes

08 from, rich family

09 Instead, living, always, gambling

10 why, which, ruins, fortune

11 gambled away, asking for

12 have, left, would, whenever

13 yell at, angrily, empty-handed

14 Bring, more

15 had already made, arrangement

16 part, tradition, chest, clothes

17 Right before, taken, money

18 angrily, such, horrible thing

19 What should, do

20 have no choice

21 have to take, chest

22 How embarrassing, behind, back

23 Since, marriage, been difficult

24 dear, continued, story

25 was not, gambler

26 family money, independence fighters

27 made himself, keep, secret

28 sure if, telling, truth

29 afterwards, out, realized, wrong

30 since, proud, devoted, movement

21 You'll have to take

22 How embarrassing, whisper behind my back

23 marriage, had been difficult for me

24 continued his story

25 a gambler   26 independence fighters

27 made himself, keep this a secret from, Japanese officers

28 if, telling, truth

29 afterwards, had been wrong

30 had devoted his life to, independence movement

1 아버지의 비밀

2 1946년에, 낯선 남자가 나를 찾아와 물었다. "당신이 김용환 씨의 딸입니까?

3 나는 파락호의 딸이라고 불리는 것이 더 익숙했으므로 나에게 이것은 이상한 질문이었다.

4 "나는 당신 아버지의 친구입니다.

5 당신은 이것이 사실인지 의아하겠지만, 당신의 아버지는…," 이라고 그 남자는 말했다.

6 나는 내 아버지에 대해 좋은 기억을 가지고 있지 않았으므로 그 순간에 실망스러운 소식을 예상하고 있었다.

7 1920년대에 마을에서 사람들이 나를 볼 때마다 그들은 "저기에 파락호의 딸이 가네."라고 말하곤 했다.

8 나의 아버지는 매우 부유한 집안의 아들이었다.

9 선비의 삶을 사는 대신, 아버지는 항상 도박장에 계셨다.

10 그것이 그가 집안의 재산을 탕진하는 사람이라는 뜻의 파락호로 불린 이유이다.

11 "네 아버지는 도박으로 모든 돈을 써 버리고 지금 더 요구하고 계신다.

12 가서 더 이상 남아 있는 돈이 없다고 말씀드려라."라고 나의 어머니는 나를 도박장으로 보낼 때마다 말씀하시곤 했다.

13 그러면, 아버지는 나에게 화를 내시며 소리치셨다. "왜 빈손으로 왔니?

14 돈을 더 가져와!"

15 내가 16살이 되었을 때, 나의 가족은 나를 서 씨와 결혼시키기로 이미 결정을 했었다.

16 결혼 풍습의 일부로, 서 씨네 가족은 새 장롱을 사라고 우리 가족에게 돈을 보냈다.

17 결혼식 바로 전날, 나의 어머니는 내 방에 들어오셔서 말씀하셨다. "네 아버지가 장롱을 살 돈을 가져가 버렸다."

18 나는 화가 나서 물었다 "어떻게 그리 끔찍한 일을 하실 수 있나요?

19 우린 이제 어떡해요?"

20 "우리에게 선택권은 없구나.

21 큰어머니의 옛 장롱을 가져가야겠구나."라고 어머니가 말씀하셨다.

01 Secret, Father

02 a strange man visited, asked

03 an odd question, was more used to being called

04 your father's friend

05 wonder if, true

06 expecting disappointing, since, good memories

07 Back, whenever, There goes

08 from, rich family

09 Instead of living, gambling house

10 That is why, was called, which, ruins

11 has gambled away, asking for

12 have no more money left, would, whenever, sent

13 would yell at, angrily, empty-handed

14 Bring me, money

15 had already made an arrangement, marry

16 As part of, a new chest for clothes

17 Right before, came into, has taken the money

18 angrily, such a horrible thing

19 What   20 no choice

22 "가문에 부끄러운 일이야."라고 사람들이 내 뒤에서 속삭이곤
했다.

23 결혼 첫날부터, 남편의 집에서의 생활은 나에게 힘겨웠다.

24 "당신의 아버지, 나의 친애하는 친구…," 나의 아버지의 친구분은
그의 이야기를 이어가셨다.

25 "그는 도박꾼이 아니었어요.

26 당신의 아버지는 가족의 돈을 만주에 있는 독립운동가들에게
보냈답니다.

27 그는 이것을 일본 순사들에게 비밀로 하기 위해 그 자신을
도박꾼처럼 보이게 했어요."

28 처음엔, 나는 그분이 사실을 얘기하시는 건지 확신할 수 없었다.

29 그러나 나중에, 나는 나의 아버지에 대한 진실을 알게 되었고
내가 아버지에 관해 오해하고 있었다는 것을 깨달았다.

30 그 순간부터, 나는 독립운동에 그의 인생을 헌신하신 파락호의
딸인 것이 자랑스러웠다.

1 The Secret of My Father

2 In 1946, a strange man visited me and asked, "Are
you Mr. Kim Yonghwan's daughter?"

3 For me, this was an odd question because I was
more used to being called the daughter of a
parakho.

4 "I'm your father's friend.

5 You may wonder if it is true, but your father….," the
man said.

6 At that moment, I was expecting disappointing news
since I did not have good memories of my father.

7 Back in the 1920's, whenever people saw me in the
village, they would say, "There goes the *parakho*'s
daughter."

8 My father was a son from a very rich family.

9 Instead of living the life of a seonbi, he was always
at the gambling house.

10 That is why he was called a *parakho*, which
means someone who ruins his family's fortune.

11 "Your father has gambled away all of the money,
and now he's asking for more.

12 Go and tell him that we have no more money left,"
my mother would tell me whenever she sent me to
the gambling house.

13 Then, my father would yell at me angrily, "Why did
you come empty-handed?

14 Bring me more money!"

15 When I was sixteen years old, my family had
already made an arrangement for me to marry Mr.
Seo.

16 As part of the wedding tradition, Mr. Seo's family
sent my family some money to buy a new chest
for clothes.

17 Right before the wedding day, my mother came
into my room and said, "Your father has taken the
money for the chest,"

18 I asked angrily, "How could he do such a horrible
thing?

19 What should we do now?"

20 "We have no choice.

21 You'll have to take your aunt's old chest," my
mother said.

22 "How embarrassing for the family," people would
whisper behind my back.

23 Since the first day of marriage, life at my
husband's house had been difficult for me.

24 "Your father, my dear friend….," my father's friend
continued his story.

25 "He was not a gambler.

26 Your father sent the family money to the
independence fighters in Manchuria.

27 He made himself look like a gambler to keep this
a secret from the Japanese officers."

28 At first, I was not sure if he was telling the truth.

29 But afterwards, I found out the truth about my
father and I realized that I had been wrong about
him

30 Ever since that moment, I have been proud to be
the daughter of a *parakho* who had devoted his
life to the independence movement.

Grammar in Real Life A

1. have many questions, your plans

2. Are, going to release

3. interested in various, genres

4. plans to work with other artists

5. going to go on, would tour

Grammar in Real Life B

1. got back home, had gone

2. seemed a little bit strange

3. remembered, had left

4. saw, had broken

5. found out, had eaten

6. At last, who did it

7. found small footprints

After You Read: Read and Write A

1. Secret
2. thought
3. was known as
4. was born into, gambled away
5. even took, a new chest for clothes
6. Actually
8. sent, independence fighters
9. made himself look like, keep this a secret

단어 TEST Step 1 p.23

01 배경	02 (뉴스 등의) 진행자	03 지휘자
04 전하다	05 엄지손가락	06 상상하다
07 울림, 맥박; 때리다, 두드리다		08 추천하다
09 재능이 있는	10 악기	11 방송하다
12 합창단	13 현지의, 지역의	14 고통, 아픔
15 주로, 대부분	16 끝없는, 무한한	17 감동시키다
18 관심, 주목	19 집중하다	20 보물, 보물 같은 것
21 ~이라고 여기다, 생각하다		
22 (경기 등에) 출전하다		23 긍정적인
24 완전히, 전부	25 쓸모없는, 가치 없는	
26 쓰레기	27 재검토하다, 복습하다	
28 환경의, 환경과 관련된		29 재활용하다
30 오케스트라, 관현악단		31 ~을 알아차리다
32 빛나는, 반짝거리는		
33 공연하다, 수행하다		34 깨끗한, 순수한
35 처음에, 초반에	36 진정하다	
37 ~와 조화를 이루어		38 ~와 비슷하다
39 ~을 돌려주다	40 ~을 신청하다, ~에 가입하다	
41 ~로 가득 차다	42 ~하는 한	
43 ~을 하고 싶어 하다		

구석구석지문 TEST Step 2 p.22

Grammar in Real Life A

1. Mary Jane, your fans have many questions about your plans.
2. 1. Are you going to release a new song this month?
3. 2. Are you interested in various music genres?
4. 3. Do you have any plans to work with other artists?
5. 4. Are you going to go on a would tour this year?

Grammar in Real Life B

1. When I got back home, my parents had gone out for a walk.
2. The house was dark and quiet, but it seemed a little bit strange.
3. I remembered that I had left the door in my room open.
4. I saw that someone had broken the lamp.
5. I found out that someone had eaten my cookies on the table.
6. At last I knew who did it!
7. I found small footprints of my dog, Lucy, and the cat next door

After You Read: Read and Write A

1. The Secret of My Father
2. I thought my father was ...
3. My father was known as a *parakho*.
4. He was born into a rich family but he gambled away all of the money.
5. He even took the money for a new chest for clothes.
6. Actually my father was ...
7. My father was not a gambler.
8. He sent the family money to the independence fighters in Manchuria.
9. He made himself look like a gambler to keep this a secret from the Japanese officers.

단어 TEST Step 2 p.24

01 broadcast	02 choir	03 entirely
04 anchor	05 touch	06 attention
07 mostly	08 positive	09 background
10 imagine	11 index finger	12 instrument
13 local	14 compete	15 talented
16 garbage	17 concentrate	18 beat
19 consider	20 worthless	21 review
22 endless	23 perform	24 recycle
25 pain	26 thumb	27 conductor
28 deliver	29 recommend	30 treasure
31 notice	32 pure	33 serious
34 environmental	35 as long as	36 calm down
37 send back	38 be filled with	39 sign up for
40 be eager to	41 in the beginning	
42 be similar to	43 in harmony with	

1 endless, 끝없는, 무한한   2 instrument, 악기

3 positive, 긍정적인   4 treasure, 보물, 보물 같은 것

5 musician, 음악가   6 worthless, 쓸모없는, 가치 없는

7 talented, 재능 있는   8 picker, 줍는 사람, 채집자

9 recycle, 재활용하다   10 shiny, 빛나는, 반짝거리는

11 tank, (물, 기름 등의) 저장 통   12 perform, 공연하다

13 concentrate, 집중하다   14 conductor, 지휘자

15 garbage, 쓰레기   16 recommend, 추천하다

Listen & Talk 1 A-1

won, swimming competition, Congratulations / compete, find it helpful / keeps, awake, helps, focus

Listen & Talk 1 A-2

off to / going, choir practice / forgot, choir, find, interesting to sing / in harmony with others

Listen & Talk 1-B

heard, you recorded / find it easy to write them / beginning, draw on, keep a journal / No pain, no gain, with

Listen & Talk 2 A-1

sign up for / Are you planning to sign up for / to perform with / are, going to / with, violin, cello

Listen & Talk 2 A-2

sign up for / planning to take the class, during / planning, weekday class, offer / another one, Both / sign up

Listen & Talk 2-B

musical instrument, recommend, is similar to, Playing, to use, thumb nails to play

Communication

help, with something / up / which seat I should choose / planning to, orchestra / orchestra / get the seats, second floor, various musical instruments / better to hear, from the second floor / find it better, other seats

Wrap Up

have, been / I've read / have you, for visiting / find, post, latest / spread news

Listen & Talk 1 A-1

W: Hey, Jake. I saw you won the swimming competition yesterday. Congratulations!

M: Thanks, Anna.

W: You always seem to listen to music before you compete. Do you find it helpfu to listen to music before you swim?

M: Yes, it keeps me awake and it helps me focus.

Listen & Talk 1 A-2

M: Hi, Sally. Where are you off to?

W: I'm going to the music room. I have choir practice.

M: Oh, yeah. I forgot that you've joined the choir. Do you find it interesting to sing in the choir?

W: Yeah, it's great to sing in harmony with others.

Listen & Talk 1-B

W: Hi, Jason. Great to see you again. I've heard the new rap song, *Young and Wild*, that you recorded. It's really cool.

M: Oh, thanks.

W: I really like your songs. Do you find it easy to write them?

M: Well, it was hard in the beginning, but now it's getting easier. I draw on my experiences and keep a journal.

W: Wow! As they say, "No pain, no gain." Best of luck with your new song!

M: Thank you.

Listen & Talk 2 A-1

W: Hey, Tommy. When is the last day to sign up for the talent show?

M: This Friday. Are you planning to sign up for it, Megan?

W: Yeah, I'm going to perform with a couple of people.

M: How cool! What are you going to do?

W: We will play K-pop music with the violin and cello.

Listen & Talk 2 A-2

W: Hello, I'd like to sign up for a drum class.

M: Okay. Are you planning to take the class during the week or during the weekend?

W: I'm planning to take a weekday class. When do you offer them?

M: There is a class on Tuesday and another one on Thursday. Both classes start at 6 o'clock.

W: Great. I'd like to sign up for the Tuesday class.

Listen & Talk 2-B

W: Are you planning to learn a musical instrument? I'd like to recommend the *kalimba*, a small African musical instrument. The sound it makes is similar to that of a music box. Playing the *kalimba* is very easy. You can learn to use your thumb nails to play beautiful music in just one lesson!

W: Hey, Anthony. Can you help me with something?

M: Sure, what's up?

W: I'm going to a concert at the Arts Center, but I don't know which seat I should choose.

M: Are you planning to go to the orchestra concert?

W: Yes. I'm going to watch the orchestra concert.

M: Then, you should get the seats on the second floor. You can hear the beautiful sounds of various musical instruments better.

W: Oh, do you find it better to hear the performance from the second floor?

M: Yes. I find it better than from other seats.

Wrap Up

M: Hey, Alice.

W: Hi, Sam. How have you been?

M: Great. Actually, I've read a lot of pop news from your blog.

W: Oh, have you? Thanks for visiting my blog!

M: Do you find it interesting to post the latest pop news?

W: Yes, I love to spread news to people.

본문 TEST Step 1　　　　　　　　p.30~31

01 Junk Orchestra

02 written by, blogger

03 sends, garbage, back music

04 write on, back, given

05 musical, was called

06 made entirely out of

07 imagine, kind, eager, out

08 thought, might, sound strange

09 few minutes, walk, stage

10 thing, noticed, made, with

11 with, playing, on, shiny

12 was shocked by, deep

13 into, with, made, recycled

14 After, eager, write, about

15 met, conductor, asked, orchestra

16 Why did you start

17 work on, filled with

18 something positive, share, with

19 use, to make instruments

20 garbage, another, treasure

21 local garbage picker, lot

22 possible, making, out, garbage

23 thing, instruments, worry, spending

24 want, to learn through

25 even, worthless, inspiring music

26 matter, as long, into

27 formed, not by instruments

29 seconds, moving, how, lives

30 power, music, endless

31 found, possible, played, recycled

32 talented, deliver, serious, attention

본문 TEST Step 2　　　　　　　　p.32~33

01 Junk　　　02 written by, music blogger

03 garbage, send back music

04 written on the back of, was given

05 was called　　　06 made entirely out of garbage

07 was eager to find out

08 thought, might sound strange

09 After a few minutes, began to walk

10 The first thing I noticed, made out of

11 with a girl playing, on, shiny cello

12 was shocked by, deep sound

13 was, into, made from recycled materials

14 was eager to write

15 the conductor, asked

16 Why did you start

17 to work on, saw, living, was mostly filled with garbage

18 something positive, so, share, with

19 to make instruments

20 garbage, another person's treasure

21 a local garbage picker, a lot

22 it, for children, out of garbage

23 The wonderful thing, didn't have to worry about, spending

24 to learn through

25 even something worthless, inspiring music

26 interviewing, doesn't matter, as long as, into

27 formed by, not by instruments　28 Comments

29 seconds, how, lives　　　30 endless

31 played with

32 Not only do, talented young, deliver, bring, to our attention

1 정크 오케스트라

2 음악 블로거 Lucy White 씀

3 "세상이 우리에게 쓰레기를 보내면, 우리는 음악을 돌려준다."

4 이것은 내가 받은 음악회 입장권의 뒷면에 쓰여 있었다.

5 그 음악 그룹은 '정크 오케스트라'라고 불렸다.

6 그들은 완전히 쓰레기로만 만들어진 악기를 연주했다.

7 나는 그런 악기들이 어떤 종류의 소리를 낼지 상상할 수 없었고, 그래서 나는 알아보고 싶어졌다.

8 음악회가 시작되기 전에 나는 그 악기들이 이상한 소리를 낼지도 모른다고 생각했다.

9 몇 분 후에 한 무리의 젊은이들이 무대 위로 걸어 올라오기 시작했다.

10 내가 처음으로 알아차린 것은 그들의 악기였는데, 그것들은 반짝이는 기름통으로 만들어진 첼로, 포크로 만들어진 바이올린, 수도관과 단추로 만들어진 플루트였다.

11 음악회는 한 소녀가 자신의 반짝이는 첼로로 바흐의 〈첼로 모음곡 1번〉을 연주하는 것으로 시작되었다.

12 나는 그 깊은 소리에 충격을 받았다.

13 나는 음악에 너무 심취해서 그들이 재활용된 재료들로 만들어진 악기를 연주하고 있다는 것을 잊었다.

14 음악회가 끝나고, 나는 그 오케스트라에 대한 이야기를 몹시 쓰고 싶었다.

15 나는 지휘자인 Favio Chávez를 만나서 그에게 오케스트라에 대해 물었다.

16 Lucy White: 왜 당신은 정크 오케스트라를 시작하셨나요?

17 Favio Chávez: 2006년에 새활봉 프로그램에서 일을 하기 위해서 내가 파라과이의 카테우라라고 불리는 작은 마을에 갔을 때, 나는 대부분이 쓰레기로 가득 차 있는 마을에 살고 있는 어린이들을 보았습니다.

18 나는 그들의 삶에 긍정적인 무엇인가를 더해 주고 싶어서, 음악에 대한 나의 사랑을 그들과 나누기로 결정했습니다.

19 Lucy White: 왜 당신은 악기를 만들기 위해 쓰레기를 이용했나요?

20 Favio Chávez: 한 사람의 쓰레기는 다른 사람의 보물입니다.

21 그 지역의 쓰레기 줍는 사람인 Nicolás Gámez가 나를 많이 도와주었습니다.

22 그는 쓰레기로 악기를 만들어 줌으로써 어린이들이 음악을 연주하는 것이 가능하도록 만들었습니다.

23 이 악기들의 멋진 점은 어린이들이 악기에 많은 돈을 쓸 것을 걱정하지 않아도 된다는 점이었죠.

24 Lucy White: 당신의 음악을 통해서 사람들이 무엇을 배우기를 원하십니까?

25 Favio Chávez: 나는 가치 없는 것도 영감을 주는 음악을 만들어 낼 수 있다는 것을 사람들이 알게 되기를 원합니다.

26 Chávez를 인터뷰한 후에 나는 사람들이 악기를 연주하는 데 마음을 쏟아붓는 한, 그 사람이 연주하는 악기가 무엇인지는 별로 중요하지 않다는 것을 깨달았다.

27 카테우라의 어린이들은 나에게 오케스트라는 악기에 의해서가 아니라 사람에 의해 이루어지는 것이라는 것을 보여 주었다.

28 감상평

29 Annie: (23초 전) 음악이 삶을 바꿀 수 있다는 것을 보아서 너무 가슴이 뭉클하다.

30 음악의 힘은 끝이 없다!

31 Thomas: (1분 전) 음악회가 끝난 후, 나는 재활용 악기로 연주되는 음악으로 사람들에게 영감을 주는 것이 가능하다는 것을 알았다.

32 Kate: (5일 전) 이 재능 있는 젊은이들은 훌륭한 음악을 전할 뿐만 아니라, 또한 심각한 환경 문제에 우리가 주목하게 한다.

1 The Junk Orchestra

2 written by a music blogger, Lucy White

3 "The world sends us garbage, we send back music."

4 This was written on the back of a concert ticket I was given.

5 The musical group was called "The Junk Orchestra."

6 They played instruments made entirely out of garbage.

7 I could not imagine what kind of sound these instruments would make, so I was eager to find out.

8 Before the concert, I thought that the instruments might sound strange.

9 After a few minutes, a group of young people began to walk on the stage.

10 The first thing I noticed was their instruments: a cello made out of a shiny oil tank, a violin made with forks, and a flute made with a water pipe and buttons.

11 The concert began with a girl playing Bach's *Cello Suite No. 1* on her shiny cello.

12 I was shocked by the deep sound.

13 I was so into the music that I forgot that they were playing with instruments made from recycled materials.

14 After the concert, I was eager to write a story about the orchestra.

15 I met Favio Chávez, the conductor, and asked him about the orchestra.

16 Lucy White: Why did you start The Junk Orchestra?

17 Favio Chávez: When I went to a small town called Cateura in Paraguay to work on a recycling program in 2005, I saw children living in a town that was mostly filled with garbage.

18 I wanted to add something positive to their lives, so I decided to share my love of music with them.

19 Lucy White: Why did you use garbage to make instruments?

20 Favio Chávez: One person's garbage is another person's treasure.

21 Nicolás Gómez, a local garbage picker, helped me a lot.

22 He made it possible for children to play music by making instruments out of garbage.

23 The wonderful thing about these instruments was that the children didn't have to worry about spending a lot of money on them.

24 Lucy White: What do you want people to learn through your music?

25 Favio Chávez: I want people to know that even something worthless can make inspiring music.

26 After interviewing Chávez, I realized that it really doesn't matter what instrument you play with as long as you put your heart into playing it.

27 The children of Cateura showed me that an orchestra is formed by people, not by instruments.

28 Comments

29 Annie: (23 seconds ago) So moving to see how music can change lives.

30 The power of music is endless!

31 Thomas: (1 minute ago) After the concert, I found it possible to inspire people by music played with recycled instruments.

32 Kate: (5 days ago) Not only do these talented young people deliver great music, but they also bring serious environmental problems to our attention.

구석구석지문 TEST Step 1   p.40

After You Read A

1. Junk Orchestra
2. sends us garbage, send back
3. About, concert
4. played instruments made out of garbage
5. with a girl playing the cello, a shiny oil tank
6. was shocked by
7. The Interview with

8. to work. on a recycling program
9. decided to share, with
10. local garbage picker
11. by people, not by instruments

Grammar in Real Life

1. visited, broadcasting company
2. sat at, where
3. There were, hanging on the wall
4. read aloud sentences moving across
5. came out of, myself recorded
6. liked the background created with

Wrap Up 2

1. Where are, going
2. going, this Sunday
3. Are, planning to perform
4. How, know about
5. is going to play the piano, going to, too
6. Come, watch, performance

구석구석지문 TEST Step 2   p.41

After You Read A

1. The Junk Orchestra
2. The world sends us garbage, we send back music.
3. About the concert.
4. The young people played instruments made out of garbage.
5. It started with a girl playing the cello made out of a shiny oil tank.
6. I was shocked by the deep sound.
7. The Interview with Mr. Chávez
8. He went to Cateura in Paraguay to work. on a recycling program.
9. He decided to share his love of music with the children.
10. A local garbage picker helped him.
11. An orchestra is formed by people, not by instruments.

Grammar in Real Life

1. I visited a broadcasting company.
2. In the news room, I sat at the desk where anchors give the news.
3. There were two screens hanging on the wall.
4. I could read aloud sentences moving across the screen.
5. After I came out of the room, I could see myself recorded on the TV screen.

6. I really liked the background created with computer graphics.

Wrap Up 2

1. M: Hi, Julie. Where are you going?
2. W: Hi, Chris. I'm going to my guitar lesson. Our band has a concert at the hospital this Sunday.
3. M: This Sunday? Are you planning to perform at the Happy Children's Hospital?
4. W: Yes. How do you know about the concert?
5. M: Oh, my sister is going to play the piano there, so I'm going to the concert, too.
6. W: Great. Come and watch our performance!

Lesson 5

01 진지하게, 심각하게		02 인정하다, 자백하다
03 비판적으로	04 끔찍한, 지독한	05 극도로, 극히
06 가짜의, 거짓의	07 고백하다, 인정하다	
08 위험한, 위독한	09 해로운, 유해한	10 시민
11 잘못 이끌다, 오해하게 하다		12 키, 신장
13 강하게 하다, 더 튼튼하게 하다		14 성인, 어른
15 논쟁, 언쟁	16 발행하다, 출판하다, 게재하다	
17 알아보다	18 사건	19 비난하다
20 입증하다, 증명하다		21 현재의, 지금의
22 참사, 재난	23 달아나다, 탈출하다, 벗어나다	
24 판단하다	25 기술하다	
26 그럼에도 불구하고	27 믿을 만한, 신뢰할 만한	
28 상처를 입히다	29 근육	
30 (사실임을) 입증하다, 뒷받침하다		31 광산; 채굴하다
32 측정하다, 재다	33 출처, 자료	34 가슴, 흉부
35 ~와 연관되다	36 조사하다, 들여다보다	
37 지어내다, 만들어 내다		
38 ~을 부수다, ~을 무너뜨리다		39 ~에 따르면
40 ~의 관심을 …로 끌다		
41 고정관념에서 벗어나다		42 ~에게 유용하다
43 잡히지 않은, 탈주 중인		

01 admit	02 muscle	03 nevertheless
04 competitor	05 seriously	06 adult
07 mislead	08 mine	09 criticize
10 prove	11 critically	12 disaster
13 escape	14 public	15 strengthen
16 fake	17 confess	18 extremely
19 harmful	20 incident	21 argument
22 reliable	23 awful	24 citizen
25 judge	26 measure	27 current
28 publish	29 critical	30 recognize
31 source	32 describe	33 support
34 wound	35 look into	36 search for
37 be related to	38 draw one's attention to	
39 fall asleep	40 break down	41 according to
42 be useful for	43 make up	

1 shoot, (총 등을) 쏘다   2 fake, 거짓의   3 citizen, 시민
4 disaster, 참사, 재난   5 describe, 기술하다
6 panic, 겁에 질려 어쩔 줄 모르다   7 chest, 가슴, 흉부
8 spell, 철자를 말하다, 쓰다   9 criticize, 비난하다
10 source, 출처, 자료   11 wound, 상처를 입히다
12 incident, 사건   13 publish, 발행하다, 출판하다
14 trust, 신뢰하다   15 prove, 입증하다
16 argument, 논쟁, 언쟁

Listen & Talk 1 A-1

caught a cold, because, dress warmly / article, cold, body temperature, low / more about it / because of viruses

Listen & Talk 1 A-2

a glass of warm milk, fall asleep / help, fall asleep / tell me more about it / chemicals, make, sleepy, amount, too, to, effect

Listen & Talk 2 A-1

What are you reading / riddles / for / Actually, useful for adults / say so / help, think, creatively, think outside the box to find

Listen & Talk 2 A-2

poetry books / written by / write better pomes / say so / honest, feelings, more creative than adults

Listen & Talk 2 B

I should buy this drink, help, lose weight / Let me read, label, closely, strange / you say so / enough information, what's, drink / right / how much you have to drink to lose weight

Communication

pieces of information, facts, completely wrong / there were, examples, facts that are wrong / what / goldfish, goldfish, actually smart / tell, more / recognize their owners / know that

Wrap Up 2

interesting article, where it is / between, and, right / What color, it is / guess / called, tell moe more / because, dangerous

Listen & Talk 1 A-1

W: I think I caught a cold because I didn't dress warmly yesterday.

M: Well, I've read an article saying that you don't catch a cold because your body temperature is low.

W: Really? Can you tell me more about it?

M: The article said that people catch colds because of viruses.

Listen & Talk 1 A-2

W: I usually drink a glass of warm milk before I go to bed, but it doesn't help me fall asleep.

M: I saw a show on TV, and a doctor said that a glass of warm milk doesn't actually help you fall asleep.

W: Oh, it doesn't? Can you tell me more about it?

M: Milk has special chemicals that make people sleepy. But the amount in a glass is too small to have any effect.

Listen & Talk 2 A-1

W: What are you reading, John?

M: I'm reading a book of riddles.

W: Riddles? Aren't they for children?

M: Actually, no. Books of riddles are really useful for adults.

W: Really? Why do you say so?

M: They help us think more creatively. We need to think outside the box to find the answers.

Listen & Talk 2 A-2

M: Are these all poetry books?

W: Yeah. These are all poems written by children.

M: By children?

W: Yeah. I think children write better poems than adults.

M: Why do you say so?

W: They're really honest about their feelings and much more creative than adults.

Listen & Talk 2 B

M: Hey, Sandy. Do you think I should buy this drink? It is said that it can help me lose weight.

W: Let me read the label more closely. Hmm, it looks a bit strange to me, David.

M: Why do you say so?

W: There isn't enough information about what's in the drink.

M: Oh, you're right.

W: Also, it doesn't tell you how much you have to drink to lose weight.

Communication

W: There are so many pieces of information we call "facts" that are completely wrong.

M: Why do you say so?

W: I read a book, and there were a lot of examples of these facts that are wrong.

M: Like what?

W: Well, most people think goldfish are not smart. But, goldfish are actually smart.

M: Really? Can you tell me more about that?

W: They can recognize their owners.

M: Oh, I didn't know that

Wrap Up 2

W: I read an interesting article about the Black Sea. Do you know where it is?

M: Yes. It's between Eastern Europe and Western Asia, right?

W: Right. What color do you think it is?

M: Well, black, I guess.

W: No, it isn't. It's blue.

M: Really? Then why is it called the Black Sea? Can you tell me more about it?

W: People call it the Black Sea because it is very dangerous.

24 had, argument during

25 led, shot, twice, chest

26 in critical condition

27 ran away after, shooting

28 searching, warning citizens, dangerous

29 there anything strange, article

30 Read, backwards, spells

31 Who wrote, why

32 so that, competitor, stealing

33 published, article, caught stealing

34 admit, harshly criticized, public

35 special cases, articles published

36 critically, judge whether, fake   37 How to spot

38 Consider, Source

39 from, reliable source

40 Can, trust, writer   41 Check, Date

42 new, old story

43 Is, related to current

44 Beyond the Headlines

45 headline match, content

46 Supporting Sources

47 related, provide similar content

---

01 Spot Fake News

02 watch, hear, interesting news

03 seriously considered whether, article

04 what if, made up

05 harmful, less informed, misled

06 Nevertheless, various, throughout history

07 written such false information

08 thinking, hidden motives behind

09 AWFUL DISATER

10 broke down, cage, escaped

11 broke down, other, cages

12 ran dawn, injured hundreds

13 still on the loose

14 stay, until further notice

15 incident described, taken place

16 article, laughed out loud

17 Those, got really worried

18 Not knowing, false, panicked

19 Some, escape, others, hunt

20 make up such news

21 confessed, up, attention, unsafe

22 SLAV SHOOTS, IN ARGUMENT

23 shot, wounded, near, mining

---

01 Spot Fake News

02 interesting news

03 have, considered whether

04 what if, completely made up

05 harmful in that, less informed, misled

06 Nevertheless, various fake, throughout history

07 written such false information

08 Let's look into, thinking, the hidden motives behind

09 AWFUL

10 broke down, escaped

11 broke down, the other

12 ran down, injured hundreds of   13 on the loose

14 Citizens, until further notice

15 described above, taken place

16 laughed out loud

17 got really worried

18 Not knowing, false, panicked

19 Some, to escape, others, to hunt

20 make up such news

21 made it up so that, could, readers' attention to

22 SHOOTS, IN ARGUMENT

23 was shot, seriously wounded by

24 had an argument during

25 led to, twice, in the chest

26 in critical condition

27 ran away after the shooting

28 are searching for, are warning, extremely dangerous

29 anything strange, article   30 backwards

31 wrote, why

32 pubilshed, so that, could, if, their articles

33 got caught stealing

34 had to admit, were harshly criticized

35 special cases, published

36 As, critically, judge whether, or   37 How to spot

38 Consider, Source

39 reliable source   40 trust, writer

41 Check   42 new, old story

43 Is, related to current

44 Beyond the Headlines

45 match the content

46 Supporting Sources

47 related, similar content

본문 TEST Step 3   p.55~57

1 당신은 가짜 뉴스임을 알아챌 수 있는가?

2 매일 우리는 흥미로운 뉴스를 보고, 듣고, 읽는다.

3 그러나 당신은 뉴스 기사가 정말로 진실인지 심각하게 고려해 본 적이 있는가?

4 모든 사람이 흥미로운 뉴스 기사를 좋아하지만, 만약 그것이 완전히 지어낸 것이라면 어떻게 할 것인가?

5 가짜 뉴스는 사람들에게 정보를 부족하게 제공하거나 사람들을 잘못 이끌 수 있다는 점에서 매우 해로울 수 있다.

6 그럼에도 불구하고, 역사를 통틀어 다양한 가짜 뉴스 보도들이 존재해 왔다.

7 왜 어떤 사람들은 그러한 거짓 정보를 써 왔던 것일까?

8 그 뒤에 숨겨진 동기를 생각하면서 몇 가지 뉴스 기사를 살펴보자.

9 끔찍한 참사

10 어젯밤, 화가 난 코뿔소 떼가 동물원 우리의 벽을 부수고 도망쳤다.

11 그들은 또한 다른 야생 동물 우리의 벽도 부수었다.

12 이 동물들은 거리를 뛰어다니며 수백 명의 사람들에게 부상을 입혔다.

13 그중 열두 마리의 동물들이 아직 잡히지 않았다.

14 시민들은 추후 안내가 있을 때까지 집 안에 머물러야 한다.

15 위에 기술된 어떤 행동이나 사건도 일어나지 않았다.

16 그 당시 이 기사를 주의 깊게 읽었던 사람들은 크게 웃었다.

17 그것을 끝까지 읽지 않은 사람들은 정말로 걱정하였다.

18 그 기사가 거짓이라는 것을 알지 못했기 때문에 많은 사람이 겁에 질려 어쩔 줄 몰랐다.

19 어떤 사람들은 도시를 빠져나가려고 했고 다른 사람들은 그 동물들을 사냥하기 위해 총을 들고 공원으로 나갔다.

20 그렇다면 왜 헤럴드 사는 이러한 뉴스를 만들어 냈을까?

21 나중에 그들은 동물원의 안전하지 않은 상태에 대해 독자들의 주의를 끌기 위해 그 기사를 지어냈다고 고백했다.

22 슬라브인이 언쟁 중에 친구에게 총을 쏘다

23 목요일 저녁 채굴 야영지 근처에서, 컬럼비아 광산 소속의 슬라브인 노동자 Mejk Swenekafew가 John Pecitello 에 의해 총상을 입어 심각하게 다쳤다.

24 그 두 사람은 회의 중에 언쟁을 벌였다.

25 언쟁이 싸움으로 번졌고, Pecitello가 Swenekafew의 가슴과 다리에 두 번 총을 쏘았다.

26 현재 그는 위독한 상태로 입원 중이다.

27 Pecitello는 총격 이후 도주했다.

28 경찰이 지금 그를 찾고 있으며, 그가 극히 위험하다고 시민들에게 경고하고 있다.

29 이 기사에 뭔가 이상한 점이 있는가?

30 그 슬라브인의 이름을 거꾸로 읽어 보아라. 그것의 철자는 " 우리는 뉴스를 조작한다."가 된다.

31 누가 이것을 썼고 왜 그랬을까?

32 데일리 텔레그램 사는 그들의 경쟁자인 데일리 뉴스 사가 그들의 기사를 훔치는지를 증명하기 위해서 이 거짓 기사를 발행했다.

33 데일리 뉴스 사는 그 다음 날 'Swenekafew'에 대한 동일한 기사를 발행했고 그래서 훔친 것이 발각되었다.

34 데일리 뉴스 사의 사람들은 그들의 행동을 인정해야만 했고 대중들로부터 혹독한 비난을 받았다.

35 이 두 기사는 특별한 경우였지만, 매일 발행되는 '가짜' 뉴스 기사는 많이 있다.

36 독자로서, 우리는 비판적으로 읽고 그 뉴스가 진짜인지 가짜인지 판단할 필요가 있다.

37 가짜 뉴스 판별 방법!

38 출처를 고려하라

39 그것은 믿을 만한 출처에서 온 것인가?

40 우리는 그 필자를 신뢰할 수 있는가?

41 날짜를 확인하라

42 그것은 새로운 이야기인가 혹은 오래된 이야기인가?

43 그것은 현재의 사건들과 관련된 것인가?

44 기사 제목 그 이상을 읽어라

45 기사 제목이 기사 내용과 일치하는가?

46 뒷받침하는 자료를 찾아라

47 다른 관련된 이야기도 비슷한 내용을 제공하는가?

1 Can You Spot Fake News?

2 Every day we watch, hear, or read interesting news.

3 However, have you ever seriously considered whether an article is really true?

4 Everyone likes an interesting news story but what if it is completely made up?

5 Fake news can be very harmful in that it can make people less informed or even misled.

6 Nevertheless, there have been various fake news reports throughout history.

7 Why have some people written such false information?

8 Let's look into some articles thinking about the hidden motives behind them.

9 AWFUL DISASTER

10 Last night, an angry group of rhinoceroses broke down the walls of the cage at the zoo and escaped.

11 They also broke down the walls of the other wild animals' cages.

12 These animals ran down the streets and injured hundreds of people.

13 Twelve of the animals are still on the loose.

14 Citizens should stay indoors until further notice.

15 Not a single act or incident described above has taken place.

16 At that time, those who read the article carefully laughed out loud.

17 Those who didn't read it to the end got really worried.

18 Not knowing the news was false, many people panicked.

19 Some tried to escape the city while others went into the parks with guns to hunt the animals.

20 So why did *The Herald* make up such news?

21 Later, they confessed that they made it up so that they could draw the readers' attention to the unsafe conditions at the zoo.

22 SLAV SHOOTS A FRIEND IN ARGUMENT

23 Mejk Swenekafew, a Slav worker at the Columbia Coal Mine, was shot and seriously wounded by John Pecitello near the mining camp Thursday evening.

24 The two men had an argument during a meeting.

25 The argument led to a fight, and Pecitello shot Swenekafew twice, in the chest and leg.

26 He is now at the hospital in critical condition.

27 Pecitello ran away after the shooting.

28 The police are searching for him now and are warning citizens that he is extremely dangerous.

29 Is there anything strange about the article?

30 Read the Slav's name backwards; it spells, "we-fake-news."

31 Who wrote this and why?

32 *The Daily Telegram* published this fake article so that they could prove if *The Daily News*, their competitor, was stealing their articles.

33 *The Daily News* published the same article about "Swenekafew" the next day and thus got caught stealing.

34 The people at *The Daily News* had to admit their act and were harshly criticized by the public.

35 The two articles were special cases, but there are many "fake" news articles published every day.

36 As readers, we need to read critically and judge whether the news is real or fake.

37 How to spot fake news!

38 Consider the Source

39 Is it from a reliable source?

40 Can we trust the writer?

41 Check the Date

42 Is it a new or an old story?

43 Is it related to current events?

44 Read Beyond the Headlines

45 Does the headline match the content?

46 Find Supporting Sources

47 Do other related stories provide similar content?

Wrap Up 3

1. title says, going to have a longer vacation

2. should check, if it is true

3. Why, say so

4. uses a shocking title, its content may tell

5. should read beyond

Read & Think After You Read B

1. write, Awful Disaster

2. draw the readers' attention, unsafe conditions

3. Actually, were very upset to find, false. How about, motive

4. wanted to prove that, was stealing their articles

1. Among, think is the most important

2. finding supporting sources is, because, if, information is correct

구석구석지문 TEST Step 2 p.65

Wrap Up 3

1. A: Wow! The news title says "Longer Vacation for Students." Hey, we're going to have a longer vacation!

2. B: Wait! We should check first if it is true.

3. A: Why do you say so?

4. B: Some news uses a shocking title but its content may tell a different story.

5. A: Oh, I see. I should read beyond the news title.

Read & Think After You Read B

1. Reporter: Why did *The Herald* write the "Awful Disaster" story, Mr. Right?

2. Mr. Right: They just wanted to draw the readers' attention to the unsafe conditions at the zoo.

3. Reporter: Actually, readers were very upset to find that it was false. How about "Slav Shoots a Friend in Argument?" What was the motive?

4. Mr. Right: *The Daily Telegram* wanted to prove that *The Daily News* was stealing their articles.

Read & Think After You Read C

1. A: Among the four tips, which do you think is the most important, and why?

2. B: I think finding supporting sources is the most important because I can check if the information is correct.